Nicholas Rhea is the pen-name of Peter N. Walker, formerly an inspector with the North Yorkshire Police and the creator of the *Constable* series of books from which the Yorkshire TV series *Heartbeat* has been derived. In the two *Constable* books in this volume, *Constable around the Green* and *Constable beneath the Trees*, Nicholas Rhea recounts more of the amusing incidents which happen to the colourful and eccentric characters encountered by a country constable, stories which have provided the basis for the adventures of PC Nick Rowan, played by Nick Berry, in the TV series. Peter N. Walker is also author of *Portrait of the North York Moors*, *Murders & Mysteries from the North York Moors* and *Folk Tales from the North York Moors*. He is married with a family and lives in North Yorkshire.

BOOKS BY PETER N. WALKER

CRIME FICTION
The *Carnaby* series pub. Hale:
Carnaby and the Hijackers (1967)*
Carnaby and the Gaolbreakers (1968)
Carnaby and the Assassins (1968)
Carnaby and the Conspirators (1969)
Carnaby and the Saboteurs (1970)
Carnaby and the Eliminators (1971)
Carnaby and the Demonstrators (1972)
Carnaby and the Infiltrators (1974)**
Carnaby and the Kidnappers (1976)
Carnaby and the Counterfeiters (1980)
Carnaby and the Campaigners (1984)
Fatal Accident (1970)
Panda One on Duty (1971)
Special Duty (1972)
Identification Parade (1972)
Panda One Investigates (1973)
Major Incident (1974)
The Dovingsby Death (1975)
Missing from Home (1977)
The MacIntyre Plot (1977)
Witchcraft for Panda One (1978)
Target Criminal (1978)
The Carlton Plot (1980)
Siege for Panda One (1981)
Teenage Cop (1982)
Robber in a Mole Trap (1984)
False Alibi (pub. Constable 1991)
Grave Secrets (pub. Constable 1992)
  *reprinted Chivers (Black Dagger) 1993
**   "   "   "   "   "   1994
WRITTEN AS CHRISTOPHER CORAM
pub. Hale:
A Call to Danger (1968)
A Call to Die (1969)
Death in Ptarmigan Forest (1970)
Death on the Motorway (1973)
Murder by the Lake (1975)
Murder Beneath the Trees (1979)
Prisoner on the Dam (1982)
Prisoner on the Run (1985)
WRITTEN AS TOM FERRIS:
Espionage for a Lady (pub. Hale 1969)
WRITTEN AS ANDREW ARNCLIFFE:
Murder after the Holiday (pub. Hale 1985)

WRITTEN AS NICHOLAS RHEA:
Family Ties (pub. Constable 1985)
EMMERDALE TITLES:
WRITTEN AS JAMES FERGUSON:
A Friend in Need (pub. Fontana 1987)
Divided Loyalties (pub. Fontana 1988)
Wives and Lovers (pub. Fontana 1989)
Emmerdale Book of Country Lore
(pub. Hamlyn 1988)
Emmerdale Official Companion
(pub. Weidenfeld & Nicolson 1988)
Emmerdale's Yorkshire
(pub. Weidenfeld & Nicolson 1990)
The *Constable* series pub. Hale
WRITTEN AS NICHOLAS RHEA:
Constable on the Hill (1979)
Constable on the Prowl (1980)
Constable around the Village (1981)
Constable across the Moors (1982)
Constable in the Dale (1983)
Constable by the Sea (1985)
Constable along the Lane (1986)
Constable through the Meadow (1988)
Constable at the Double (1988)
Constable in Disguise (1989)
Constable among the Heather (1990)
Constable beside the Stream (1991)
Constable around the Green (1993)
Constable beneath the Trees (1994)
Constable in the Shrubbery (1995)
Heartbeat Omnibus I (1992)
Heartbeat Omnibus II (1993)
*Heartbeat – Constable among the
          Heather* (pub. Headline 1992)
Heartbeat – Constable across the Moors
          (pub. Headline 1993)
Heartbeat – Constable on Call
          (pub. Headline 1993)
Heartbeat – Constable around the Green
          (pub. Headline 1994)
Heartbeat – Constable in Control
          (pub. Headline 1995)
Heartbeat – Constable along the Lane
          (pub. Headline 1996)

Heartbeat

Constable Around the Green and Other Tales of a Yorkshire Village Bobby

Nicholas Rhea

HEADLINE

First published in this edition in 1994
by HEADLINE BOOK PUBLISHING

10 9 8 7 6 5 4

ISBN 0 7472 4725 0

Typeset by CBS, Felixstowe, Suffolk

Printed and bound in Great Britain by
Cox & Wyman Ltd, Reading, Berks.

HEADLINE BOOK PUBLISHING
A division of Hodder Headline PLC
338 Euston Road
London NW1 3BH

Contents

Constable
Around the Green

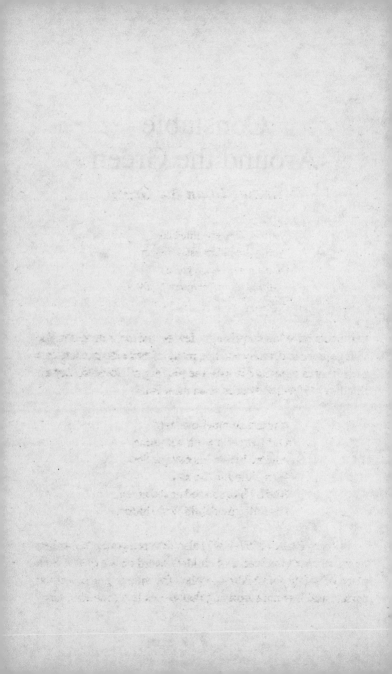

1 Games Upon the Green

As some divinely gifted man,
Whose life in low estate began
On a simple village green
Alfred, Lord Tennyson (1809–92)

Our poets have, on surprisingly few occasions, referred to the village green and, oddly enough, many of their references to this blissful area associate it with the playing of children. Robert Southey (1774–1843) does so in these lines:

It was a summer evening,
Old Kaspar's work was done,
And he before his cottage door,
Was sitting in the sun.
And by him sported on the green,
His little grandchild Wilhelmine.

William Blake (1757–1827) also featured youngsters when he wrote about the voices of children heard on the green. As a place of safety for children to play, the village green seemed perfect and it is not surprising that games like rounders, leapfrog, cricket and tig were played there and that the open space was used for the village fair, maypole dancing and other communal activities. Because the parents' homes were often clustered around the green, the children would be supervised.

There is of course, the archetypal village green. This is a flat, well-tended patch of lush grass of indeterminate size in the centre of the village. Around it are the most important buildings of the community – the church, the rectory, the inn, the manor-house, the shop and an array of delightfully rural cottages, probably with thatched roofs. On the green itself there may be some old stocks and an equally old pillory, a market cross or war memorial, a well, a maypole and even a pitch for playing cricket, football, bowls, rounders or quoits, plus a rippling stream nearby or a pond with ducks.

One vital element of a village green is that it is common land and therefore freely available to all, but in fact the nation's greens do vary enormously in shape, size and usage. A tour of the splendid English countryside will reveal the variety of our greens, and those on the North York Moors are no exception. Here, in villages like Goathland, Lealholm or Hutton-le-Hole you will find enormous stretches of undulating grass shorn smooth by the steady munching of free-range blackfaced sheep, but sadly some of the existing greens are now utilized as weekend car parks. Children of the visiting hordes now play between rows of parked vehicles while their parents snooze in the summer sun and leave behind their plastic litter and empty beer cans for the villagers to remove before the following weekend's onslaught. Sadly, the children of the local residents are compelled to go elsewhere for their own recreation and amusement.

In the dales, the greens are perhaps smaller than those of the more elevated moorland villages. Although some are not much larger than football fields, they do serve a similar communal purpose. But not every village boasts a green – indeed, in today's motorized society, many villages quietly congratulate themselves for not being blessed with a village green.

In these days of mass rural visiting, those villages without greens consider themselves fortunate because there is nowhere for the hordes to stop; those with village greens now suffer an awful loss of privacy from Easter until the end of October, the only compensation being that the influx of people does generate wealth for some of the more enterprising villagers and so keeps the rural economy viable. The greens of many pretty villages are therefore still being used by the public, albeit not by the residents, and this is done in a far less cheerful manner than in the past. Some visitors are very rude and intolerant of the residents' need to go about their daily lives and work, somehow oblivious to the fact that people actually live and work in such beautiful surroundings.

Happily, however, there are still a few quiet communities well off the proverbial beaten track in which the village green exists as it did in former times, and in which it continues its former role. One of those places is Slemmington which lies just off the southern edge of the North York Moors between Ashfordly and Eltering. Its green has all the features of a typical picture postcard setting.

The church with its tower and superb lychgate overlooks the green and all around are pretty stone cottages with red pantile roofs; a quiet stream flows through the village and it boasts mallard, teal and even swans in addition to its grayling and minnows. There is an ancient stone cross in the centre of the green and not far away, a set of stocks which were last used less than a century ago. There is a wishing-well with a dated cupola and, at the side of the green furthest from the stream, there is a pond which also attracts a variety of ducks, swans and wild water-fowl such as moorhens and coot.

There is an ancient ford across the stream too, but one curious factor concerns the stream. Here it is called Slemmington Beck, while two miles upstream, it is Gelderslack Beck and even higher, it is Shelvingby Beck. It changes its name to take on the identity of every village through which it passes before entering the River Rye near Malton and thus this single stream has a dozen different names.

But by far the most famous of Slemmington's attributes can also be seen on the green – it is the gigantic maypole which stands in its concrete base like a massive, slim and multicoloured tower. It is one of the tallest maypoles in the region, rising to some 72 feet in height and tapering towards the top. The tip bears a beautiful weather-vane in the form of a running fox; this splendid piece of metalwork is a present from a former blacksmith. The figure of the fox is re-gilded from time to time to keep it in pristine condition.

Painted in a range of bright colours, the maypole has been renewed several times due to the effects of weather, use and age, and the present one dates to 1987, being a gift to the village from Lord Ashfordly's estate.

Each May Day, the village children dance around the pole having been trained since before Easter by their enthusiastic schoolteacher; the boys wear white shirts and red shorts, while the girls wear white dresses with red sleeves and collars. All wear white socks and black shoes. Their well-rehearsed repertoire of maypole dances is a charming sight and their display attracts an audience from near and far. Early in March every year, the maypole is lowered and repainted in readiness for the new season and once the pole has been re-positioned in April, the children begin their practising.

I used to enjoy my visits to Slemmington for it was always such a peaceful and friendly place with little or no crime. But the village became the scene of some curious criminal activity. Every time my patrolling took me through the village, I was reminded of that dramatic interlude; it happened shortly after I became the village constable at Aidensfield.

One bright sunny morning in early March, my telephone rang. I was seated at my desk in the office adjoining my police house and was typing a report about a minor traffic accident. I wondered who was calling at this time of morning, for it was only 8.30 a.m. I was slightly annoyed because I had wanted an early start in order to conclude some paper work.

'Jack Lawson.' I recognized the voice at the other end of the phone. He was clerk to Slemmington Parish Council.

'Morning, Jack,' I greeted him. 'What can I do for you this bright and sunny day?'

'It's our maypole, Mr Rhea, it's gone.'

'Gone?' I responded. 'Where's it gone?'

'Search me, but I think somebody's nicked it.'

'Nicked it? Who would want to steal a maypole?' I asked.

'There was a lot of good wood in it, it would make a useful pile of logs, Mr Rhea.'

'But if anybody tried to cut it up and sell it for firewood, it would be recognized immediately, it was all red, white, blue, yellow and green paint,' I retorted.

'Exactly, Mr Rhea. Fresh paint an' all. We'd just painted it for the bairns, to encourage them to practise their dancing. They'll be right upset and it'll take ages to find another, maypoles don't grow on trees, you know. Anyroad, I must report it, it belongs to the whole village. I just hope you fellers can help us get it back.'

'I'll come straight away,' I promised.

Jack also ran the village store and post office and when I arrived, his first action was to show me the empty socket on the village green. I could see wheelmarks in the soft turf; a large vehicle of some kind had obviously been used. It would be impossible to hoist the huge and weighty pole from its deep socket by manpower alone; lifting gear would have been used.

'It's been lifted clean out of there,' he pointed to the empty hole. 'Now, to shift a thing that size needs muscle, and not human muscle. Mechanical muscle, Mr Rhea, like a bloody crane or summat with a grab or lifting gear.'

'What's it worth?' I put to him.

'Worth? Well, I mean, I can't put value on it, can you? You can't value a maypole.'

'But as firewood, Jack? As logs?'

'Well, you'd only get seventy or more logs out of it, that's not a lot, not a wagon-load by any means. So chopped into logs, I reckon I'd do well to get a couple of quid.'

'Thanks,' I said, pointing out that no one in their right mind would hire or use a huge vehicle of the kind that had been so obviously necessary to move it, merely to chop up the pole to earn themselves a couple of pounds. It did not make economic sense and thieves usually stole because they wanted to make an easy profit. This theft did not seem to fit into that category and I wondered if Claude Jeremiah Greengrass was behind this crime – stealing a maypole was the sort of daft thing he would do, although I did doubt whether even he had access to the necessary lifting gear.

I examined the surrounding green for further evidence. I drew a rough diagram of the large tyre tread marks in the hope I might be able to make some plaster casts of the tracks before they deteriorated, but there was nothing else of use to me.

I interviewed Jack in his kitchen over a cup of tea and a scone and obtained the necessary statement for my crime report. It included facts such as the last time it had been seen and the time it had been missed, together with a nominal value and a note saying that no one had any authority to remove it. Next I made a search of the village and began my enquiries. I asked if anyone had heard or seen anything odd during the night, but no one had. So far as my search was concerned, there were not many places to conceal a 72-foot-long multicoloured maypole, but if I did not search, Sergeant Blaketon would ask why I hadn't done so. Thus I searched behind all the local hedgerows, in the timber yards, along the banks of the stream and every other likely place. I even plodded through a copse of pine trees on the outskirts, thinking that the maypole might have been hidden upright among them. Then in all honesty, I could report a careful search of the vicinity. I knew what Sergeant Blaketon would think – he would think it was not a theft but a prank of some kind. To be honest, I was still unsure myself; I needed either to find the pole or to find a motive for the theft. But whether it was a theft or a prank, or even a publicity stunt of some kind, it was unfair to the children. I found myself dearly wishing I could find it so that the children's rehearsals were not unduly disrupted. I returned to Jack's shop and told him what I had done, saying I would circulate details to all surrounding police officers and would keep him informed of any progress.

'Should I try to find a new one?' he asked, worried about the consequences if there was no maypole dancing this year.

'Let's give it a day or two,' I said, more in hope than in realism. 'If it is a joke, it'll turn up somewhere. Those who moved it won't want to disappoint the children.'

'I've called an emergency meeting of the parish council tonight,' he said. 'I've invited the May Day committee too. What can I tell them?'

'Tell them the matter is in the hands of the police,' I suggested. 'You could ask everyone to keep their eyes open for it and to help us find it. You might tell the local papers, there's a good tale for them in this, and the publicity might just help.'

'It might persuade the thieves to cut it up an' all,' he worried. 'But, Mr Rhea, where can you hide a maypole?'

'I don't know.' I sympathized with him in his moments of agony and promised my very best efforts to recover it. My first enquiry would be to Claude Jeremiah Greengrass.

When I walked into his untidy yard, Claude Jeremiah was busy sawing wood and, at my approach, his scruffy dog, Alfred, loped away into hiding; at first, I regarded that as a dual ominous sign but quickly saw that the timber was a pile of old railway sleepers and not the maypole. Alfred the lurcher, I felt, had an instinctive desire to hide from police officers, perhaps due to his breeding or else because of his dubious partnership in various illicit poaching expeditions.

As Alfred scrutinized me from an outbuilding with his hairy

grey face poking through a gap in the rotting woodwork, Claude Jeremiah was reducing the sleepers to bundles of kindling which he'd sell around the district. He did not see or hear my approach due to his noisy actions and this gave me a brief opportunity to look around his buildings for signs of the maypole. But there was none.

'Morning, Claude,' I shouted above the noise of his saw.

He stopped work. His face dropped when he saw me standing behind him and said, 'I wasn't me, Mr Rhea, definitely not me.'

'What wasn't you?' I asked.

'Whatever you're here for, whatever's happened, it wasn't me. I didn't do it.'

'What have you done with the Slemmington maypole?' I decided to pull his leg a little, a way of getting my own back for the hassle he caused me from time to time.

'Me? I've done nowt with any maypole, Mr Rhea.'

'Not even chopped it up for firewood?' I eyed his pile of cut timber.

'Railway sleepers, Mr Rhea, all creosoted, a job lot, they're closing lines and selling 'em off cheap. They make real good kindling.'

'I believe you, many wouldn't,' I laughed and then began to walk around his rubbish-cluttered premises, lifting lids off bins, moving old tyres and peering into sheds.

Alfred emerged and slunk into a position of safety behind his master and the pair of them followed me around with Claude Jeremiah explaining where he had obtained the objects of my pretended interest. Finally I stopped.

'Someone's stolen the Slemmington maypole,' I told him. 'Sometime during the night. We want it back for the kids,

Claude, so if you come across it during your travels, let us know, eh?'

'Right you are, Mr Rhea, yes, I'll keep my ears open. A maypole, eh? Now there's a thing. Fancy pinching a maypole.'

'My sentiments exactly, Claude. Who on earth would do that?'

Claude Jeremiah scratched his head and pretended to think deeply. 'Somebody with a use for one, I reckon, Mr Rhea,' he grinned. 'And not many folks have any use for a maypole these days, either new or second-hand.'

'So in your opinion, there's not a big market for second-hand maypoles, Claude?'

'Definitely not, Mr Rhea.'

'But if there was, you might be tempted?' I watched him with interest.

'Now then, Mr Rhea, that's putting ideas where there was none. No, I'd never pinch a maypole; well, I mean, I'd never get it out of the ground, would I? I'd need heavy lifting gear which I haven't got.'

'You could always steal a crane, Claude. Or borrow one. Now, somebody's got it out of the ground and spirited the thing away. Even I reckon that's beyond you, so I won't keep you away from your honest labours any longer.'

And I left man and dog to continue their chores. My next journey was to Ashfordly police station where I had to formally record the crime and to circulate it in our various publications. But Sergeant Blaketon was not at all pleased.

'You're not serious, Rhea?' he bristled. 'Who'd pinch a maypole? It'll have been taken down for redecorating or whatever they do. Maintenance. Repairs.'

'No, Sergeant,' I said. 'That's all been done. It had just undergone its annual service and had been reinstated, all new and shining bright. Then it was spirited away during the hours of darkness, sometime between nine o'clock last night and eight o'clock this morning.'

'There's no market for stolen maypoles, Rhea, not like jewellery and antiques . . .'

'It's not even an antique maypole, Sergeant,' I couldn't resist that retort. 'I can't see any antique dealer buying it.'

'I can't see anybody in their right minds taking it, Rhea. Are you sure it's been stolen? This isn't a prank of some kind is it? Somebody preparing for April Fool's Day? A stunt of some sort?'

I explained that I had considered all those possibilities and after making enquiries from the local people, plus a search of all likely maypole hiding-places and an interview with Claude Jeremiah Greengrass, I had to conclude that it was a genuine crime. This meant it would become part of our crime statistics, and if we didn't trace the thief, it would become part of our 'unsolved crime' figures. It would look as if there was a crime wave in Slemmington.

'It won't look good in our crime stats. and monthly returns, Rhea,' worried Sergeant Blaketon.

'Then we'll have to trace the culprit,' I said. 'How about writing me off normal duties to concentrate on detecting this heinous crime?' I suggested.

'Don't be so bloody daft, Rhea,' was all he said.

The inspector at Eltering, the superintendent at divisional headquarters and the detective superintendent at force headquarters, all queried the crime; each thought the maypole's disappearance was nothing but a prank. In spite of their reservations, however, a genuine crime report had been made and so the fate of the Slemmington maypole became part of our official crime statistics.

I returned to Slemmington later that day to continue my enquiries, the only development coming from a young mother who'd been awake at night tending her crying baby. Around 2 a.m., she'd heard the noise of a heavy vehicle moving slowly through the village, but hadn't looked out to see what it was.

If she had, I reckon she'd have noticed the removal of the said stolen property.

Three days passed without any useful maypole-detecting information coming into my possession. Slemmington Parish Council was growing increasingly concerned about my lack of results and were putting pressure on Jack Lawson to obtain a replacement. Meanwhile, the local weekly paper had not yet been published and so wider publicity among the public had not yet been achieved. It was a harrowing time for all.

And then the following day, as in all good detective stories, a piece of timely good fortune came my way. Living in a large converted farmhouse on the edge of the moors near Lairsbeck was a retired military gentleman who rejoiced in the name of Colonel Cuthbert Cruikshank-Carstairs. Three days after the maypole vanished, I had to visit him about the renewal of his firearms certificate and, as always, he welcomed me into his spacious, book-lined study while his wife brewed some strong coffee from home-ground beans. Colonel Cuthbert, as everyone called him, was an authority on country life; he wrote books and articles for magazines like *The Field* and *Country Life* and lectured to organizations ranging from the Women's Institute to adult educational courses about all aspects of rural living. His expertise ranged from fox hunting to folk lore by way of local customs, rural superstitions and ancient herbal cures.

Knowledgeable about all kinds of wildlife from fish to flowers, birds to bees and ferrets to foxes, he was a veritable treasure-house of country knowledge. Having completed the business of my visit, we chatted over our coffee and he asked me what was happening in the constabulary world beyond his village. I told him about the maypole theft and he smiled.

'Revenge,' he beamed. 'That will be Waindale getting their own back.'

'Waindale?' I must have sounded puzzled because he laughed at my reaction.

'You've not heard about the feud?' he asked.

'No,' I had to admit, wondering why, if there was a feud between Waindale and Slemmington, Jack Lawson hadn't told me.

'Years ago,' he said, 'Waindale had a lovely maypole, the tallest in this area. The villagers held a May Day festival every year and there is little doubt it was the finest display for miles around. The other villages were jealous, some tried to compete by arranging their own maypole dancing but none could match Waindale's dancing and none could produce a maypole of such impressive height. But of all the competing villages, Slemmington almost succeeded. Lord Ashfordly donated them a fine pole from his woods, it was not quite as tall as Waindale's but it was a very fine specimen. The acquisition of a fine pole encouraged Slemmington to recruit and train its own fine troupe of dancers led by a lovely maiden called Susanna Browning.

'But the trainer of the Waindale group got his eye on her. He

wooed her and wed her, thus taking away Slemmington's
leading dancer. Well, no one could forgive Waindale for that act
of piracy and so, the next thing that happened was that
Waindale's fine maypole vanished over night. Miraculously, at
that very same time, Slemmington acquired a very tall one, far
taller than any of its earlier specimens. The suspicions were
always there, rumours abounded. It was said that if Slemmington
couldn't have Susanna, they would have the finest maypole.
There is no doubt that the Waindale-ites believed Slemmington
had purloined their pole, but the Slemmingtonians have always
denied they were criminals.'

'When was this?' I asked.

'March 1766,' he told me. 'In March 1866, Slemmington
was raided overnight and its maypole was stolen. A similar one
was found in Waindale, but no one could prove it was the same
pole. Sadly, Waindale's maypole ceremonies never maintained
their earlier attraction and, in 1907, they ended. Waindale has
never had a maypole, or a maypole ceremony, since that time. In
contradiction, Slemmington's ceremony has flourished.'

'And now,' I said. 'It is March 1966, two hundred years
since the feud started.'

'Exactly,' beamed Colonel Cuthbert. 'The anniversary of the
original battle. So it would not surprise me that if you were to
pay a visit to Waindale, you might find a handsome maypole
sitting in the old socket . . .'

'I was there early last week,' I said. 'There was no maypole
on the green then.'

'Precisely,' he said.

I thanked him and after leaving his comfortable house, drove
through the winding lanes and across the windswept moors to

Waindale. This is a tiny community comprising a few stone cottages and a couple of farms around the village green, but there is no inn, no post office, no shop and no church. Its only feature is a telephone kiosk, although there is a timber-yard on the outskirts. There was rarely any reason for me to visit Waindale but now, as I drove in, I could see the enormous maypole which dominated the skyline.

It was rooted firmly into the old concrete-surrounded socket. To my inexpert eye, it looked identical to the one which had vanished from Slemmington but to my official police officer's eye, I knew there was no way of proving, to the satisfaction of a court of law, that this was that very same pole. As I studied the mighty edifice, I noticed that the top bore the metal carving of a team of shire horses drawing a wagon. That type of wagon is known as a wain in this area; wagons were once constructed here and the village was rich with skilled wainwrights, hence the name Waindale. A local farmer, Robin Hartree, noticed my interest and wandered across.

'Now then, Mr Rhea,' he smiled. 'Two quick visits, eh? It's not often we see you hereabouts on such a regular basis.'

'It's not often I need to come,' I said. 'I only come like this every hundred years or so when somebody decides to pinch a maypole.'

'Ours is safe enough,' and his eyes twinkled. 'Nobody's pinched ours.'

'But somebody's pinched one from Slemmington,' I said.

'They got their famous big maypole by pinching it from us, Mr Rhea. They've always made do with second-hand maypoles.'

'And Waindale doesn't?'

'Nay, lad, ours are allus new 'uns, just look at that paint, glistening like new. We're reviving our old custom, in honour of Susanna Browning. You'll not know of Susanna Browning?' he grinned.

'But I do,' I said, telling him the story as told to me by Colonel Cuthbert. And when I finished, I told him that I knew all about the story of the oft-stolen maypoles, adding that it might just be a coincidence that there was a timber-yard on the edge of Waindale, a business belonging to a man from Waindale which had all the gear necessary for lifting tree-trunks from the woods and maypoles from their sockets.

'Well, Mr Rhea,' he said. 'I'd say Waindale has only got what's rightly theirs, and that doesn't mean I'm saying the pole came from Slemmington.'

If indeed this was the Slemmington pole, then it did not rightly belong to Waindale because this particular pole had been a recent gift to Slemmington from Lord Ashfordly.

Even so, I did have some sympathy with the Waindale folk who were, even after the passage of two centuries, still smarting over their lost maypole.

When I returned to see Jack Lawson, he launched immediately into a tirade of anger without waiting to hear my news. He said he was furious because during the night someone had left the village's metal fox, minus the maypole, on his front doorstep and this piece of cheek had been aggravated because he had managed to find a replacement pole, but it was a mere 36 feet tall instead of 72 feet – only half the size of the missing one.

'Calm down, Jack,' I said. 'I think I've found your missing pole,' and I told him of my discoveries, not forgetting the story of Susanna Browning.

'I never thought anybody would remember that anniversary,' he said. 'I mean, I read about it when I was a lad, in an old local history book, but it's never been mentioned for generations. To be honest, we don't pay much attention to it in this village, it happened two hundred years ago so it's really got nothing to do with us now. Anyway, Waindale's got our maypole, so when do we get it back?'

'I can't prove it's yours, Jack,' and I explained the legal difficulties. 'All I can say is that there is a pole which matches yours exactly, and it is standing on Waindale village green.'

'But it is ours, Mr Rhea!'

'I know that and you know that, but there's no way to prove it if Waindale deny they removed it. Now listen, if someone was to remove that pole and replace it on Slemmington green, then put the smaller one in its place, I'd say the same logic would apply. One pole is just like another . . .'

'Are you saying no questions would be asked?'

'I'm saying it would be difficult to distinguish one brightly painted maypole from another, especially one with a fox on top . . .'

'I'll make a fuss about erecting our new one,' he grinned. 'That'll mislead Waindale . . . I'll have words with our Maypole Action Committee. When's your night off, Mr Rhea?'

'Friday,' I said.

On Saturday morning, I made a point of touring Slemmington and noticed the tall, gleaming maypole with the fox on top. It was in position on the green and a small committee of men were admiring it. I stopped and Jack came over to me.

'We've got a nice new pole, Mr Rhea,' he grinned. 'Exactly the same height and colour of the one we lost.'

'That's amazing,' I said. 'I trust you've anchored it well into its base?'

'We have,' he said. 'Concreted it in and we're erecting a secondary structure around the base, like a flagpole has, to give it added security. You and Mrs Rhea will be coming to our May Day ceremonies?'

'I might look in,' I said. 'Well, I must be off. I thought I might have a look at Waindale's new maypole.'

'They tell me they've got a good 'un, Mr Rhea, but not quite as tall as ours.'

I smiled as I drove away. Waindale did indeed have a fine maypole and it was considerably smaller than the one I'd seen there earlier. Robin Hartree saw me examining it and came across for a word.

'Someone's given us a nice new maypole, Mr Rhea,' he smiled.

'Someone must love Susanna Browning,' I countered. 'You'll be celebrating May Day perhaps?'

'Now we've got a maypole of our own, we might just do that,' he said. 'But none of us here knows owt about maypole dancing, Mr Rhea; we need someone to show us how to cope with all those ribbons and things.'

'There's some very knowledgeable folk in Slemmington,' I said. 'They've some maypole experts there, I'm told, quite friendly folk they are, when you get to know them.'

Each village was therefore quite happy with the outcome of the great maypole mystery and each village now stages its own maypole ceremonies. The feuding has been suspended until 2066, but the lack of positive and legally acceptable identification of each pole meant the police could never be sure that the precise pole that was stolen had ever been replaced.

Replacement by a substitute meant that the original was still recorded as missing and because of that, the crime is still listed as 'undetected'.

The next piece of villainy in Slemmington's crime wave also occurred on the village green. It involved the scorer for the cricket team which was known throughout the district as The Chadwicks. The Chadwicks was Slemmington's village team, but the entire team comprised men with that surname – brothers, cousins, fathers, sons, grandfathers and uncles. The team had been playing for years, always comprised entirely of Chadwicks; even the reserves were called Chadwick so it required a scorer with more than average acumen to keep track of their runs, wickets, bowling and resultant analyses.

Such a man was Cyril Pulling, a bespectacled and meticulous clerk who worked in the accounts office of a nearby animal feeds production company. Small, neat and extremely tidy, Cyril was married with an equally neat and tidy wife and two equally neat and tidy children. The house was small and neat and the family ran a small and neat Morris mini car.

Cyril's Saturdays during the summer consisted of scoring for The Chadwicks and he drove to all their matches in his immaculate little car. It was always polished and gleaming; in spite of having two small children, Cyril's car was never full of childish things like sweet papers, toys and games, neither were its windows greasy with finger marks.

Cyril was a serious fellow; he tackled his scoring duties with the same commitment as his company results or his own income tax returns, but he never seemed to smile. Those who knew him realized that this was his means of enjoying himself, of getting himself out of the office. Even if it meant working with columns of figures, Cyril regarded it as a holiday and therefore a welcome break. Scoring for The Chadwicks was his relaxation.

Unfortunately, his serious nature often meant he was a butt for jokes and one Saturday, when he parked his beautiful car behind the pavilion at the edge of Slemmington's village green, he left the doors open and the key in the ignition switch. The temptation was too much for three of the village lads. Whilst the first half of the match was in progress, they pushed the little car onto the lane and down the gentle slope, then drove it into an old barn just across the narrow bridge and closed the barn doors. This was their idea of a joke; they never thought for a moment that their prank would be considered theft of a motor vehicle.

Cyril noticed its absence during the break when he went for his sandwiches and flask; realizing he had left his key with the car, he knew he had been foolish and that someone was now driving around in his pride and joy. Cyril knew precisely what to do when a crime was committed and so, without wasting a moment, he dialled 999.

I was on patrol between Ashfordly and Eltering that afternoon and when I received the call on my radio, I diverted to the cricket ground and arrived within ten minutes. Play had not resumed so I was able to talk to Cyril; I doubt if he would have abandoned his scoring just to talk to me had I arrived after the recommencement of play. I had the registration number – that had been circulated after his 999 call – but I needed more detail and listened as he explained about parking it. As we chatted, I noticed three youths hanging around and watching my activities, but did not regard their interest as unusual or significant. When play resumed, I decided to search the vicinity for the car – we always searched the area when a crime had been reported. I began by driving along the lane.

Very quickly, I spotted the wheelmarks in the soft grass and the three sets of footprints, one at the steering-wheel side and two at the rear . . .

Equally quickly, I saw the flattened grass at the entrance to the old barn. It had been depressed by the opening and closing of the huge doors; I could also see the twin tracks leading inside. It was the work of a moment to find the car.

As I hauled open the heavy doors, I became aware of the presence of those three youths, all about sixteen and all watching me from behind the shelter of a thick hedgerow. They thought I could not see them . . . Either they had hidden the car as a prank, or else it had been concealed here to be collected later by the thieves or perhaps a receiver.

Either way, I could deal with the matter. I radioed Control and requested that Scenes of Crime be informed, asking them to attend to examine the car for fingerprints and other evidence. The good news was that the Scenes of Crime vehicle was in the vicinity, having just attended an office-break-in in Strensford. It would arrive within a matter of minutes.

I closed the barn doors to await their arrival, thus securing the car. In the absence of a lock on the barn, I parked the police van in front of the doors and locked it, then returned on foot to the village green. I went into the pavilion and waited for the over to finish before informing Cyril of my discovery. He was delighted; I said the car did not appear to be damaged but that our Scenes of Crime people were en route and the car would be restored to him once they had concluded their investigation. I then said I suspected a prank by the three youths who, by now, were outside the pavilion watching me chat to Cyril. From their demeanour, I thought they were plucking up courage to talk to me.

I went out to them.

'What do you lads know about Cyril's car?' I looked at each in turn. Three frightened faces peered at me, so I decided to capitalize on this fear. 'If it's been stolen and if I find the culprits, they'll be in serious trouble. Our Scenes of Crime officers are on their way now, to examine the car for finger-prints . . . so let's suppose I asked for your fingerprints, all of you? I wonder what I'd find?'

'It was us, Mr Rhea,' said the taller one. 'But we didn't steal it, we just hid it, as a joke . . . honest.'

'Ah!' I peered down at them, trying to appear fierce. 'Well, it seems your joke has backfired, doesn't it? I have received a report that the car was stolen, and when you take someone's property without permission, that is stealing, especially when you hide it so the owner can't find it . . .'

I was about to lecture them about dishonesty when SOCO, the name we gave to the Scenes of Crime Officers, eased on to the village green parking area in their marked vehicle. The boys' faces showed their dismay and one of them, whom I later discovered was called Andrew Staples, began to weep.

'I think you lads have learned a lesson,' I said. 'Now wait here. I'll have words with our officers, then I'll come back to you. Right?'

They waited, huddled in a sorry group as I went to speak to SOCO.

'Hello, Sarge,' I greeted Detective Sergeant Power.

'Stolen car, Nick?' he asked. 'Can you show us?'

'Sure, down here,' and I led the way back to the old barn, moved my police van and showed them the car.

'Right,' said Power. 'I'll fetch my troops.'

'Since calling you,' I said. 'I've found the culprits,' and I told him the story. He listened and smiled.

'I don't think we can crime this one, Nick,' he said. 'Can we have a word with the loser and ask him to withdraw his complaint? They're only kids, juveniles, and no court would convict them.'

'Suits me.' I was happy to go along with this. 'But I think we should teach those lads a lesson.'

'That's easy,' grinned Power. 'Let's have a word with the owner first.'

'He's scoring, we'll have to wait for a break in the game,' I said.

'That's fine,' said Power. 'There'll be a cup of tea around, I expect, and I like watching cricket anyway.'

Cyril Pulling listened to Sergeant Power's plan and actually smiled as he nodded his agreement. 'I'll agree to that,' he said. 'There's no damage to my car and no harm's been done.'

When Power had had three mugs of tea and umpteen scones and cakes made by the cricket team's wives, we returned to Cyril's mini, eased it out of the garage and drove it back to the side of the cricket pitch. The three youths watched us with some apprehension. Then Sergeant Power and his two colleagues, both detective constables, set to work.

One was the official photographer, the other a Scenes of Crime officer and under the directions of the sergeant, they literally smothered the car in grey fingerprint powder. There was thick powder everywhere.

Within five minutes, that lovely little vehicle looked like something which had been stored in a dusty shed from the time that Adam was a lad.

'Right, you three,' shouted Sergeant Power before brushing the powder in his search for prints. 'Come here.'

The three youths came across, nervous and apprehensive.

'You took this car for a prank, right?'

'Yes, sir,' said Andrew Staples.

'Well, it needs cleaning, doesn't it? It needs to be as clean as it was before it got covered in all this powder. Now, I have cleaning materials in my van, plenty of dusters and so on, and so that's your job. Mr Pulling wants his car as clean as a new pin by the time the cricket match finishes. Right? And I'll remain here to make sure it is. Got it?'

'Yes, sir,' said the three chastened lads.

It was a good match. The Chadwicks won by a wicket and ten runs, each of the police officers present, including myself, had a grandstand view of the game aided by endless cups of tea and lots of scrumptious home-made food, while three hard-working lads made a superb job of polishing Cyril's car.

'It's cleaner than when I lost it,' said Cyril afterwards – and smiled again.

2 Fiends in High Places

There are no tricks in plain and simple faith.
William Shakespeare (1564–1616)

The practised confidence trickster is a curious mixture of evil cunning and winsome appeal; by using his combination of characteristics he or she may persuade others to part with gifts, money, accommodation or even to permit use of the so-called secret parts of their bodies. Over the centuries, unscrupulous men have charmed their way into the beds of gullible girls, scheming women have persuaded rich men to marry them for better or for a lot worse, and there is a roaming army of pestilent confidence tricksters who prey on old folks, vicars, charity workers and others who are blessed with warm hearts. This plague of wandering charlatans comprises villains and parasites who live off the generosity of innocent victims in their constant effort to feed and clothe themselves, often in luxury. Con men have been known to charm hard-won life-savings from poor pensioners, only to lose the lot in a moment of high living or reckless gambling. There is deep-seated cruelty in people who will do such evil things and although some would admire their devious skills, the police know their true worth and do their utmost to warn their potential victims, to trap the rouges and to bring them to justice.

But trapping such wily characters is like seizing an eel; no matter how sure your grip, the eel will wiggle in its own slime until it is free from your clutches – and confidence tricksters are very similar. They are as slippery as the proverbial eel but infinitely more cunning and nasty.

They rely upon their silver tongues and well-rehearsed charm to get them out of trouble. It is a sad truth that many of them do evade justice. They know how to use the letter of the law and the sympathy of their victims to their full advantage in some cases, their charm is such that even the victims refuse to believe that their new 'friend' is a wrongdoer. In many cases, the victims do not wish to prosecute and while this protects that victim from the scorn of their neighbours, it leaves the villain free to prey on others.

In Yorkshire, we call such people 'slape tongued', which means slippery tongued; I believe it was the Red Indians in cowboy films who called such people fork-tongued because a snake's tongue is often forked – and who can trust a snake? God made the serpent the lowest of the low, a beast destined to crawl for ever on its belly, and this is an apt comparison with the guile of a confidence trickster. They are among the lowest of humanity's low and I believe there is a famous quotation, whose origin escapes me, which says 'There is no heart below the head of a serpent'.

The famous nineteenth-century criminologist, Dr Hans Gross, had a lot to say about confidence tricksters too – in one paragraph he describes them as 'generally men who have received a good education in their youth, or who at least have had the opportunities of picking up the appearance of such. Without exception, they are men of ability, full of dexterity and presence of mind, but with a love of easy and idle life'.

He offers a picture of a typical fraudster and it is perhaps worthy of inclusion here.

> Fashionably dressed, he steps into a jeweller's shop and steals while pretending to select, or he causes the valuable selected to be brought to his hotel, takes delivery and disappears through another door; he goes to the banker and collects the amount of a forged cheque; he manages to get introduced to the highest social circles, runs up heavy debts and disappears; he cheats at play and that on a large scale; he becomes engaged to one or more wealthy young ladies and makes off with money borrowed from presumptive fathers-in-law; he buys houses and estates without paying for them, mortgages them and disappears; he gets into business relations with a merchant and runs up debts in his name; in a word, he knows marvellously well how to play upon that weakness in mankind that allows itself to be bluffed by a high-sounding name, fine clothes, and easy and self-possessed manners; he knows there are fools to be found always and everywhere, and lives at their expense until he is caught.

Whilst a constable at Aidensfield, I was often in receipt of police circulars which warned of tricksters on the move. In such cases, we would then warn any potential victims who lived and worked on our beats. Bed-and-breakfast establishments were commonly targeted by travelling con men who slept and ate, then left without paying, and so we would tour those on our respective patches to alert them. Some confidence tricksters would specialize in visiting vicarages where they told a sorrowful and harrowing tale of some kind, following which the vicar gave them tea, sympathy, a pocket full of money and sometimes a bed for the night. Off would go the fraudster to another vicarage where he would repeat the yarn and the sneaky side of such acts often remained unknown until one clergyman chanced to be talking to another about their daily work and compared notes about helping the poor.

The tale that had been told so well to both was usually enough for the vicars to realize they had been well and truly tricked out of their hard-earned money; they would ring the police and we would circulate a description of the wanted villain, by which time, of course, he was usually miles away in another diocese doing exactly the same thing. No matter how widely we circulated his activities, he usually managed to select a vicar who hadn't been warned or who, if warned, did not believe that the charming fellow in his study was indeed the biblical wolf or false prophet in sheep's clothing.

In one case, a con man was actually arrested in our area and he had to be transported to the Midlands where he was wanted for serious offences in the Birmingham area. He was taken to Birmingham by train, being handcuffed to a detective *en route*, but during the journey he even managed to persuade the detective to give him £5! He said he had no money but wanted to buy some flowers for his granny who would be most upset at his arrest. Of course, there was no upset granny . . .

This incident shows that policemen are human too, and that some of us can be persuaded to believe the sorrowful stories of a skilled confidence trickster. Of course, that sort of thing would never happen to me . . .

Clever disguise was sometimes resorted to by confidence tricksters and a favourite was a clergyman's dog collar. This was one of the most simple to effect. If one is approached by a man in a dark suit and a back-to-front collar, then one is usually tempted to believe that he is trustworthy. As a consequence, there are many travelling rogues who dress up as priests or vicars, nuns or monks but perhaps the most interesting of the clerical con men within my knowledge was the one who came to Aidensfield to establish a monastery. To be honest, I am still not sure whether or not he was a genuine man of God with a desire to perpetuate his faith or whether he was a charlatan.

When the impressive figure of Father Severus Sanandaj, a priest from the Patriarchate of the Karakumian Branch of the Orthodox Adiaphoritic Apostolic Church arrived in Aidensfield, we all warmed to him in a spirit of ecumenical love, hope and joy. He was a majestic figure some six feet five inches tall, with long black hair aided by a heavy black beard and moustache. Underneath all that hair, his age was difficult to determine, but I guessed he was in his middle forties. He was a fit man who enjoyed physical activity; he walked miles and from time to time would disrobe and enjoy a hectic swim in the local swimming-baths.

During his daily routine, he wore the long, all-embracing black vestments of a priest of the Orthodox Church, the kind which can still be seen in Greece, and upon his head he wore a tall tubular black hat with a rim around the top. To see him, fully robed, walking down the main street of Aidensfield was indeed a memorable and remarkable sight.

He was a quiet man who seemed to be totally content with his religious life and he lived in a rented cottage along one of the quieter lanes of the village. I was never sure precisely when or how he arrived; he just seemed to materialize upon the village scene but with Maddleskirk Abbey only two miles away, the sight of a foreign priest, monk or nun in the area was not regarded as unusual. Many came from all over the world to Maddleskirk Abbey for retreats or spiritual renewal, or to attend conferences relating to church matters.

Thus Father Severus was regarded as just another foreign and interesting priest who had been drawn to this place of religious succour.

When I asked George in the pub if he knew about the Orthodox priest, George confirmed those thoughts by saying,

'He's summat to do with the abbey, Mr Rhea, he walks along there to see the monks, joins them in church and for meals and things. They're supporting him, he fled from the Soviet Union by all accounts, got away from the Communists and made his way across Europe to England. He's from some obscure branch of the Orthodox faith and reckons he's trying to keep his church alive. He wants to establish a small monastery in Aidensfield.'

It all made sense. The Roman Catholic monks of Maddleskirk Abbey did encourage those of other faiths to join them and I did know they were very active in keeping christianity alive in various Communist countries. This man had undoubtedly contacted them when he was in dire need of help – and he had come to live amongst us, at least for a short time. I knew the villagers would make him most welcome.

Soon after his arrival, a caravan appeared in the garden of his cottage and within a week or so, it had sprouted something that looked like a huge onion with a leek standing beside it. The caravan was his church, the central point of his new monastery, and the onion-shaped thing was its dome; the leek beside the dome was a small decorative copy of a minaret.

Soon, the dome was painted with gold paint, the minaret was gilded in parts, and a splendid icon of the Virgin Mary appeared on the side of the caravan. The entire complex looked like a cross between a miniature Kremlin and model of Brighton's Royal Pavilion but when I saw what had appeared in that lane, I wondered from where he drew his congregation and how he intended to support himself. But such problems were no real concern of mine – I knew that many monastic establishments had had very modest beginnings and had survived through the faith of their founders and the devotion of their supporters. Perhaps the Orthodox Adiaphoritic Apostolic Church of Aidensfield would similarly flourish?

My duties and those of Father Severus never came into contact. From time to time, however, I did have to visit the administrative offices of Maddleskirk Abbey and sometimes found myself talking with the abbot. On one such occasion, I took the opportunity to refer to Father Severus and his onion.

I discovered that he was already well known in the abbey. The cottage he was using was owned by the abbey trustees; it was a spare house which could be used by guests to the abbey. One common use was for Anglican priests who had left their own church to become Catholics, but who needed a period for contemplation away from all religious influences. They would stay there to gather their thoughts; Catholic priests facing a crisis of faith would also use it, as would any other deserving person.

Father Severus, I was told, having fled from oppression and Communism, was one such deserving case. He lived there free of rent, his food was supplied by the abbey and he could join the brethren for lunch and evening meals whenever he wished. He was even given a small allowance of cash for his daily essentials, and had been allowed use of all the abbey's comprehensive facilities and contacts. Hence his caravan, onion and icon.

Neither I nor anyone else had cause to suspect he was not genuine. But, eventually, tiny hints began to appear. He took up swimming in the local baths where he presented a splendid figure and attracted the interest of many women, some of whom, I am sure, felt sorry for the celibate man and his onion. I do know that he took one or two ladies out for expensive meals.

Or perhaps they took him out? I never found out who paid the bills but I reckoned it might be either the abbey trustees or the ladies in question. On another occasion, he ordered a case of wine from the Brewer's Arms and told George to send the bill to the abbey. Later, I saw one or two ladies journeying individually to Aidensfield to attend his monastery and admire his minaret; once or twice, I saw well-dressed ladies emerging with a smile from his church and wondered if they had been on a pilgrimage or a therapeutic visit to the handsome priest.

Father Severus expanded his range of powerful physical activities, going for long, fast runs, swimming or playing rugby football with a local team.

He performed other feats of strength and endurance too, such as running a marathon and weight-lifting. He once joined some TA volunteers on an exercise involving abseiling, rock climbing and a fearsome assault course, and left a lot of the younger men breathless. In time, tales of his prowess became commonplace and there was no doubt that he was a strong and very fit man. Rugged, powerful and tough, he was not the conventional image of a man of God.

But as I received no complaints about his behaviour, I could not therefore take any specific action against him. Besides, his way of life was none of my business. If he was living off the generosity of the local abbey and some local lonely women, then was that wrong? Certainly, it was not wrong if they volunteered to support him as he came to terms with his exile, but was he using deceit and trickery to achieve those comforts? I must admit that I did have some anxieties about him, particularly as his use of English was so good.

Conscious of my duties towards the people of Aidensfield and district, I did try to find out a little more about the Karakumian Branch of the Orthodox Adiaphoritic Apostolic Church. But the more I delved into the complexities of the historic links between the Catholic and Orthodox churches, the more confusing it became. I did learn, however, that there had been a branch of the Eastern Orthodox Church whose followers were known as Monophysites; there was a breakaway group of this sect, and they were known as Adiaphorites.

And I did discover that towns called Karachev, Karakuny, Karakumskiy and Karakulimi did exist in various parts of the USSR. I also found out that one of the bishops of the Monophysitic Orthodox Church was called Severus. He was Bishop of Antioch in AD 513. Our chap had taken his name.

But having made these minor discoveries, I also knew that the hallmark of a good con man was to establish what appeared to be an authentic base for his story. This man had done that – it would take a great deal of infinitely more detailed research to prove that his church did not exist and equally, because communication with the Soviet authorities was so difficult, it would probably be impossible to establish the bona fides of Father Severus. So who was he? Was he English? German? Russian? Hungarian? I had no idea.

In my policeman's mind, this man was a mystery and when I had a rendezvous with Sergeant Blaketon one morning, I decided to voice my concern. I told him about Father Severus and he listened intently.

'Have you had any complaints about him, Rhea?' he asked.

'No, Sergeant,' I had to admit. 'Not one.'

'Then it's no concern of ours, is it?'

'But if he is conning all those monks and those women, then he ought to be stopped. If they are being charitable because they think he's genuine when in fact he might be a rogue, then he's nothing more than a cunning and evil scrounger.'

'If one of them makes an official complaint, we can do something about it, but what's he done wrong, Rhea? There's nothing wrong in people being charitable! And well-meaning people do create new religions and churches. Jesus did it, didn't he?'

'Jesus got crucified because folks thought he was a villain,' I reminded Blaketon.

'There'll always be miscarriages of justice, Rhea, and I don't want one in the case of your Father Severus. If there's no formal complaint, it suggests he's done nothing wrong, and that means we can't – and shouldn't – take action. And he hasn't done anything wrong, has he?'

'He hasn't been found out, you mean,' I retorted.

'So he charms the ladies and persuades holy men to support

him. Where's the criminality in that, Rhea? It's being done the world over, and has been for centuries.'

I realized I was not making any headway and decided to keep my ears and eyes open for any further hints about the background of Father Severus. I even paid a visit to his church, just to have a look inside, and he was charming and helpful, speaking in good English with what appeared to be a strong Eastern European accent. He showed me into the caravan with its small altar, its icons and its ornate gold leaf decor. Before the altar stood half a dozen chairs and there was the all-pervading smell of incense. It was an Orthodox Church in miniature.

In the few months he had been in the village, he did muster half a dozen regular members of his congregation, all ladies of means. Lonely ladies, I believed. Ladies with husbands out at work all day and absent for most of the night.

Severus remained with us for more than a year and not once did I receive any complaint about him or his church. I did make discreet enquiries into his claims and into his name and background, but found absolutely nothing. Other than searching his house, I realized I could learn nothing of the man – and I could not search his house unless he was arrested for a crime.

Then it became known that he had had a calling to visit America, there to establish yet another of his monasteries. Notices appeared on the parish noticeboard and in the local paper; there were papers pinned to the door of his church because he was attempting to raise funds to finance his visit to America on a missionary basis. And, of course, the rich ladies provided their support. They organized events in the village like raffles, jumble sales, whist drives and other gatherings with the

sole aim of raising money for his charitable and religious work
in the pagan USA.

And, sufficient funds having been raised, he conducted a
thanksgiving service in his church, thanked everyone for their
support and left Aidensfield.

The cottage remained empty for a long time, and the caravan
with the onion on its roof began to look rather neglected.

No more ladies came to pray there, although some did
receive postcards from America signed 'Severus' and saying it
was a wonderful country for the free and that he had managed to
establish several small churches in various neighbourhoods.
But there was no address or contact number on any of the
correspondence, and no hint about where precisely those
churches had been established. In time, Maddleskirk Abbey
Trustees recovered their caravan, took the onion and leek off its
roof then removed the icon and other adornments. It was needed
to house a new cowman who worked on the abbey farm.

And that, I reckoned, was the end of Father Severus, except
that two or three years later I was watching a colourful police
thriller at a local Odeon. I forget the title now, but suddenly, in
a daring sequence where a trapped man leapt from a high
building which was on fire and threatening to collapse, I saw
Father Severus. He was the man who was about to jump; his
tall, powerful figure, his handsome face with its beard and thick
hair were unmistakable and then I realized why he had gone to
America. There he would find lots of pretty women with plenty
of money but I don't think they would be the kind who'd be
happy spending their spare time in a caravan with an onion on
the roof. In Hollywood, there was a different religion and he had
found it – but he looked very happy.

When the credits came up, I saw that the stuntman was called Igor Stepnyak. I wondered if the American police would try and establish who precisely he was.

But, as I had had no complaints from Hollywood, it was not my job.

If priests and vicars were prey to confidence tricksters, then so were the occupiers and owners of large country houses. One of their chief difficulties was the recruiting of reliable and trustworthy members of staff; even when landowners were being penalized relentlessly by the advance of socialism, they did manage to keep their homes and life style. They found new methods of keeping the homes which had been in the family for centuries, even if it meant opening them to the public.

Fortunately, many were still able to provide much-needed employment for local people, but it was a changing world which forced them to advertise for staff. Fewer and fewer recruits could be found in the surrounding villages and many young people would not tolerate the long hours, high demands and meagre wages which accompanied this kind of work. The outcome was that even though butlers, housemaids, laundrymaids, gardeners, estate workers and their kind were still in demand by the owners of mansions on my beat, such staff had to be recruited from afar, often from towns and cities, and often from a class of person lacking loyalty, honour and trustworthiness. Gone were the days when you could hire a maid or a manservant for life; no longer was it considered an honour to work for his Lordship. Rather, it was considered to be drudgery.

But the polish of a trained butler was still necessary and who

better to fill the role of butler than a highly skilled confidence
trickster?

Many of them did apply for such posts and many were
appointed, only for his Lordship to discover later that items of
the family silver or priceless bottles of wine from his cellar had
vanished, often at the same time that the butler no longer
responded to his bell.

Our circulars were rich with examples of this kind of treachery
and theft and we did try to educate their Lordships into taking
care over staff appointments. One simple method was to actually
check any proffered references. Many prospective employers, in
places ranging from factories to fancy houses, took written
references on face value without checking that the signature was
genuine or that the supposed signatory had, in fact, written such
glowing prose about the chap applying for the post.

There is a theory, of course, that if a referee writes highly
praiseworthy words about an employee, then it is done with a
desire to part company with that employee. The ploy was often
used in the police force. If an officer in one force was not very
proficient, he usually had an unhappy time and felt that a
transfer to a quieter area would be beneficial. When he applied
for a post in the new force of his choice, his chief would write
glowing praises about him, in the hope that someone would be
daft enough to take him off his hands.

Sometimes, that ploy worked, but very soon discerning chief
constables realized that high praise from another chief constable
was often an indication that he was trying to offload some
rubbish. It was akin to the prose of a second-hand car salesman
or a less-than-honest antique dealer. You finished with something
that looked good but which did not work. In those respects,

second-hand policemen were often like second-hand cars.

In our attempts to thwart confidence tricksters, we tried to educate all potential employers to check references with great care and, until the Labour Government said it was wrong for us to check a person's criminal record in such cases, we could even make discreet enquiries on their behalf. After all, it was in the interests of the local constabulary and also the local community not to have a known and active criminal living in the village, even if he was employed at the big house at the end of the drive and even if he said he'd reformed.

But the socialist creed said otherwise – the socialists said we must give all villains a fair chance to continue their crimes. And so they did. With no check on their activities and precious little punishment to deter them, they continued to commit their crimes and to accumulate an increasing list of victims. But in the days preceding those doctrinaire edicts, we did check a person's criminal record if he or she was applying for certain posts and I do know that a lot of crime was thus prevented.

In spreading the message of caution when making vital appointments I did, I know, influence Lord Ashfordly on more than one occasion. Several checks of submitted references proved them to be false and as a consequence, he did not make the appointments in question. Today, of course, the Theft Act of 1968, section 16, deals with dishonestly obtaining a pecuniary advantage by deception and this now makes it a crime to obtain a job with forged references or through the use of invalid or faked qualifications.

But even the most careful checks can fail to flush out a clever villain and so it was with a butler appointed by Lord Ashfordly.

He called himself Gilbert Chaldecott-Montefiore and upon

applying for the post of butler with Lord Ashfordly, had produced glowing references from his last employer, the Earl of Labberford. He had worked for the earl at his London house, so he had claimed.

Lord Ashfordly, not knowing Labberford in person, had written to the impressive address on the high quality headed paper and had received a reply to the effect that Chaldecott-Montefiore was a splendid fellow worthy of anyone's hire. He had left Labberford's employment simply because Labberford, a widower of some years, was going into a private nursing home for an extended period and would not therefore require a butler in the foreseeable future. Lord Ashfordly had congratulated himself upon the acquisition of such an outstanding chap.

In fact, Lord Ashfordly was so pleased with his new butler that for once he did not ask me to discreetly check his credentials.

But in the weeks that followed, the demeanour of Gilbert Chaldecott-Montefiore led his Lordship to believe that the fellow was not everything that he claimed. His knowledge of fine wines was very limited, his treatment of the other servants was not in keeping with the position of butler, his attitude to Lord Ashfordly's guests was not of the kind one would attribute to a trained man . . .

Lord Ashfordly, with the beginnings of suspicion deep in his heart, rang me one morning.

'Ah, Mr Rhea,' he always called me Mr Rhea, not just Rhea, 'I would like a word with you, on a private matter.'

'I'll be in your area this afternoon,' I said. 'I could call around three o'clock?'

'That will be perfect.' He sounded relieved.

Wondering what could be worrying him, I drove to Ashfordly

Park, his magnificent country house, and rang the bell. It sounded deep within the mansion and a maid responded. When I announced that his Lordship was expecting me, I was asked to wait in the library, and was eventually shown into the study. A silver tray of tea and biscuits was waiting, and the maid poured a cup for each of us before handing around the biscuits. As she worked, Lord Ashfordly made small talk about the weather and increasing tourism in the market town which bore his name.

When she'd left us, he began, 'This is a delicate matter, Mr Rhea. I must insist on complete confidence and the utmost discretion on your part.'

'Of course,' I assured him. I liked Lord Ashfordly. A sturdy man in his early fifties with a good head of hair, he was a tireless worker for the townspeople, sitting on the parish council and the county council and protecting the town against unwelcome development. He had a known dislike of square concrete buildings and characterless shopping developments and, fortunately for Ashfordly town, was in a position to resist hurtful change. I had a lot of respect for him.

'Last month,' he said, 'I appointed a new butler, a man called Gilbert Chaldecott-Montefiore. Excellent references, good bearing, fine manner, good command of the English language, smart and tidy. Ideal in many ways. You've met him, have you?'

'No, I haven't,' I said, explaining that from time to time I did meet the butlers of such houses, but to date, had not had the pleasure of the company of Mr Gilbert Chaldecott-Montefiore.

'It is his day off today,' smiled Ashfordly. 'He has gone to Scarborough, there's an outing been arranged from the town; he's away all day, hence my call to you.'

'You are worried about him?' I anticipated. 'He hasn't been stealing from you, has he?'

'I fear that might follow,' and he told me about his worries which were chiefly based on his butler's lack of finesse and skill in his chosen profession. As his Lordship itemized the growing number of small errors, I realized they were the kind of fault I would never have recognized, nor indeed would any ordinary person. But to a blue-blooded member of the British aristocracy, those errors and lack of the social graces would be like loud warning bells. With reasonable cause for concern, Lord Ashfordly suspected that the fellow was a charlatan.

'So, Mr Rhea,' he said. 'I am asking if there is any way you can check his antecedents for me?'

I had no wish for a theft to be committed at Lord Ashfordly's house; worse still, it might become an unsolved crime if the villain was very clever. And no self-respecting constable wants an unsolved crime on his books. I was therefore keen to help.

'His name,' I proffered. 'Is it genuine? It sounds more like the name of an employer than an employee.'

'That's the name he uses, Mr Rhea, and it was on all his documents; medical card, National Insurance and so on.'

'Thanks.' I knew that it was not difficult to obtain forged documents of that kind. 'Have you any of the papers he supplied to you? References and so on? I need something to base my enquiries upon.'

'There's his personal file, in the safe. I'll get it.'

Unlocking his safe, he produced a file of papers and passed them across. I made notes of the names, addresses and other salient factors provided by Gilbert Chaldecott-Montefiore in applying for the post, and returned the file to him. I then asked for a physical description of the butler and was told he appeared to be between thirty-five and forty years of age, his documents showing him to be thirty-eight. He was 5' 11" tall, well built without a beer drinker's belly, dark hair cut short and kept tidy with a regular application of hair-oil, no bald patch, good strong white teeth, grey eyes, clean shaven and he did not wear spectacles. He was always smartly dressed and when off duty favoured a dark blue blazer with the top pocket bearing a badge depicting a yacht, a white shirt, a striped tie and grey trousers. He was well spoken with no discernible accent, but did not own a car or any transport of his own. He had no known tattoos or other obvious identifying features.

'I'll check our records,' I assured him. 'We do have a pool of information about confidence tricksters who are operating up and down the country but if this name has not been used before, we might have trouble identifying him. His description could fit thousands of men. But I'll let you know what progress I make.'

I ran a check with our local criminal record office and with the national CRO in Scotland Yard, but the name of Gilbert Chaldecott-Montefiore was not listed as a suspicious character.

Likewise, I asked the Metropolitan Police in London to find out if the Earl of Labberford was resident at the address given by the butler. They said it would take a few days to produce an answer.

As I suspected, the butler's physical description was of little value, a surprising number of active con men having a similar appearance. Having done this, rather than show my uniform at the Park when the butler was working, I rang Lord Ashfordly with my lack of positive news.

'What I need, sir,' I told him, 'is a set of fingerprints. If he has been convicted, they'll be on record. Can you get them for me, surreptitiously?'

'How on earth would I do that?' he chortled.

'I need to have something he has handled, something with a smooth surface like a wine-glass, a bottle of wine perhaps, or a piece of silver, an ashtray maybe, something that his prints will adhere to. And you would not have to touch it either . . . you will need to persuade him to handle the object and then leave it in your office, without anyone else touching it, for me to collect . . . you could ask him for an opinion about a new wine, perhaps? A glass would be better than a bottle, it has no paper label. Paper doesn't show prints very well.'

'Got you!' Lord Ashfordly sounded pleased. 'Leave it with me, I'll call you when I've done my Sherlock Holmes bit.'

It would be three days later when he called me.

'Mr Rhea,' he almost whispered into the telephone, 'I have a wine-glass which our friend has handled, no one else has touched it.'

'I'll be there right away,' I promised him.

Lord Ashfordly told me he'd asked the butler to test a new claret and the fellow had used the glass which now stood on a tray on a side table in the office. The butler had offered to clear away the glass after the tasting, but his Lordship had suggested he leave it for the maid. After all, that was her job. And then Lord Ashfordly had locked the tray and the glass in his safe. I took possession of both the tray and glass.

Taking infinite care with the samples, I placed them in a secure box and took them home from where I rang our Force Scenes of Crime department and asked if they would check the items for fingerprints. I told them the full story and completed the necessary forms. They said it would be no problem. Two days later, the SOCO van arrived, having been on another investigation in the vicinity, and a detective constable took away the exhibits.

The next day, I received a telephone call from Lord Ashfordly.

'He's gone,' he said. 'Chaldecott-Montefiore has left my employ, Mr Rhea. He's just vanished. Gone like a puff of wind.'

'Has he taken anything from the house?' was my first question. 'Anything of yours, I mean.'

'No, not a thing. He's just packed his bags and left, he's not even taken his personal papers.'

'He'll get some new ones in another name,' I said. 'He doesn't need the ones he's left behind. Did he give a reason?'

'Not to me, but I've asked the other staff if they know why he left. It seems he had words with the maid about the removal of that wine-glass, Mr Rhea, and she said she'd not moved it nor even seen it . . . I think he was suspicious of what I'd done, I think we flushed him out, Mr Rhea.'

'All that suggests he *was* a con man,' I laughed. 'But our own results aren't through yet. I'll let you know what turns up, sir. You'll be applying for a new butler now?'

'Well, actually, there is a chap in town, he had to leave his post as waiter in one of my hotels, not in the best of health, you know, but I think he can cope here, so I'm offering him the post. And I do know him of old, Mr Rhea.'

The Metropolitan Police did ring to say there was no record of anyone called the Earl of Labberford, and that the address was now occupied by tenants who were law-abiding and who had no idea who either Labberford or Chaldecott-Montefiore were. When the results of the fingerprint check came through, I learned they belonged to a confidence trickster whose real name was Charles Brown. He had a string of convictions in dozens of false names which included Crispin Carnegy, Nicholas Rochford, Auriel Blake-Edwards, Guy Furness-Brown, Dougal MacTavish-Rochford, Benedict Irvine, Peter Charles Monthiem-Muirhead, Derek Kelligan, Owen Walwyn-Jones and many more. His last conviction had resulted in two years' imprisonment for stealing silver from a country house where he had secured work as the butler.

I rang Lord Ashfordly to acquaint him with the character he'd welcomed to his home, and also to say that it looked as though the Earl of Labberford was also a fictional character. He thanked me, saying he was pleased that our joint actions had warned off the villain before he'd had the chance to steal anything.

Lord Ashfordly did say he'd done some of his own detective work too, by using his London contacts, and he had also discovered that the supposed Earl of Labberford did not exist. The address was genuine, it had been rented for a few months by a man called Jean-Paul Vericompte who had vanished. His appearance was remarkably similar to that of Gilbert Chaldecott-Montefiore. Lord Ashfordly was able to tell me more than Scotland Yard had bothered to unearth.

'The cunning of the fellow!' Lord Ashfordly had apparently enjoyed his piece of detective work and I felt he would relate the tale at many a dinner party. 'Damned clever really, it's a shame he was such a villain. If he'd used his brains properly, he might have been a success in life. Charming fellow, Mr Rhea, damned good in many ways. Sorry to burden you with my problems.'

'Not at all,' I said. 'That's why I'm here, to prevent crime.'

'I wonder where he's gone?' asked Lord Ashfordly.

Nine months later, our circulars told the story of the theft of a substantial amount of silver-plate from a mansion at Arridgeford in the Yorkshire Dales. The butler, who'd vanished, was the chief suspect; he had given the name of Ogden Garnon-Evans but his description was remarkably similar to that of Gilbert Chaldecott-Montefiore.

I rang the village constable at Arridgeford with an account of my own experience at Ashfordly and said we had a set of fingerprints if they were of any value.

Then I rang Lord Ashfordly to pass on that piece of news — it would add to the stories he would relate to his guests.

3 Do You Really Have To Go?

I pray thee leave.

Michael Drayton (1563–1631)

Most of us have had the experience of guests who have outstayed their welcome, but by any known standards, the staying power of Henry Hubert Houghton was exceptional.

Shortly after my arrival at Aidensfield, I heard his name mentioned in hushed tones and was advised not to show the hand of friendship towards him. Being fairly new to the district, I understood this to indicate that Henry was a rogue of some kind, or an undesirable fellow, the likes of which young constables should not befriend, but when I first saw him, he seemed a perfectly reasonable gentleman. Middle-aged, well spoken, smartly dressed and of fairly affluent means, he looked like any normal middle-class man albeit with perhaps just a hint of lingering ginger, a profuse moustache, a penchant for smoking a pipe full of pungent tobacco and a wardrobe full of expensive, tweedy clothes placed him firmly within the country set, and certainly not within the realms of local villains. I don't think he followed a profession but he did seem to have a fairly comfortable life style; he was a bachelor who lived in a large house and ran a vintage Rolls Royce.

Most certainly, there was no reason to suspect that he was a sexual deviant, mentally sick or a villain of any kind, so why should I keep him at a distance? I was enlightened somewhat further when another villager warned me never to invite Henry Hubert Houghton for dinner or even for a cup of coffee.

'I've already had a veiled warning about him, but he seems a decent enough chap,' I said. 'He's not a rogue so I'm at a loss to know why I should keep clear of him.'

'Oh, he's decent enough, and honest,' said my informant. 'But there's one major problem with him – if he gets into your house, he'll never leave. He'll be there all night, mark my words. And I mean all night, not just an extra hour or two. That's the problem with Henry, he just won't go home.'

When I first heard this, I thought it was an indication that Henry perhaps stayed a fraction longer than was mannerly, something that lots of people did from time to time, but I was to learn that this was an understatement. If Henry got into anyone's house, he stayed – and stayed – and stayed.

My first direct experience of this phenomenon came from Dr Alex Ferrenby. I espied the bearded doctor ambling down the village street around ten o'clock one morning; he looked as if he'd been up all night for his hair was awry and there were large black rings around his eyes.

'You look a bit rough, doctor,' I smiled at him.

'Rough?' he coughed. 'I look a bit rough, I feel a bit rough and I am a bit rough. More than a bit rough, Nick, old son. I'm shattered, mentally, physically and emotionally.'

'Anything I can do?'

'Nope, not a thing. I've got my football pools to get off today

– got to get my priorities right – so I'm off to the post office for a postal order and then, God willing, I'll crash out on the surgery lounger for a few hours.'

'A late night call-out, was it?'

'Nothing of the sort,' grunted the old doctor. 'I wish it had been. No, it was that confounded fellow Houghton. I should never have invited him, I know him well enough to avoid having him, but, well, it was his birthday and I felt sorry for him. So he came for a meal last night and just would not go. I mean, I tried, I said it was bedtime, I even put my pyjamas on and the milk bottles out, but he just stayed and stayed . . . I went to bed and left him – he was still there this morning, sitting on my settee with a glass of whisky in his hands. I've left him again just now, perhaps he's still there!'

'I've heard about his staying power,' I chuckled. 'I thought it was exaggerated local folk lore or common talk.'

'Talk? It's not mere talk, old son, it's genuine. He just won't go. Don't you ever let him come to you for dinner, Nick; he'll stay all night. I mean it. That's good advice from a sincere friend.'

Over a period of months, I began to hear other like tales of Henry Hubert Houghton and warned Mary about him, not that we would have any reason to invite him as a guest. But it did make sense to be prepared for the worst. I began to wonder how I would persuade him to leave should we ever be faced with the problem. Short of physically carrying him from the premises there seemed no polite way of persuading him to leave.

I was to learn that Dr Ferrenby had literally propelled him from the house. Others had done likewise – and Henry Hubert was never offended by those drastic measures. Indeed, such treatment became normal for those who had to deal with him and I began to suspect that he had come to terms with the fact that all his departures would be forced upon him. I think he had reached the stage where he would never leave unless someone pushed him out of the house. One clever lady had offered to take him shopping in York upon finding him still sitting in her lounge when she came down for breakfast and he'd gone shopping with her, but once in York, she'd managed to lose him among a crowd of American visitors. Somehow or other, he'd found his own way home. It seems that the ploys for evacuating Henry Hubert were many and varied, and I did realize that his vagueness and lack of appreciation of events going on around him meant he was never upset by this treatment. Armed with this knowledge, I felt sure I could cope should I be faced with such a problem.

It was inevitable in a small village like Aidensfield that the challenge would eventually arise – and so it did. I was about to leave home at 8.30 one morning for a patrol of Aidensfield and district in my police van, when the telephone rang. I answered it to find a distraught lady at the other end. It was Mrs Riley who lived in a fine house overlooking the green at Slemmington.

'Mr Rhea,' she breathed. 'Thank God I caught you . . . Henry Hubert is here, he's been here all night just sitting in my lounge and I must go out, I've an appointment, but he won't leave . . . can you help me?'

I hesitated. Domestic matters of this kind were hardly within the scope of a police officer's duty, but in a rural community, the constable always tries to help where possible. This seemed a good means of establishing good relations with the public while helping a lady in dire distress.

'I'll be there in twenty minutes,' I promised her.

Mrs Riley, a handsome woman in her late thirties, was waiting at the front door, wringing her hands and almost on the point of tears. 'Oh I do hope I'm not being a nuisance, but he just won't go ... my husband asked him to join us for dinner last night, Mr Rhea, God knows why. When it got to midnight we dropped hints but he just sat and sat, and so, in the end, in sheer desperation, we went to bed and left him on the sofa. He was still sitting there this morning, I don't think he'd been to sleep and I don't think he even noticed we'd gone to bed.'

'He's always like this,' and I explained what I'd learned about the fellow. 'I'll take him home.'

'I would be so grateful,' she sighed. 'I really would.'

'Come along, Henry.' I gently eased him to his feet by taking his arm. 'Time to go home.'

'Oh, really? That's awfully kind of you, Mr Rhea,' and he thanked Mrs Riley for a splendid meal and warm hospitality. He seemed to think that whatever was happening to him was quite normal and as he had no transport of his own, having come by taxi, I settled him in the passenger seat of my police van. He sat there very quietly, rather like a huge warm teddy bear, but when I was driving away from Slemmington, the radio burbled into life with my call sign. I responded, hoping this wasn't a call-out to an emergency for I didn't want to be lumbered with Henry Hubert if I had to cope with a traffic accident or anything else of a serious nature.

'Location please,' requested the radio set and I recognized the distinctive voice of Sergeant Blaketon broadcasting from Ashfordly police station.

'Slemmington, heading towards Brantsford and Ashfordly,' I responded.

'Received. Please attend High Row House, Thackerston, home of a Miss Morris. Report of intruders. Over.'

Thackerston was some distance from my present location so I asked, 'Understood. ETA – twenty minutes. Is there another mobile in the vicinity who can attend more speedily?'

'Negative,' came Blaketon's blunt response. 'This is not considered urgent, the intruder might be a cat in the loft. The lady has heard noises up there. You're on duty, Rhea, you're the nearest, you will attend. Over.'

'Ten four,' I responded.

If I drove Henry Hubert home first, it would add a further quarter of an hour on to the journey to Thackerston even if I could get him out of the van immediately; I wondered why Sergeant Blaketon couldn't have driven to Thackerston to check out the intruder report; he was much closer than I and could be on the scene before I reached the halfway stage. As I pondered the reasons for his lethargy, I did wonder if he was perhaps afraid of searching lofts for things that made mysterious noises . . . but of course, I would never suggest that! As I drove along, I felt it would be a risk taking Henry Hubert with me. If he settled himself into High Row House over a cup of Miss Morris's coffee, he'd be there all day and he might even stay all night too. In view of the lack of urgency and the suggestion that there was no rampaging housebreaker, I decided to offload Henry *en route*, and what better place than Ashfordly police station? As my journey took me right past the front door, it would, I hoped, be a simple matter to drop off Henry and he would have a bit of companionship too because Sergeant

Blaketon was clearly *in situ*, keeping out of the way of nerve-racking tasks. I felt Henry Hubert would be a good companion for Sergeant Blaketon!

Minutes later, I drove into the yard of Ashfordly police station, helped Henry Hubert out of the cramped little van and escorted him into the front passage of our highly polished police station.

'Who's this, Rhea?' Sergeant Blaketon looked up from his typewriter as I bustled Henry inside. The expression on Blaketon's face indicated that he thought I'd arrested a housebreaker. I had to disillusion him.

'This is Mr Houghton, Sergeant, he was stranded at Slemmington and I was taking him home when I got your call. He lives in Aidensfield. But I thought, in view of the urgency of my call-out, I could drop him here, he can catch a bus home from the market-place. There's a timetable on our noticeboard, that's why I brought him, to have a look at it . . .'

'Rhea, you are not supposed to give members of the public lifts in official vehicles except in an emergency duty situation. We are not a taxi service . . .'

As he launched into the official ruling about the use and misuse of official vehicles, I rushed out, jumped into the van and roared away towards Thackerston. I chuckled to myself – I thought my disposal of Henry Hubert had been very neatly done and I congratulated myself.

When I arrived at Miss Morris's pretty cottage, she told me how she'd heard strange noises in the loft; they were still there. I listened. It was weird, a sort of scratching sound accompanied by loud rustling movements in the roof void.

I could understand why a maiden lady in her seventies should be worried. I made a search of the house downstairs and could find no sign of a forcible entry and she said she'd not let anyone in. The cottage was detached and so it was impossible for anyone to creep into the loft from adjoining premises; the loft door was in position above the landing and so I was sure there was no one lurking up there. However, I decided to climb in to investigate.

I discovered that the noises came from a pair of starlings. They had entered the loft through a hole beneath the tiles and were busy constructing their nest. The sound of their claws and the rustling of their movements among the rubble and the loft insulation had been amplified – this kind of problem was a regular event for country folk. Upon my arrival, the birds fled through the hole and flew off, so I blocked it with some heavy pieces of rubble I found lying about the loft. I didn't think they'd be able to return.

She was very relieved when I explained and offered me coffee. Having dealt with this intruder, I relaxed over the warm drink, then radioed Ashfordly police station to make a situation report. Sergeant Blaketon answered.

'Ten four,' he acknowledged, and then added, 'Rhea, that man you brought is still here, he will not leave to catch his bus . . . I have asked him to go, I even gave him a coffee at my own expense, but he's just sitting on the bench in our entrance hall . . . you'd better come and take him away.'

'I'm not supposed to use my official vehicle for carrying members of the public,' I reminded him. 'Besides, Sergeant, I have an appointment at The Aidensfield Arms in quarter of an hour, I'm meeting the chairman of the parish council to discuss an occasional licence for a parish event . . .'

'But, Rhea, this fellow will not leave the police station, I can't get him out . . .'

'I'm sure a man of your vast experience will cope with him, Sergeant,' I said. 'Over and out.'

Some unfortunate people will refuse to leave premises for perfectly sound reasons and such a person was Victor Pyman. For the whole of his working life, he had been employed upon Lord Ashfordly's estate. He had no particular trade but if anyone asked what he did for a living, he would say he was an estate worker. This included a wide range of skills, from felling and dressing timber to erecting and maintaining fences, hedging, building rough roads, repairing stonework and roofs, ditching, cutting grass, tractor driving and even repairing heavy machinery. Victor, like his father had been, was a very versatile man and an undoubted asset to his employer.

Indeed, so valued was Victor that the estate manager had agreed to keep him in employment even though he had passed the retiring age of sixty-five. But as he approached seventy, the estate manager, a Mr Taylor, felt it was time for Victor to retire. Victor had not wanted to finish but had reluctantly agreed.

Lately, he had begun to feel his age, a fact gently pointed out to him by Mr Taylor who had realized that Victor was slowing down and tiring easily. Besides, as Mr Taylor had pointed out, Victor had enough interests to keep him busy at home. During his life, he had assembled a large flock of hens which he kept at his cottage, he had pigeons in a loft, a family of ferrets, several Golden Retrievers, an unknown number of cats and even a tame roe deer. In retirement, he could spend more time with his beloved animals and so, at last, he warmed to the idea of having more free time.

During his life, he had been totally content in his work, his father having been employed in a similar capacity for the old Lord Ashfordly. Victor now lived in the house previously occupied by his father. That house was owned by the estate but it had been occupied by the Pymans for many years. Victor had been born there and had lived there as a child; indeed, he had lived there all his life, sharing the house with his parents until their deaths. He had married late, but had produced no children and his wife had died some five years before I came into contact with him. Now, therefore, Victor was the sole occupant but, having no heirs, the family's long occupancy of that quiet woodland cottage would come to an end when Victor departed.

I was never sure how Mr Taylor intended to deal with Victor's cottage so far as his retirement was concerned because, sadly, Mr Taylor died suddenly from a heart attack.

We shall never know what his intentions were because it was the long-standing practice of the estate that, unless there were siblings who continued to work for the state, the occupants of estate-owned houses would have to vacate the premises upon their retirement. Alternative accommodation would be found for them and their family. If there were no available estate cottages, then a council house would be arranged.

The way for a family to retain an estate-owned house was to persuade one of their offspring to work for Lord Ashfordly and in the past, lots of them had done this. They had thus remained in their home, with their parents living with them in retirement. Through this system, an estate cottage was occupied by the same family for many generations and many had died in the house in which they had been born. But in the 1960s, there was a changing attitude towards working for the aristocracy and there was no commitment to the continuity of family service. Young people were moving away and besides, few desired to be employed in what they regarded as humble work. When their parents retired, therefore, there was no one to take over the family home on the estate. Other workers moved in, often being recruited from afar, and few had the commitment of those past workers. Some cottages, located in Ashfordly town, were sold and so the overall atmosphere on the estate had changed dramatically within a few years.

For Victor, therefore, having followed in his father's footsteps, there had been no trouble finding a house – he had simply continued to live in the cottage where he had spent his happy childhood, and now, approaching the age of seventy, he hoped he would be allowed to die in peace in the same old house. But if Mr Taylor intended to allow Victor to remain, he had never told anyone; he had died before making those intentions known either to Victor or to the estate management.

A new estate manager was appointed at rather short notice and he arrived at this critical stage of Victor's life. Official wheels grind very slowly but very surely and quite suddenly, Victor found himself served with an order to quit Woodland Cottage. And if he went, it would mean that all his beloved livestock would also have to go. And you couldn't keep pigeons, hens, dogs, cats, ferrets and a pet deer in the garden of a town house or on a council estate.

It was Victor's misfortune that, at this critical moment of his life, there had been a change of estate manager. The newcomer was from Hertfordshire, a Mr Simon Furnace, and from the day of his appointment, things seemed to go wrong for Victor. There can be no excuses for sloppy work and bad personnel management, but there can be reasons. Victor was an unwitting key character in the sad drama which followed.

During the change-over from one regime to the other, there had been a lamentable breakdown in internal communications.

That was the reason that poor Victor found himself with a notice to quit Woodland Cottage. In fact, this was a perfectly normal procedure because the council would not rehouse people unless they'd been given an order to quit their tied houses. What normally happened was that people in Victor's position were told they would receive a formal notice to quit but not to regard it as anything personal; it was all part of the system and it was done so that they could then inform the council of that fact, and the council would have to rehouse them. If such tenants voluntarily left their tied houses, the council would not rehouse them. Thus these notices were important to the tenants, but due to an administrative clanger, no one had told Victor of the real purpose behind his notice. Mr Furnace probably thought Victor had been told by Mr Taylor, whereas he had not; there was no doubt Victor was under the impression he could stay in Woodland Cottage for the rest of his life.

The shock of receiving the notice to quit was almost fatal, but once he'd gathered himself together, he thought the estate was rejecting him after all those years of work. It is an understatement to say he was extremely upset. In his loneliness, his sorrow turned to deep anger, and his deep anger turned into determination. He became determined that no one would force him, or his animals, to leave Woodland Cottage.

It is a fact in many such cases, that if there is a gross error at the outset, then that error is compounded during subsequent developments.

In his abject misery, poor old Victor did not seek help from anyone; from that initial anger and misery, his mood turned to one of dogged determination as he began to take measures to barricade his home against all-comers. The new management, on the other hand, became increasingly agitated at the old man's determination to stay put and could not understand his attitude. As time went on, Victor passed the age of seventy and thus ceased to be employed by the estate, but he stubbornly refused to leave the cottage, and so the estate's notice to quit was eventually reinforced by a court order. A copy was served on Victor. Even at that stage, the management thought Victor would have taken steps to secure for himself a council house, or at least would have warned the council of his impending homelessness, but that had not happened. Victor had no intention of living in a council house. He was sitting tight in the only home he had known as the official wheels were put inexorably in motion. Victor was about to be evicted.

The lack of communication, which grew worse instead of better, convinced Mr Furnace that Victor was a troublemaker, and Victor regarded Furnace as an evil man who now represented the true nature of Lord Ashfordly. Furnace became determined to have the old man out of Woodland Cottage with the minimum of fuss because, he claimed, it was needed for a new estate worker, while Victor was determined to stay with his menagerie. It seemed that an unhappy confrontation of some kind was inevitable.

At that time, one of the worst duties that could befall a police constable was to be ordered to attend an eviction. When a tenant ignored the court order to quit the premises, the next stage was for the bailiffs to move in.

Quite literally, the bailiffs' task was to remove all the furniture and belongings of the tenant, then remove the tenant and secure the premises against the evicted person and/or the family. It was a very distasteful duty; it was even more distasteful for the police officer who had to attend. Every police officer hated being associated with this sort of thing, for their duty was not to evict the family – their duty was to prevent a breach of the peace. It was inevitable, however, that the victims of the court order regarded the police as officers who were helping to enforce the court order. This was not so – enforcement of such court orders was never a police matter but as we stood by to prevent fights and attacks on all parties, it was inevitable that we got the blame.

There was, however, a little-known Act of Parliament called the Small Tenements Recovery Act of 1838, still in force in the 1960s, by which a warrant could order a police officer to effect an entry, by force if necessary, to eject the tenant and remove his furnishings so that the owner could recover possession of rented accommodation. I thanked God that I had never known that statute ever be used in my part of Yorkshire and that I had never had to enforce such an order. And I hoped I never would be put in that terrible position.

It was with some trepidation, therefore, that I found myself instructed to present myself at Woodland Cottage, there to prevent a breach of the peace while bailiffs evicted the tenant, a Mr Victor Pyman. This was the first intimation I'd had of any trouble with Victor – and I thanked God that I was not being ordered to carry out the eviction.

I decided to visit Mr Furnace, the new estate manager, to find out precisely what had prompted the issue of legal process in this case. As he called me into his office with its stuffed birds, display of antlers and beautifully polished oak panelling, the first thing that impressed me was his utter pomposity and total lack of interest in people. What on earth had prompted Lord Ashfordly to appoint him was beyond me. He was one of those rare people who immediately persuade others to dislike them.

'The facts are clear, Constable.' A tall, fair-haired man with a narrow, cruel face, he stood with his back to the fireplace of his office with his heels on the fender, and he did not offer me a seat or a coffee. 'The stupid oaf will not leave the house, the house belongs to the estate, and the estate is seeking repossession. Pyman has been there five years longer than normal, he's had all the time in the world to secure another home. It's time for him to go, that's all there is to it. It's my job to house my current workers and I need that cottage for a new man. Pyman has had the usual notice to quit, which he has ignored.'

'Perhaps he needs help,' I ventured. 'He is an old man.'

'That is not my function, Mr Rhea. The situation is that Pyman is ignoring the court order to vacate the house. Your job, as I understand it, is to stop Pyman doing anything stupid, like shooting at us or attacking the bailiffs. I fail to see why you need to come and discuss it with me.'

I could see Furnace's secretary looking at me through the adjoining door as Furnace pontificated from his fireside perch, and I knew by her face that she, and, I suspected, the other office staff, were far from happy with this idiot in charge. As he bore on about maintaining the efficiency of the estate, I found myself incredulous at what I was hearing. I knew Victor was not the troublemaker that this fellow was implying and I realized the poor old fellow could never expect a sympathetic hearing from this obnoxious character. But duty was duty. As a policeman, I was supposed to do my duty without fear or favour but I must admit that my sympathies were with Victor.

Even if it might be said I was exceeding my duties, I decided to have a word with Victor. Having listened to Furnace I was uncertain about my reception from poor old Victor, but went to see him none the less. I parked on a grassy area beneath some sycamores within sight of Woodland Cottage and walked towards the building. Hens were pecking about the place and at my approach, two of Victor's retrievers barked and raced towards the white-painted fence which surrounded the house.

I noticed Victor's pale face at one of the downstairs windows and waved towards him.

'Victor, it's me, PC Rhea,' I shouted. 'Can I have a word?'

The window opened and Victor shouted, 'What do you want?'

'A word with you,' I called back. 'A quiet word.'

'There's nowt to say, Mr Rhea. If you've come to chuck me out, I'm not going and that's that.'

'I haven't come to chuck you out, Victor. I've come for a chat.'

'You think I believe that? All them papers I've got, threatening me with bailiffs . . .'

'Victor, those papers are nothing to do with me or my colleagues.' I stood my ground. 'I just want a chat.'

He hesitated; he was from a generation who could trust the police and I did know he'd been friendly towards the Ashfordly officers in the past. Victor was a true countryman, as honest as a person could be.

'Hang on,' he said, closing the window. Minutes later the front door opened and he peered out, as if checking to see if I had any colleagues among the trees, but when he was satisfied I was alone, he bade me enter. We went into his kitchen where a kettle was singing on an old-fashioned hob over the fire. Without a word, he made a pot of tea, produced some scones from a tin and pointed to a chair at the polished pine table.

I told him I had just come from Furnace's office and explained what had transpired, then asked for his version of events. He told me, his old eyes brimming with tears as he related his family's long occupancy of Woodland Cottage, concluding by saying, 'And to think it's all come to this, chucking me out with nowhere to go . . . it's disgraceful, I never thought his Lordship would stoop to such a thing, the old Lord would never have, he was good to his staff . . .'

'Hang on, Victor,' I said. 'Has Lord Ashfordly spoken to you about this?'

'Spoken? No, how can he? He's in Switzerland, skiing, been there weeks . . . nobody knows where he is, he's touring, moving from hotel to hotel. He's due back on Wednesday but it'll be no good talking to him, not now, not when his office has done this.'

'Those papers, Victor, you've got them handy?'

'Aye, in my bureau,' and he produced a sheaf of them which he spread on the table. I fished through them, finding the notice to quit which the estate had issued, pinned to the back of which was another letter. This was a note explaining how, upon receipt of the notice to quit, the recipient should make application to the council to be rehoused; the note also explained that the purpose of the notice to quit was indeed to persuade the council to allocate a council house and it advised the recipient to take the notice to the council offices. Then I saw that the notice was dated almost ten months ago.

So poor old Victor *had* been notified of the procedures. I suspected he had not understood the purpose of the letters, which were couched in legal jargon. Or, of course, he had never even read the letter. In the shock of reading the notice, he might not have turned it over to study the small print attached to it. And, I was conscious of the fact that the deceased Mr Taylor might have promised he could remain in the cottage. But notwithstanding all those possibilities, it would have been good personnel management for someone to have come out and explained things to him in simple terms.

When I began to explain the contents, it was clear that he had not read all the correspondence, he had not discussed it with anyone nor had anyone come to enlighten him. I asked whether Taylor had made any promises about the house and he said, 'Well, he did say he'd keep me on, Mr Rhea, working. That meant I could stay here . . .'

'But you know that when a person retires, the estate needs the house for someone else . . .'

'Aye, well, but we've been here years, Mr Rhea, our family has used this old house for longer than I can remember and I thought I could stay.'

What precisely had been said to Victor was uncertain, but there was no doubt that the whole affair was, in simple terms, a cock-up. That he was being badly treated was not in doubt, at least not in my mind, and I did not know whether I could halt the relentless machinery of the British legal system.

The bailiffs were due on Thursday; it was Monday now.

When I explained it all to Victor, saying how other workers in his position had been found nice accommodation, he assumed his stubborn attitude.

'That's mebbe so, Mr Rhea, but I don't want a council house. I want to stay here, with my animals. That's all. It's not a lot to ask and I've not long for this world, not at my age.'

'So you're staying put?'

'Aye, I am. If they carry me out of here, Mr Rhea, they'll carry me to my grave.'

'Mr Furnace said they need the house for another worker,' I said. 'You can't hold up the work of the estate.'

'There's no other worker coming here, it's just an excuse, Mr Rhea. They're going to turn this into a holiday cottage, they don't want more staff, they're cutting back on workers now. When I finish, they'll not replace me, Lord Ashfordly told me that himself, months ago.'

'Is that right about the cottage?' I asked. 'It's going to be used by holidaymakers?'

'It's as right as I'm standing here, Mr Rhea. My home, I was born here, and it'll be used by folks who don't know me and who don't care a jot . . .'

This news did make me angry; it was not the fact that it was to become a holiday home but the fact that the estate had misled the authorities about the future use of the house.

I was also annoyed that an old man had been made to go through such agony and turmoil. At that moment, I decided that something should be done. But what?

'Leave it with me, Victor,' I said, hoping that I sounded confident I could help him. 'I'll see what I can do – but if I can't stop things, I might be back on Thursday,' and I explained why I might be back and that it wouldn't be a pleasant visit for either him or me. If I couldn't halt the inexorable wheels of the British legal process, he might not regard me in such a trusting manner.

As I left the cottage, I had no idea how I should tackle this problem; in truth, it was nothing to do with me and in that respect, Mr Furnace was correct. Even so, I could stick my neck out in a vain attempt to get the estate to reconsider their decision; I could alert Lord Ashfordly to the situation, but he was away until just before zero hour; I could speak again with Simon Furnace to ask him to rethink the situation and seek the court's permission to withdraw their warrant or I could have a word with the court authorities themselves about the legal aspect of supplying false information in order to obtain a warrant. That could, in some circumstances, be regarded as perjury, although I did know that the estate did have the right to evict Victor in any case. Whether the future use of the cottage as a holiday home was material to the issue in question was a matter for debate.

I could examine the Perjury Act of 1911 to research those crimes where perjury could be committed when making false declarations, not on oath, and not in a court of law. That looked like using a sledgehammer to crack the proverbial nut.

Brooding over Victor's plight, I drove home and was in a somewhat angry and subdued mood as I finished my shift. Mary had tea ready so I went upstairs to change, then came down for a few minutes with the children before eating.

'You're very quiet,' said Mary over the meal. 'Is something wrong?'

I told her about Victor's plight and she sympathized with

him, but did remind me that it was not my duty to interfere in cases of that kind. If the estate had seen fit to issue legal process, then that was their business, not mine. That evening, I relaxed with the children and helped Mary get them ready for bed, then said, 'I think I'll pop to the pub for a drink. I feel like a pick-me-up.'

'You need cheering up!' she said. 'But don't take Victor's case to heart, it's nothing to do with you.'

'He needs help. Anyway, how about you?' I asked. 'Would you like to come? Mrs Quarry would come and baby-sit at short notice, I'm sure.'

'No, you go, I'm finishing a dress for Elizabeth.' Mary made a lot of clothes for our children and she was an expert with a needle and sewing-machine.

And so, shortly after nine o'clock, I walked down to The Brewer's Arms to enjoy a couple of pints of best bitter. I enjoyed these relaxed times with the local people for the pub was the centre of information for Aidensfield and district. And as I sipped my beer, I noticed Edmund Fowler enter the pub.

He was a freelance journalist whom I often came across in the magistrate's court and when he saw me, he asked if I wanted a drink. I accepted a pint, making a vow to buy him one in return.

As we chatted, with him probing for stories and me trying to avoid revealing professional secrets, I realized that Victor's plight would make a cracking tale for the press.

'Pint, Eddie?' I asked when he'd drained his glass.

'Thanks.'

I took him to a quiet corner and asked if he was interested in a good story. Naturally, he said he was. I told him about an old man who was being evicted from his family home so that it could be turned into a holiday cottage, and that the owners had wrongly claimed the house was required for another worker. Eddie Fowler recognized the potential of this tale, saying it was a story for the national papers, and so I gave him details. I did add that Lord Ashfordly had no idea of recent developments. He said he'd love to do the story and promised not to divulge my name as the source.

On the Wednesday morning, the sorry tale of Victor Pyman was front page news in the *Northern Echo*, the *Yorkshire Post* and several national dailies. There were pictures of Victor with his animals, with photographs of his mother and father, and a quote from Mr Furnace saying that a mistake appeared to have been made.

When I reported to Ashfordly police station on Thursday morning to rendezvous with the bailiffs, I was told that the warrant had been withdrawn. Victor would be allowed to remain in the cottage for the rest of his days.

I was to learn that, in order to make him qualify for the tenancy in accordance with the estate's rules, he had been offered a part-time post. Victor thus became an estate worker yet again – men like him never retire anyway.

When Lord Ashfordly heard about the rumpus upon his return, he speedily arranged a meeting which was designed to improve relations between his office workers and the rest of his staff. I think it worked, because the next time I went into the estate office in the course of my duty, I was offered a cup of coffee by the new estate manager.

* * *

Another case of reluctant departure was very different because it featured a hearse.

A man called Angus Warriner, who lived in a small house tucked behind the main street of Aidensfield, had discovered the rotting hearse years ago.

From time to time when I was passing on a Saturday afternoon, I would pop in to have a look at it because Angus was 'doing it up'. In fact, he'd been doing it up for years. Week by week, however, there would be a small degree of progress, perhaps a corner of metal had been meticulously shaped to replace a missing corner, a decorative piece of ironwork on the exterior had been crafted or he had completed a unit for the interior, a brass rail perhaps or a discreetly fitted light. The hearse was in a multitude of pieces spread about his garage and I wondered if it would ever be put together in one piece; Angus seemed to have no plan, apparently doing odd jobs when he felt like it and not working to an identifiable system. But he was highly confident that he would achieve his objective, which was to put the hearse back on the road in its original black and shining glory complete with brass rails, wood-lined rear interior, subdued lighting and luxurious leather upholstery.

The story was as follows. About ten years before my arrival at Aidensfield, Angus had discovered the 1932 Austin hearse in an orchard at Lairsbeck. Complete but neglected, it was being used as a hen-house. Although it had been smothered in hen dirt and straw, the fabric had been fairly sound, if somewhat rusty in places, and Angus had persuaded the owner, a smallholder, to part with it for a modest but welcome sum.

Over the following years, Angus had spent hours restoring the old vehicle. Not being a mechanic, he had bought books, discovered photographs of similar models, talked to hearse users of the past and had steeped himself in the history of this model. He had scoured scrapyards and old village garages in his quest for genuine spares, he had escorted coffins to the graveyard to see how the vehicle operated and in truth he had become a veritable expert on this type of hearse.

Then, quite suddenly, the vehicle began to look like a hearse once again. From the heap of spare parts which had gathered around the shell over the years, a Phoenix-like hearse had reappeared.

'What do you think o' that then, Mr Rhea?' he said to me one Saturday morning.

'Wonderful,' I said looking around. 'You've really worked a miracle, Angus.'

'She's not quite finished yet, mind. There's bits o' wiring to connect up, lighting to fettle, engine to get in tune and then she'll need a complete respray and polish, but we're getting there. She'll be out on the road soon, that's when I get her tracking right . . .'

There was always something else for Angus to do on the vehicle. Each time I called, Angus had not quite finished, but there could be no doubt that, instead of a pile of scrap pieces and an old shell where hens once clucked and mucked, there was now a gleaming hearse in all its former glory.

Now, when I called, it was standing there in his garage and then, one day in June when I popped in, I noticed that the entire garage floor was clean and empty. Everything had been swept up, the garage was tidy and in the centre, shining in the light which filtered through the windows, was the most beautiful vehicle I had ever seen. Shining black with highly polished chromium on its wheels, bumpers, windows and door handles, the interior of the rear portion was of some highly polished wood with glistening brass fittings.

'Listen to this engine, Mr Rhea.' He opened the door and the scent of polish emerged. He pressed the starter and the engine struck up; it purred like a sewing-machine.

'Wonderful,' I breathed. 'That's wonderful Angus, you must be a very proud man.'

'I am, Mr Rhea, I am,' he sighed. I wondered how he was going to fill in his spare time now that the hearse was finished, but said to him, 'Well, Angus, you'll be wanting to get it taxed and insured, eh? To take it out for a drive?'

'Nay, Mr Rhea, I'll not do that. She's far too good to take on t'road, I'd be frightened of rust and getting it damaged . . . she'll stay here, safe and sound. I can polish her from time to time, you see . . .'

And so the hearse never saw the light of day. As the months went by, I still popped in, but the hearse was now gathering dust and when Angus took up breeding cats, some of them nested in the back of the lovely vehicle.

Many years afterwards, long after I had left Aidensfield, I saw a report that Angus had died. I never went back into that garage, but I wondered if the old hearse was still there, full of cats and waiting for someone to come and do it up.

4 She Who Wears the Trousers

Lord of yourself, uncumber'd with a wife
John Dryden (1613–1700)

Society, especially the male section of it, has always had to tolerate bossy, nagging and bad-tempered women. This trend continues in spite of a curious range of punishments designed to stay the whiplash of their cruel and muscular tongues.

One such implement was the ducking-stool; this was a type of seesaw or similar device, one end of which extended over a pond or river. The scold was seated upon the end which protruded over the water while the operators controlled the other end. At the appropriate time, the unfortunate woman was lowered into the water, perhaps several times, in an attempt to stop her tongue, but there are reports of women emerging with their tongues still going at full throttle.

A similar device was known as the cucking-stool but this was not used over water; an example of its role occurred at Leicester in 1467. It was known as 'a seat of infamy where strumpets and common scolds with bare feet and head were condemned to abide the derision of those who passed by'. In Leicester's case, it was operated by the mayor and the offending women were placed on the cucking-stool before their own doors, and then carried to the four gates of the town.

There are reports of large spheres of bare female flesh other than heads and feet being on display, because some cucking-stools sported a large hole in the seat.

One vicious punishment for scolds was the brank, sometimes known as the scold's bridle or gossip's bridle. The people of Macclesfield referred to their scold's bridle as 'a brydle for a curste queane'. The brank was a metal frame, rather like a heavy cage, which was placed over the woman's head and locked in position. At the point where her mouth faced the framework, there was a protruding piece of metal which went into the mouth, thus effectively halting her tongue. In some cases, these tongue-like protrusions were covered with sharp spikes so that if the woman moved her tongue, she suffered severe injuries. It seems that not even this cruelty was sufficient to halt some nagging tongues.

There were many varieties of brank, some of which are now held in museums or even in churches. One on display in Walton-on-Thames parish church bears the date 1632 and the verse:

> Chester presents Walton with a bridle
> To curb women's tongues that talk too idle.

In some cases, men at the receiving end of such tongues organized their own punishment for vicious wives. One example comes from the severely nagged men of Congleton in Cheshire. They installed large hooks beside their fireplaces. If their wives scolded them, they would call in the jailer, at the same time asking him to bring the town brank or scold's bridle.

The offending woman was then fastened to that hook for a few hours, being released only when she promised to curb her tongue. The last known public use of a brank occurred as recently as 1824 at Congleton when a woman called Ann Runcorn was prosecuted for scolding and using harsh language. She launched a tirade against the churchwardens and constables one Sunday morning as they toured the town emptying public houses then closing them during the church service. Ann Runcorn was found guilty and the penalty said that there and then she must 'have the town's bridle for scolding women put upon her, and that she be led by the magistrates' clerk through every street in the town as an example to all scolding women'.

In some towns, scolding women were placed in the stocks or the pillory, there for bored youths to pelt them with rotten eggs or mouldy fruit, and it may be of interest to learn that the common law offence of being a common scold remained active in England until 1967 – the Criminal Law Act of 1967 abolished it. To my knowledge, it was never used during the 1960s!

In spite of scolding being a criminal offence even while I was serving at Aidensfield, I never had occasion to place guilty ladies in the stocks or to bridle them. Even so, there were several who richly deserved some kind of preventative treatment! There were some ladies whose tongues were never still and who could deliver the most humiliating of lectures, sometimes in private and sometimes before an audience of astonished bystanders.

Before I refer to those charming examples of the female sex, I am reminded that there are some lovely words to describe such women, including shrew, spitfire, termagant, xantippe and harridan and, in spite of the punishment meted out in the past, such ladies do continue to plague us – even after death! Happily, most gentlemen can make fun of them; this occurs especially after the tongues have been stilled by death, perhaps in deep gratitude for the sudden and blessed relief that follows. For example, there is the story of a Yorkshireman whose nagging wife died. Immediately after the funeral, he was leaving the churchyard when a crack of thunder rent the air. 'Well,' he said to bystander, 'she's got there.'

In another case, this epitaph adorns a woman's tombstone at Torryburn in Scotland:

> In this churchyard lies Eppie Coutts,
> Either here, or somewhere hereabouts,
> But where she is, none can tell
> Till Eppie rise and tell hersel'.

The respite experienced by men upon the death of their nagging wives can perhaps be shown in the following epitaphs:

> Here lies my wife, a sad slattern and shrew,
> If I said I regretted her, I should lie too.

> Underneath this sod lies Arabella Young,
> Who on the 5th May began to hold her tongue.

> Here snug in her grave my wife doth lie,
> Now she's at rest – and so am I.

> This spot is the sweetest I've seen in my life,
> It raises my flowers and covers my wife.

And perhaps the shortest and most apt is upon a Cumberland tombstone: 'Tread softly – if she wakes, she'll talk.'

Those of us blessed with reasonable wives and female relations may find it difficult to comprehend the power over meek husbands which is so vociferously exercised by the harridans to which I have referred. Men who would journey to the frozen wastes of Siberia, who would fight for their country or rescue drowning cats from raging floodwaters, will wilt and quiver when confronted by a tongue-lashing from such a wife. If the pen is mightier than the sword, then a woman's tongue is mightier still.

I came across one of those husbands shortly after my arrival at Aidensfield. In reflecting upon the poor fellow, I wondered about his domestic dilemma long before I met him because he would be seen around the village wearing a permanent hangdog expression on his face as he did the shopping, ran errands and confronted people on his wife's behalf whenever she complained about anything – which was very frequently.

She was the sort of woman who would write to the television companies or the radio if she disagreed with the content of a programme; she seemed to think that her opinion was the only one that mattered. She wrote to the newspapers, to women's magazines, to the parish council, to Members of Parliament and even to the Prime Minister, and her letters were always of the complaining type. She never wrote to say 'thank you'. But when it came to confronting those who, in her misguided opinion, had wronged her, she rarely met them face to face. She made her husband fire all her bullets. If she found a bad potato in a sack, it was her husband who had to complain to the grocer; if she bought new clothes and found a fault, it was her husband who had to ring up and grumble; if the postman was late, she made him ring the post office and even, if she objected to a television programme, it was her husband who was made to ring the BBC. She wrote to them but she made him telephone them. In short, she ordered him about until he had almost abandoned any chance of having a mind of his own.

His name was Richard Cornforth; he would be in his late forties and walked with a slight stoop, doubtless through bearing such a heavy burden all his life. His clothes always seemed to be ill-fitting, with his jackets being too long or baggy, his trousers often being worn at half-mast and shirt collars crumpled. I'm sure his wife nagged him about his appearance, but in this, he never seemed to improve. He was never dirty or scruffy; he just looked eternally crumpled.

Richard worked for a local brewery called Heather Ales whose premises were at Eltering. I was never quite sure what he did, but it was something to do with supervision of the wort as the hops were added to the brew-kettle prior to boiling, the full recipe for their beers being something of a local secret. He drove to work in a smart Ford Anglia which he polished lovingly whenever he could escape from his wife's nagging, although I had patrolled past while hearing her exhorting him to clean the ashtray, sweep the interior and make sure the windows were clean, back, front and sides. Richard was a quiet, law-abiding fellow, the sort who would excite mothering instincts in a woman rather than any sexual interest, but my links with him were few because I never had any cause to visit his home. Indeed, I kept well away.

It was a small semi-detached house on the edge of Aidensfield with a neat garden and ceramic ornaments on the interior window-ledges. Mrs Cornforth was often to be seen outside the house, polishing the windows, sweeping the paths, washing the woodwork of the doors and keeping the exterior in pristine condition. Even though I had never been into the house, it was strongly rumoured around the village that it was unbelievably immaculate inside with never a speck of dust to be seen. It was one of those houses whose contents glistened in the sunshine, but where, when the sun shone, the curtains were closed to prevent it fading the carpets and furniture and where stair-runners covered the carpets to prevent wear and tear.

Local legend said you could literally eat a meal off the kitchen floor without getting the tiniest mite of dust in your spaghetti bolognaise. It was the sort of house which 99 per cent of all known germs never dared to visit.

Then one spring weekend, Mrs Cornforth was unexpectedly called away to visit a sick aunt in Newcastle-upon-Tyne and, for the first time in his married life, Richard found himself alone. Quite unbelievably, he was left in charge of the marital home, a situation rather like a canoeist unexpectedly finding himself in command of the *Titanic*.

But, the truth is that in Richard's case, he was *almost* in charge. Esme, his wife, had organized his meals, leaving notes to tell him when to put certain casseroles in the oven and when to eat the baked items she had left. He had to wind the grandfather clock, feed the cat, shake the doormat and make the bed – she'd left him little notes to jog his memory, and secondary notes to tell him where to find the first notes. There were additional notes too, explaining about ordering meat from the butcher, greens from the grocery van, a pint a day from the milkman and the best trout or plaice from the visiting fishman. In spite of these commandments, Richard was to a large extent left to his own devices – she hadn't told him when to go to bed, for example, or when to get up.

What Esme hadn't bargained for, however, was that one of Richard's nag-free nights was a Saturday. It was not an ordinary Saturday either.

Richard, during the course of his employment, had often heard about the masculine fun that accompanied Saturday nights, especially when his workmates went off to watch football or cricket and afterwards went out to the pub. He'd heard that they went either to celebrate a win or drown their sorrows if their team lost. Whatever the outcome, they went to the pub and had chicken and chips in a basket, or fish-and-chips from the chippy in Eltering High Street, followed by a few pints.

Although Richard had been a reasonable sportsman during his youth, he had never taken part in a sporting event since his marriage to Esme at the ripe old age of twenty-two. It was during a conversation at work that his colleagues discovered Richard had a moment of freedom, a chance to enjoy a brief new life, something akin to the twenty hours of a mayfly's existence. Ever eager to make him happy, they lost no time persuading him to join them for a taste of bliss on that particular Saturday.

They knew he needed a good night out; *he* knew he needed a good night out and, hopefully, Esme would never know a thing about it. It was with some excitement, therefore, that on that fateful Saturday night, Richard joined the Heather Ales annual spring staff outing when it had been decided they would attend Eltering football club to witness Eltering play in the final of the Heather Ales Moors Trophy competition. This was a cup to be played for by all the market towns which surrounded the North York Moors; it was a fiercely fought competition and Eltering had never won the trophy in its 25-year history.

Now, they had a strong team which was highly fancied and they had thrashed all comers. On that Saturday, therefore, there was every chance the cup would be theirs and, as Richard's employers, Heather Ales, had donated the trophy, it seemed fitting that all the employees, or as many as possible, should witness the match and join any subsequent celebrations. Richard had agreed it was a good idea.

Eltering won by five goals to two, a resounding victory, and after the presentation of the trophy, there was a buffet supper, with drinking and dancing at The Bay Horse in Eltering. Richard, having been given a lift by a friend, was one of the packed host in that comfortable old inn. The drinks flowed, the food was good, the music was divine, the dancing was wonderful and Richard had the time of his life. His natural exuberance astonished his workmates, his sense of fun cheered them while his capacity for buying drinks warmed their hearts.

The woman with whom he danced away the evening told him he was handsome and clever, so he bought her lots of drinks and lots for himself, the result of which he felt very romantic and loving. But all too soon, the marvellous evening was over; like Cinderella, it was time for Richard to go home. By now, of course, he was broke and, worse still, he was paralytically drunk. The colleague who had given him a lift to Eltering knew he lived somewhere in Aidensfield, having picked him up at the war memorial, but did not know to which of the houses Richard belonged.

And, at that stage of the evening, Richard did not know either, or perhaps it is more truthful to say, he was unable to explain where he lived. As a consequence, he was assisted from his colleague's motor car and settled in a swaying position upon the lower steps of Aidensfield war memorial. The time was about 12.30 and it was now Sunday morning as his cheerful voice sang about Nellie Dean as well as producing some bawdy renderings of exceedingly rumbustious rugby songs. He remained on the steps of the war memorial to offer his rendition to the public but it is fair to say that the people of Aidensfield did not know the identity of the tuneless moron who was making such a din in the middle of the village, nor did they seem to appreciate the fine baritone voice which emanated from his lips. Several of them telephoned me with ardent requests for me to extinguish the racket and then to lock up the noisy crowd.

Half asleep, I crawled out of bed, put on my uniform jacket and trousers, and made my way into the centre of the village. I parked the van on the edge of the green and even above the noise of its engine, could hear the awful moaning sounds and strange music that came from the vicinity of the war memorial.

Upon my arrival, I saw that it was not a crowd, it was Richard, singing a Territorial Army camp-fire version of 'Eskimo Nell' in several different voices.

The fumes which issued from his wide-open mouth told me he must have consumed half of Heather Ales' daily output of beer, and the words which came from the same place told me he had no idea who he was, where he was or what he was. He was blissfully happy – but I was not. None the less, at such an early hour of the morning, I had no wish to be faced with the awful chore of making written reports about his conduct, nor did I wish to antagonize him or his wife by arresting him for being drunk and disorderly. The simple solution was to take him home – if he continued to sing in the house, it was no concern of mine, although the neighbours might complain. The Noise Abatement Act of 1960 did make provision for those who created noise and vibration to the annoyance of the public but whether its provisions would cope with Richard's music was something I dared not anticipate at that moment.

Like most of the village, I knew that Esme was away for the weekend and for that reason, the task was less fraught than it would otherwise have been. Upon reflection, of course, if Esme had been at home, this would never have happened. However, I struggled with Richard as I manoeuvred him towards the front door of his house and I managed to find the key in his pocket. I opened the door, switched on the light and said, 'Home Richard. You're home. In you go. Mind the step.'

The rapid change in his demeanour was both astonishing and bewildering. He appeared to sober up almost immediately.

'No, Mr Rhea, I can't. I cannot go in, I must not go in.'

'But, Richard,' I was puzzled. 'This is your house, isn't it? I've got the right place? The key fits . . .'

'Yes, Mr Rhea, yes indeed it is, but . . .'

'She's away, Richard, Esme's away, I can take you in . . .'

'Good heavens no, Mr Rhea, my word, no. Not at all, no. I must not go in.'

I propped him against the door pillar, shouted Esme's name and then said, 'See, she's not there, the coast is clear.'

'I'll stay out, Mr Rhea, in the garage, in my car, that will solve matters, no trouble there, no trouble at all . . .'

'Look, what on earth's the matter? I can't leave you out here, you're in no fit state and besides, if you stay here you'll freeze or you'll start singing again, and no one can abide the noises you make. So come on, in you go,' and I took his arm.

He pulled free, saying, 'No, I can't, Mr Rhea, no, not now . . .'

'But why?' I shouted at him. 'Why won't you go in?'

'I haven't got my slippers on,' he said quietly. 'Esme says I must always put my slippers on before I enter the house, the floors, you see, they're all highly polished . . .'

'Then take your shoes off,' I suggested.

'No, Esme says sweaty feet make marks on the polished floors, Mr Rhea . . .'

'Where are your slippers?' I asked.

'In a box outside the back door,' he said.

'You're joking!'

'No, Mr Rhea, I'm not.' His voice remained slurred during these exchanges, but the threat of Esme had indeed driven most of the drunken influences from his body. I supported him as he panted and puffed along the path at the side of the house and eventually we came to what appeared to be a dog-kennel. It was outside the back door and I shone my pocket-torch inside; a pair of man's slippers waited for their owner's homecoming.

'Put them on,' I said.

He obeyed. Now he was at home, he would obey my orders, just as if I was Esme. Sitting on the back doorstep, he managed to remove his shoes and replaced them with his slippers whereupon I said, 'Right, in we go. Back to the front door.'

'Not the front door, Mr Rhea. I'm never allowed to use the

front door, that's only for funerals and weddings.'

'Then we'll use this door, the back door.'

'I didn't bring the key, I took the front door key by mistake, Mr Rhea, and I can't go in there, not now . . .'

'Wait there,' I said sharply.

I went into the house via the front door, leaving a mud trail along the gleaming passage which led into the kitchen, then I padded across a shining white-tiled kitchen floor to the back door. I unlocked it, opened it wide and said to Richard, 'There, we've solved that one. In you come, Richard.'

'Thank you Mr Rhea.' He seemed most relieved. 'Thank you . . . now, what can I tell Esme, about tonight . . .'

'Nothing,' I said. 'You tell her absolutely nothing.'

'But she'll know . . .'

'Not if you clean those footmarks off the hall and kitchen floor.' I pointed to my own marks. 'That can be your punishment for coming home in this condition. I'll not say a word!'

He smiled and closed the door as I left.

But as I walked away, I heard a woman's voice from upstairs crying, 'Richard? Is that you? Where have you been? I want an answer, Richard, I want an answer this minute, I'm coming down . . .'

I left hurriedly. Esme had returned just as unexpectedly as she had departed, and as I had no wish to be on the receiving end of her tongue-lashing, I scurried away. As I trotted to my waiting van, I saw the door of Richard's house burst open as he also fled into the sheltering darkness of the night. Then I lost him. I have no idea where he spent that night, but wherever it was, he remained silent, perhaps knowing that if he sang, Esme would find him.

I do not know what transpired between him and Esme after his brief taste of freedom but he did appear to join more events in the village and his confidence increased. He even brought me a pint of beer in the pub one night.

Another bossy wife came to my notice when a hiker reported finding some stolen property, namely a bottle of Scotch whisky, hidden in a cavity in a dry stone wall.

The wall runs along the side of the lane in Rannockdale, a remote dale which contains a scattering of farms and lonely stone-built cottages. It is an ancient wall and was then in a tumbledown condition with many large holes within its length. It was hardly the place to be patronized by thieves or disposers of stolen goods, but the bottle of whisky was new and unopened. The fact that it had been thrust deep into the cavity suggested it had been hidden there, so it could hardly be classified as lost property. Some furtiveness had been involved; skulduggery was suspected.

'You'd better keep observations on that wall, Rhea,' ordered Sergeant Blaketon. 'It sounds to me like the sort of thing that Claude Jeremiah Greengrass would do. If he, or anybody else, is dumping stolen goods on your patch, it could mean somebody's coming out to collect them. A hotbed of receivers, Rhea, a nest of felons under your very nose, so you've got to nip this crime ring in the bud, eh? You've got to arrest them. And if it is Greengrass, I want him inside. Right?'

'Yes, Sergeant,' I said, knowing that if Greengrass had stolen the whisky, it would have been drunk long ago; Claude would never risk leaving any of his treasures for others to enjoy. So began a long, fruitless period of keeping unproductive observations on the activities of Claude Jeremiah and also upon a length of dry stone wall some three miles long by six feet high.

The problem was that other valuables were later found hidden in various parts of that wall and I felt sure Greengrass was not responsible. Somehow, they were always placed there while I was not keeping watch, but having said that, it is difficult keeping a simultaneous watch on every hole in a wall of that length. To achieve that degree of observation, a posse of constables would be required to keep watch for twenty-four hours a day, seven days a week.

Over the following weeks, visitors, local people, farmers, shepherds and ramblers came to me with things they had found in the wall – a bottle of sherry, a pack of 200 cigarettes, a shot pheasant, several boxes of chocolates, a hardback novel, some bottles of beer, tins of fruit, packages of butter and margarine, jars of jam and marmalade . . .

From time to time in my years at Aidensfield, I'd had reports of sneak thieves, people who enter houses through unlocked doors to steal the first thing that they see, such as a radio set in the kitchen, the butcher's money or a nice vase. Also, from time to time, I'd seen Alfred, Claude Jeremiah Greengrass's lurcher, mooching about the streets; sometimes he had a slab of wrapped butter in his mouth or a teacake or, more likely, a mutton chop, a chicken leg or a joint of roast beef. Alfred was in fact responsible for a lot of unreported crime in Aidensfield, but I did not think the dog or its master had taken to hiding goodies in a dry stone wall. Sergeant Blaketon was not convinced, however.

'I can't totally accept that Greengrass is not the culprit. I'll bet he's behind this, so have you spoken to the local shopkeepers,

Rhea?' asked Sergeant Blaketon one afternoon. 'This is mainly the sort of stuff anyone can buy from the village shops. Or nick from kitchen tables. That dog of his is a four-legged crime wave. Has Greengrass become a shoplifter and has that bloody dog of his been learning lessons from squirrels? Hiding things like this . . .'

'I don't think so,' I confirmed. 'I've had words with them all, but they've not been raided, nothing like this has been stolen. They all know Claude Jeremiah well enough to keep an eye on him, but he's no shoplifter, Sergeant. I've had no reports of break-ins at shops or houses either, so I doubt if this is stolen property after all. It's more like someone just getting rid of it . . .'

'Why would they do that? It's all good quality stuff, it's not rotten or condemned, is it?'

'And it's brand names, Sergeant,' I said. 'Good stuff.'

'Exactly, it's just the sort of daft game Greengrass would play. It's definitely a Greengrass sort of going-on if you ask me, Rhea,' he sighed. 'Well, keep at it.'

Then one Monday morning, I was in Joe Steel's shop when a rambler hailed me. He was in his sixties and warmly clad in hiking gear.

'Ah, Constable,' he said, producing a tin of peaches from his anorak pocket. 'I found this, I thought I'd better hand it in. It was hidden in the dry stone in Rannockdale, near the footpath to Flossie's Foss. I wondered if there'd been a raid, it hasn't been there long, the tin's not rusty or anything.'

Flossie's Foss was a local waterfall, foss being a local word for a high waterfall along a beck or stream. I thanked him and explained what was happening so far as hidden goods were concerned, took his name and gave him a receipt.

When he'd left the shop, Joe said, 'I gave that tin for the village hall raffle, Nick, last week. I'm sure it's the same one, I recognize the dent in the side.'

'That dent wasn't made by Alfred's teeth, was it?' I asked.

'No, it got damaged in transit. That's why I thought it was a good raffle prize, I'd have had some small difficulty selling it.'

He examined it more closely and confirmed that it was indeed the very same raffle prize he had donated.

'Have you given other things for raffle prizes recently?' I asked and I then listed some of the found articles. When he said they *all* sounded like raffle prizes, I went home and checked the dates of events at the village hall. Almost invariably, there had been an event in the hall shortly before the discovery of the hidden articles. But why would anyone conceal a raffle prize in a dry stone wall miles from anywhere?

I decided to keep discreet observations in the vicinity of the village hall during the course of the next function. The first event during my new strategy was a whist drive in aid of Rannockdale village hall funds, and there was to be a raffle. I decided to patrol the village that evening and, on the pretext of wishing to buy a raffle ticket, I went into the hall just before the drive started and bought a full book of tickets whilst eyeing the choice of prizes. There was the usual stuff – a leg of ham, a pound of sausages, tins of fruit, vegetables, bottles of whisky, rum, gin and sherry, some bottles of beer, a box of chocolates, some soap and perfume and sundry other worthy prizes.

As I strode out of the hall clutching my tickets, I tried to memorize the names of everyone present – it wasn't easy, but among the fifty or so faces I did notice the whiskered features of

Don Ledger. In his early fifties, he sported a huge grey moustache which seemed to wrap itself around his cheeks in large curls and thus he was recognizable in any crowd.

Don was prominent in my mind for further reasons because (a) he was a very staunch supporter of anything that happened in Rannockdale village hall and (b) he lived in Rannockdale. He worked Peat Hag Farm which was a small hill farm providing a very modest income from a large flock of moorland sheep and a few sturdy beasts, some Scottish Highland cattle being among them. His farm was at the top of the dale, at the far extremity of that dry stone wall.

Another of his quirks was that he never drove anywhere, having never passed a driving test; his wife did drive and she would sometimes drive over to Whitby or Eltering to do her shopping, but Don always walked.

I decided he was the man to watch.

The raffle was drawn at the interval, but no one left the hall until the end of the whist drive, and I made sure I was concealed in the darkness as the players departed. Sure enough, Don emerged and I saw he was carrying a bottle of gin. It was cradled in his arms like a baby. As he said his farewells and began the long walk back to Peat Hag Farm, I remained in the shadows and began to follow him. I was wearing my crêpe-soled boots – these were known as Brothel Creepers within the police service because they enabled us to move in total silence. And so I began a long walk, always maintaining a safe distance behind Don by making full use of shadows cast by trees, houses, haystacks and the dry stone wall itself. And then, as Don approached a stile which formed part of a public footpath across the dale, I saw him stoop against the wall.

I heard the sound of glass against stone and knew he was concealing the bottle of gin. I waited until he was out of sight and earshot, then recovered the bottle from a hole in the wall. Sure enough, it was the bottle which had been a raffle prize earlier that evening; the counterfoil of the winning ticket was still stuck to it. I decided to take it back to the police house with a view to paying Don a visit tomorrow.

Next morning, I rang Peat Hag Farm and Mrs Ledger answered.

'It's PC Rhea,' I announced. 'I thought I'd come out and sign Don's stock registers this morning about elevenish. I wanted to check he was in before I drove over to Rannockdale.'

'He'll be in,' her response was short almost to the point of curtness. 'I won't, I'm going shopping to Eltering. I'll tell him to expect you, I'll leave the 'lowance out ready.'

Before leaving, I placed all the recovered items in a box in the police van and when I arrived, I found Don pointing a wall to one of his outbuildings and he welcomed me, inviting me into the spacious kitchen where, as promised, Mrs Ledger had left out some scones and cakes. Don made a pot of coffee and we settled down for our 'lowance, as the midmorning coffee break is called hereabouts.

Following the introductory chatter about nothing in particular, I checked and signed his stock registers, then decided to ask about the raffle prizes.

'Don,' I began somewhat tentatively, 'In the back of my van, I've got a box full of groceries, drinks and things. Raffle prizes, I believe.'

'Won summat, have you?' he smiled with just a hint of guile.

'Not me, it's not often I win raffles,' I told him. 'No, these are odds and ends folks have handed to me in recent weeks, folks like hikers, ramblers, passers-by and so on. Very honest folks I might add. The stuff was found in holes along the length of a dry stone wall, the wall that runs up Rannockdale almost to this farm; when we got the stuff handed to us, naturally we thought somebody was hiding stolen goods, Don, but now I know different. It's not stolen, it's not the proceeds of crime. It's raffle prizes. I reckon the stuff belongs to you.'

'Aye, it does, all on it, ivvery bit,' he said without hesitation. 'Cheeky buggers, eh? Nicking my stuff . . .'

'They wouldn't know it was yours, Don,' I said. 'I mean, to find a whole bottle of whisky or a pack of 200 cigarettes in a hole in a wall is quite a discovery. So it can't have been all that well hidden. So they're yours, eh?'

'Aye, and Ah know what you're going to ask next,' he laughed. 'Why did Ah felt it like that?'

'Exactly,' I said, knowing that 'felt' is an old Yorkshire word for 'hide'.

'It's t'wife,' he grinned. 'She was brung up as a strict Wesleyan, an' there's nowt wrang wi' that, but she dissn't like gambling. She hates me buying raffle tickets, thoo sees, Mr Rhea, she counts that as gambling, but, well, 'cos Ah'm a big supporter o' t'village hall, Ah likes to pay my whack. So Ah maks sure Ah allus gits a ticket or two. T'snag is, Mr Rhea, Ah wins ivvery tahme. Ah can fair guarantee Ah'll win summat.'

'I don't, I buy hundreds of tickets and rarely win anything!' I grumbled.

'Well, mebbe Ah's got somebody caring for me from above, so Ah dissn't like refusing and Ah can't give 'em away late at night, so that's why Ah felt yon things, nut very well it seems. It's so as t'wife nivver sets eyes on 'em.'

'But if you hide them like that, you must intend to retrieve them later?'

'Oh aye. Ah gives 'em all away, fresh raffle prizes, them that's not takken bi other fooalks, an Ah gives 'em ti t'awd folks, needy families, hospitals, that sooart o' thing. Yon bits was nivver there very lang afoor Ah gat rid on 'em, Mr Rhea. Usually Ah'd given 'em ti somebody within a day or two.'

'But you must have wondered where they were going? Those that disappeared?'

'Nay, nut really. There's mair tourists aboot these days so it's a fair bet some o' them things'd be found. And that dissn't worry me, Mr Rhea, if they're gahin ti help some deserving case. Ah mean, Ah deearn't want them things, so other folks might as well 'ave t'use of 'em. That's way Ah sees things, Mr Rhea. Onnybody that taks things Ah've felted is welcome tiv 'em.'

'It's very kind of you, Don.' I had to admire him. 'It's very generous. So, I've got a box full of things in my van, what shall I do with them?'

'What aboot t'Orthopaedic at Brantsford? Dis thoo ivver git doon there?'

'My wife's doing some voluntary work there, on a part-time basis,' I said. 'It keeps her up-to-date with medical matters and she loves working with patients. So, yes, she can take the things to them, they'll be welcomed.'

'Right. Thoo'll nut tell oor missus?'

'No,' I assured him.

'Then t'matters owered. More 'lowance, Mr Rhea?'

'I wouldn't say no to another of those scones,' I said as he refilled my mug.

Perhaps the most impressive indication of the power of a woman over a man was revealed to myself and the other constables of Ashfordly Section when Mrs Blaketon refused to let Sergeant Oscar Blaketon watch the Cup Final.

When the inspector at Eltering arranged our duties for that auspicious day, Sergeant Blaketon found himself quivering with frustration and disbelief. He had been put on duty on the afternoon of Cup Final day and there was no other supervisory officer on duty with whom he could exchange shifts. It was 1965, the year that Liverpool played Leeds – and Sergeant Blaketon was a staunch Leeds supporter.

Once his initial anger had subsided, he had promised himself that, whatever happened, he would not miss the match. He would watch it on television.

As he made his plans, there is no doubt that Sergeant Blaketon was very suspicious about the way the duties had been allocated by the inspector – he knew the inspector was himself a keen soccer supporter as was Sergeant Bairstow and the other sergeants at Eltering. Poor old Oscar guessed there had been some collusion in fixing their duties so they would not miss the match. The fact they had all gone to Wembley on the same bus trip did add some weight to his suspicions.

But in spite of the gloom, there was a slight glimmer of hope. Sergeant Blaketon's responsibility that day, in the absence of the others, was Cover Duty. That meant he was on call for the entire day – he was allowed to take time off in between parts of his shift as long as he was always available. He reasoned that if he worked that morning and evening, he could have the afternoon at home; if he sat at home that Saturday afternoon to watch the Cup Final, then he would be on call within easy reach of the telephone and therefore available to attend to any occurrence. Once he'd overcome his initial disappointment, he did seem happy to go along with that arrangement and I knew he would pray to his favourite god there was no call-out incident of any kind during the match.

But a major problem did arise. It was one he had never foreseen. There was an old romantic film on the other channel that same afternoon, a real Hollywood weepie; it was a blockbusting tear-jerking drama of world-wide appeal, one which produced floods of tears among the world's women.

And, for the life of me, I can't remember its title.

However, Oscar Blaketon's blissful dream came to an end when Mrs Blaketon announced she had invited some friends around for the afternoon to view the weepie; tea would be served between bouts of tears, crumpets would help to appease the agony of thwarted love, beating hearts might even be assuaged with a glass or two of sherry and, all in all, the lovelorn ladies of Ashfordly were determined to have a marvellously sad time enriched with Mrs Blaketon's hospitality amid severely alternating bouts of tender emotion and fiery passion. Their desires marked the effective end of Oscar Blaketon's Cup dream.

By chance, I had popped into Ashfordly police station to leave some correspondence and was in the office just when this news had been presented to Blaketon by his wife. I could hear him pleading with her; through the door which linked his house to the police office, I could hear his desperate voice pleading with her to view the film at the house of another of the invited women. Mrs Blaketon steadfastly refused.

'Don't be silly, Oscar,' she retorted. 'Their husbands are all watching the Cup Final. You can't watch it, you're working so that's why we decided to watch the film here. They can watch their silly football in peace while we're all here.'

I could hear his pleas as he said, 'The husbands could all go to one of the other men's houses, there'd be a spare set if they did that; you could all go to that house, the one with the spare set.'

'Our arrangements have been made, Oscar,' she said.

'But,' he persisted, 'I'm sure some of the men will be viewing together, you know, with a few bottles of beer. There's bound to be an empty house or two. If you found out which house was empty, you and your ladies could all go there, and then that would leave our television free for me . . .'

'No, we can't do that, their friends aren't the same as our friends, some of the men are having their own friends in, from different families. It's not at all easy, Oscar, arranging social get-togethers like this. It's impossible to change things now, everyone's made their arrangements. I've made my plans for eats and drinks, I'm not changing anything, not now, it's too late. So that's final. No more arguments. Besides, you're on duty that afternoon so I can't see why you are making such a fuss.'

'But I want to watch the Cup Final,' he pleaded. 'I'm on cover all day, I'll be on call. I just need to be near a telephone. I can take time off at home, you see, but I can't go to some other house like they can. Surely, you could make some changes in your arrangements, just for me, just this once; those men and women are not on call, you're not on call, you don't have to sit near your telephone in case of a call-out . . .'

'I have made my arrangements, Oscar, and I am not going to change them. I've already told you that. And that's final.'

When I heard his footsteps approaching the door, I busied myself with some papers and watched his unhappy return. His face said everything; it oozed misery.

'Something wrong, Sergeant?' I ventured.

'Women, Rhea! That's what's wrong. Women. Fancy wanting to watch a nauseating old romantic film instead of the year's most famous football match. And it's Leeds and Liverpool . . . silly old cow . . .' and he went into his office.

When I looked at the duty rota, which was made up a fortnight in advance, I saw that I was off duty on Cup Final day. It was my long weekend off, i.e. Friday through to Sunday inclusive, which meant I could view the game on television; had I wished and had I known in advance, I could even have gone to Wembley to watch it live. But I am not a particularly keen football fan and have rarely, if ever, watched a match. But I enjoy the Cup Final and always try to watch it, just as I watch the Grand National, the Derby, the Boat Race and other major sporting events. And so I decided that I would watch the match.

And because I would be off duty and free to watch the game, I knew what would happen. Whoever was patrolling the area on duty would find a reason to visit my police house while the match was in progress . . . and so I did expect an influx of one or two officers; somehow, they would wangle a visit. At least one officer would be patrolling in the Eltering subdivision and another would be touring the Brantsford area.

From Ashfordly Section, there would be Phil Bellamy. Phil would surely arrive, for I saw he'd been allocated a 2 p.m.–10 p.m. duty that afternoon and he was a keen soccer fan. But Bellamy's duty was not a cover duty and so he should not officially sneak time off to watch football – but if he did, he should take care not to be caught doing so. I've no doubt he banked on Blaketon's own desire to see the match – if Blaketon was watching the Cup Final, he would not be out on patrol, trying to catch young officers skiving off duty!

In the days following my discovery of Blaketon's predicament, I began to notice that he was very considerate towards me, more so than usual; he would chat for longer periods in a very friendly manner, he would say that if I ever had problems, I should not be afraid to ask for his advice or help. Then, on the Thursday evening he met me at nine o'clock. I was due to go off duty at ten.

'A thought's just occurred to me, Rhea,' he smiled; I thought it was a rather devious smile.

'Yes, Sergeant?'

'My wife and friends are viewing a corny old romantic film on Saturday afternoon. Would Mrs Rhea like to join them? I'm sure I could arrange it.'

'Saturday? No, thanks, Sergeant, I think we'll be going shopping,' I said, having already guessed his intentions.

'Oh, well, I just thought she might like an outing . . .'

'She's not really into old tear-jerkers,' I smiled.

'But you're off duty tomorrow as well, eh? You know, Rhea, whenever I had a Friday off, I liked to get my weekend chores done on the Friday, then I had the Saturday clear. The shops aren't so busy on Fridays, you can get parked easier than

Saturdays . . . Fridays are a very good day for shopping, Rhea. You ought to try it sometimes, I really think you'd enjoy shopping on a Friday.'

'Yes, but some of our children are at school, you see, so we're tied to weekends . . .'

'Oh,' he said, obviously not appreciating the dictates of a family with tiny children. 'I like going to watch Leeds, you see . . .' I don't think he was listening to me now. 'Do you know they're in the Cup Final this year? Playing Liverpool? At Wembley?'

'No, I had no idea,' I lied. 'It should be a good match. Are you going to see them? Isn't there a bus trip down to Wembley from Eltering? I heard the inspector was going.'

'Yes,' he said. 'But sadly my duties didn't work out in my favour, I'm on call that day. I'm hoping to see it on television though. It's live coverage.'

'Oh, that'll be exciting,' I beamed at him. 'But I'm no football fan. Cricket yes, because that's a Yorkshireman's game, but apart from that, I'm not much of a sports fan.'

'You won't be watching the match then?' I knew he was struggling to induce me into offering him an invitation to view it, but he did not wish to make an overt request.

'I'm not sure, I might watch,' I said flippantly. 'If I can get Mary and the kids out to the shops and back again before kick-off, then I'll watch. But I'm not going to break my neck to rush home just to view some footballers. Besides,' I added, 'it's not easy watching television with four little children galloping about the room.'

He went away with his problem unresolved and I heard later that he'd mentioned the match to the other constables who would be on duty that afternoon. As in my case, he had never made a direct request to watch the match on their televisions, but his intentions had been very clear. Poor old Oscar . . .

I must admit I began to feel sorry for him because his dilemma became a subject of fun among the constables; they were all determined to make him miss the match.

In my own case, I had no intention of going shopping with Mary and the children; she and her friends had decided to have a joint expedition to York, leaving all the multitude of several families' children with a nursery minder, and thus making available the television sets for the whims of their husbands. Thus I had my own set all to myself. I decided to obtain a few bottles of beer, some crisps and a pork pie and then to savour the atmosphere of the game with whichever of my colleagues managed to arrive.

At 2.30 that Saturday afternoon, as the TV set was warming up with pre-match scenes from the ground, my telephone rang. It was Phil Bellamy.

'Nick,' he said. 'I'm ringing from the kiosk in Aidensfield. Any chance of a coffee? I'm on a job on your patch, report of an escaped prisoner, I thought I'd call in . . .'

'Escaped prisoner? That's a likely tale! You mean you want to watch the Cup Final?' I laughed.

'Well, if it happens to be on when I'm there . . .'

'Sure,' I said. 'Drop in.'

By three minutes to three, Phil and two motor patrol constables from Strensford were settled on our settee each with a mug of coffee as the excitement at Wembley rose to a crescendo and then, as the moment of kick-off approached, the doorbell rang.

'Pretend you're out!' shouted Phil.

'I'm not on duty,' I retorted. 'You are. So if it's a job, it's yours, mate! Besides, we can't ignore it, your police car's outside and there's a patrol car beside it. It's like a police road traffic department out there . . .'

He groaned as he anticipated an urgent request for his attention, but when I opened the door, Sergeant Blaketon was standing there in full uniform. And he was smiling broadly.

'Good heavens, Sergeant,' I said, in what I hoped was a voice loud enough for Phil and the others to hear, 'Whatever brings you out to Aidensfield when I'm off duty?'

'I just happened to be passing,' he said and I could see the glint of success in his eye.

'Really?' I detected facetiousness in his voice.

'Yes. And I saw Bellamy's car. And that patrol car, both parked outside. I wondered if they'd had any success tracing that escaped prisoner?'

'What escaped prisoner?' I asked. Had there really been an escapee in Aidensfield? I hadn't heard anything about it.

'You won't have heard, you're off duty but, well, I knew you wouldn't mind if I called in, seeing we're all in this together, this search; I know you're not on duty . . .'

The crafty old schemer had come out deliberately, I knew; he'd known I'd be at home, he'd known Mary would be out and I bet he knew Bellamy would be here too, sneaking time off to watch the Final . . .

'Fancy a coffee, Sergeant?' I asked.

'Not interrupting anything, am I?' he grinned.

'I've just made one for Phil and the others,' I said. 'They all had a job on my patch, they were all looking for that prisoner . . .'

'Were they now? And have they obtained any sightings?' asked Sergeant Blaketon.

'I've no idea, Sergeant, they haven't said.'

Then, from the living-room, I heard the roar of the crowd as the teams ran on to the pitch. Blaketon heard it and I saw the reaction. He was itching to get in there and watch.

'Watching telly, are we, Rhea?'

'My wife's gone out, the children are being looked after, so I thought I'd watch the telly. It's Cup Final day, Sergeant,' I said as if I wasn't really interested. 'Leeds versus Liverpool.'

'Is it really?'

'Would you like to join us? The kettle's boiled . . .'

But before I could say anything else, Oscar Blaketon was rushing through to my lounge, removing his cap in the process, and he was just in time to flop into a chair as the whistle blew for kick-off. I heard him say, 'Not a word, Bellamy, not one word,' as he fixed his gaze on the screen.

I took in a coffee for him, with one for myself and a second one for Phil and the others who sat just as transfixed as Sergeant Blaketon as they barely acknowledged my presence. Their addiction was complete. And so Phil and the patrol officers remained to watch the game; no other constables called to watch the game – Blaketon's car, parked outside, would have warned them off if they had made an approach – but had they known, they could have come in. Oscar was in his seventh heaven as he savoured every kick on Wembley's turf, but when Liverpool won by two goals to one, he left quietly, if a little sad. It hadn't been the dream result he'd desired.

'Thank you, Rhea,' he said as he left. 'Anything to report, Bellamy?' He turned to Phil with a look of dejection on his face.

'I think that report about an escaped prisoner must have been a false alarm, Sergeant,' Phil said. 'I can't find anyone resembling an escapee, nor anyone who made the report. You said a lady had called you from Aidensfield?'

'We heard your call to PC Bellamy on the air, Sergeant,' said one of the patrol officers. 'We were nearby, so we decided to patrol the village, just in case.'

'I thought there might just be time to make a search before kick-off,' grinned Blaketon.

'Yes, there was,' said Bellamy.

'And, as I'm on cover duty, I thought I'd better attend myself just in case it was a genuine call. You never can tell with calls like that,' he said with a strange smile on his face.

But when I checked the Occurrence Book later, there was no entry about the reported sighting of an escaped prisoner. No one had rung in to report one. I decided that Sergeant Blaketon had been very cunning on that occasion. He had scored points over his wife too, for she never knew he had seen the match and neither Phil nor I would tell her.

5 Taking Care of the Pennies

The unsunned heaps of miser's treasures.
John Milton (1608–74)

Most of us associate the word 'miser' with a man who greedily hoards his money but I cannot find a feminine equivalent of that word. One of my dictionaries fails to provide any hint as to the sex of a miser, but says that it means one who hoards wealth and lives miserably; an avaricious person. Another says the word means one who deprives *himself* of all but the barest essentials in order to hoard money. From this latter definition, one might be tempted to believe there are no female misers but in the course of my duties at Aidensfield, I did come across certain women whose behaviour might well have qualified them as miserly.

One such lady suffered a sudden and mysterious death. Her name was Adelaide Bowes, she was unmarried and she lived alone in a ramshackle cottage in Undercliffe Road. She presented a strange sight as she trudged around Aidensfield in an old brown longcoat dating to World War I, a dark headscarf which almost concealed her face and ancient wellington boots turned down at the top. Stooped and grey-haired, her age was indeterminate and the villagers said she had always looked like that; no living person could recall her appearance being any different.

Everyone considered her to be very, very poor. She bought only the most meagre of supplies from the shop, barely enough to maintain a baby let alone a full grown woman, and she never spent money on clothes or household effects. Her furniture was scrap recovered from the village tip, her house had no electricity and no running water; she relied on an open fire for heat, light and cooking upon, and she obtained water from a stream which flowed past her house to join Aidensfield Beck. Most of her time was spent wandering around the village collecting wood for her fire and even inspecting dustbins for the cast-offs discarded by those supposedly more wealthy. Those cast-offs could be clothes, shoes or even food. Miss Bowes was a recluse who shunned the friendship of everyone; no one ever went into her house and she never visited anyone in Aidensfield. She rarely washed, if the blackness of her hands was any guide to the rest of her, nor did she launder her clothes or clean the house.

As the local constable, I became aware of her shortly after my arrival, but enquiries from several villagers assured me that she was not in need of professional help or advice, and that she had lived in that manner for as long as anyone knew. Sometimes, if I bade 'good morning' to Adelaide, she would respond with a nod of her head or even a toothless smile, but she would never allow me to get into conversation with her.

As one of the village eccentrics, she was accepted by all and no one tried to interfere with her life style.

Then she was missed.

It was Joe Steel who first mentioned it to me.

'Adelaide didn't come into the shop this morning,' he said to me. 'I save old newspapers for her, she uses them to light the fire, I think,' he added.

'Is it unusual for her not to call?' I asked.

'Fairly,' he nodded. 'She's usually pretty consistent in her movements; it's coolish weather and she likes her papers.'

'I'll have a look at the house,' I assured him.

It was really a hovel. She owned the cottage, having inherited it from her family, and it stood alone in a patch of overgrown garden. There was a garden shed made of creosoted timber but it was falling down, and the path to her front door was overgrown with nettles and briars. The windows hadn't been cleaned for years, the paintwork of the house was peeling off and the woodwork was rotten. It did not look like a house which had an occupant. When I reached the front door, I knocked loudly and shouted, 'Adelaide? It's PC Rhea. Are you there?'

There was no reply. Not a sound came from within.

'Adelaide?' I tried the door handle; the door opened, scraping across the stone-flagged floor as I pushed it wide enough to enter. 'Adelaide? Anyone there?'

Calling my name, I climbed over the sacks of rubbish in the entrance hall, moved an old dining-chair and managed to get into the living-room.

It was full of books; they were stacked on the floor, the table, the window-ledges, the tops of cupboards – in fact, every flat surface contained several piles of books. And there were more books piled upon the piles, some neatly, others in a muddle and many in irregular heaps. I scrambled across them, climbing over lofty piles as I called her name. Some spun away beneath my feet but did not go far, as there was nowhere for them to go.

It was like clambering through a heap of waste comprised entirely of old books – I bet some of them were rare editions and probably worth a fortune.

I reached the kitchen, or scullery as it is known hereabouts, but there was no sign of Adelaide. The kitchen was similarly awful, a depository for dirty crockery and pans which had never been cleaned. There were scraps of waste food, half-eaten tins of beans, half loaves of bread going mouldy . . . it was almost impossible to believe that anyone actually lived here.

Shouting the whole time, I made my way up the bare wooden staircase; it was so narrow that I walked sideways and the stench was awful. But I found Adelaide. She was lying on the bedroom floor, fully clothed in her old brown longcoat, headscarf and wellingtons, and she was clutching a tin of weedkiller. I crouched at her side, doing by best to ignore the appalling stench and touched her head. She was dead; of that there was no doubt. I guessed she had died from natural causes, but that tin of weedkiller did make me just a little concerned – had she consumed any of it? Was this a suicide?

I made a brief examination to satisfy myself that there were no signs of attack upon her and then left the house, knowing better than to touch or move anything. My first job was to call Dr Ferrenby to certify the death but if he could not ascertain the cause of death, then there would have to be a post-mortem examination. In particular, we had to satisfy ourselves whether her death was from natural causes, or whether it had happened by her own hand or by some other means.

Dr Ferrenby came directly from his surgery.

'Poor old Adelaide,' he said as he gazed upon her lifeless remains. 'What a miserable life she had. Yes, Nick, she's dead.

I'll certify that. But I can't certify the cause of death, you'll need a PM. I don't like the look of that weedkiller. It's not a murder though. Felo de se, you think?'

He used an old term for a suicide, a legal term meaning felon of one's self, or unlawful death by one's own hand. In the old days, a felo de se forfeited all his or her property and was given an ignominious burial in unconsecrated ground.

'Would it kill her?' I asked.

'Depends what's in it, you'll have to get the contents of the tin analysed. So there you are, Nick, old son; a sudden death for you to deal with.'

I radioed Sergeant Blaketon to inform him of the sudden death and to express an opinion, backed by the doctor, that there were no suspicious circumstances. I said it looked like natural causes, although suicide was just a possibility.

I then asked Sergeant Blaketon if he would arrange the despatch of the shell in a van from Eltering police station. The shell is really a makeshift coffin which is used to carry away bodies in such cases, for the corpse needed to be removed to a mortuary as soon as possible.

He said he would arrange that and added, 'If it's suicide, Rhea, she might have left a note. Lots of 'em do, you know. You'd better search the house to see if you can find one.'

I did not relish that task. To search for a suicide note among such a mass of accumulated filth threatened to be a most awesome and horrible task, but it had to be done. I returned to the house, with the body still upstairs, as I began my hunt.

I found a writing bureau in a back bedroom. It contained a writing pad and envelopes and so I started there. I found no suicide note, but I did find a handwritten will, signed by

Adelaide and correctly witnessed by two people, one of whom was a solicitor. The will was simply phrased and as I read it, I saw that she had no family or relations and had left all her wealth and possessions to the Salvation Army 'in appreciation of the time you cared for me in London in 1949'. A Salvation Army captain at Eltering had been nominated as executor of her will. I wondered what they would do with all this rubbish, although the old cottage might have some value.

Then on a shelf above there was a Bible and so I decided to see if she'd placed a note within its pages – I had known that sort of thing to happen in some suicide cases.

But I was astonished at what I found. Between almost every page there was either a £1 note or a ten shilling note; as I turned the pages, the Bible revealed a fortune. I looked in some other books – and there was more accumulated wealth, hundreds and thousands of pounds. I stopped and radioed for Sergeant Blaketon to visit me urgently at the cottage. I must have a witness for this; I had no wish to be accused of helping myself to any of this hoard and so I locked the doors and waited outside. In the police service, one is always open to accusations of taking property from houses in such circumstances. It is an accusation easy to make and difficult to refute.

'What's going on, Rhea?' Sergeant Blaketon demanded as he climbed from his car half an hour later. 'Why are you standing outside the house?'

I told him, and as I was explaining, the van with the shell arrived. Before dealing with the money, we removed the body and then Blaketon and I went back inside, with me showing him the hoard of cash.

'How much more is there?' he asked, looking around the rooms and wilting at the sight of the pile of books in the living-room. I went to one of them and opened it – its pages were lined with £1 notes. I opened another – it was the same, sometimes with £1 notes and sometimes containing ten shilling notes and even fivers in some cases.

'There's thousands, Sergeant,' I said. 'Thousands.'

'We can't leave this lot unguarded, Rhea,' he said. 'What the hell can we do with it? It'll need a furniture van to shift it and besides, it's not really our problem, is it? Hasn't she any relations who'll see to it?'

I told him about the lack of relatives and of the will I'd discovered and he smiled. 'Then let's ring the Sally Army, shall we? This must all belong to them now, the house and its contents, and that executor she's named can take charge. They can do the search, Rhea; they'll be looking for money, not a suicide note. If they find one, ask them to hand it to you, although I reckon she died naturally. She looked natural, if you know what I mean. Anyway, you'd better remain on guard, I'll get PC Rogers at Eltering to contact that Salvation Army officer named in the will, and ask him and his team to come here immediately. But you'll have to stay on guard until they are in possession of their inheritance and I think I'll get the duty solicitor to come along as well, just to make sure we've done the right thing.'

The alternative was for us to empty the house and place the entire contents in police premises for safe-keeping, but that demanded manpower and time, two things in very short supply. I thought Blaketon's solution was a good one. He had enough trust in me to leave me alone with all that cash and while I was waiting for the Salvation Army to arrive I radioed Ashfordly police station to ask Phil Bellamy to arrange for the body to be taken to the pathology lab at Scarborough Hospital.

When Captain Rodney Blair arrived in his Salvation Army uniform, I explained what lay inside the premises and he said he knew Adelaide fairly well; she had often written to him and had great respect for the Army and its work following some unspecified assistance in London years ago. I formally handed over the house and contents to him and his fellow officers, then left the premises.

My next task would be to attend the post-mortem, probably sometime tomorrow, and one of the worst jobs was to prepare the body for the pathologist's examination. But it all went well – Adelaide had died from natural causes. She had not consumed any weedkiller and we had no idea why the tin was in her hand as she had died. That was another mystery.

The big mystery, of course, was why she had lived in such poverty while hoarding so much money in her house. There was more than £100,000 and it all went to Salvation Army funds – although they did give £5,000 to our own police widows' pension fund.

I have often pondered Adelaide's fate, wondering why people deny themselves the necessities of life in order to leave enormous wealth which they can never enjoy.

Another common form of miserliness is found in those with money who will spend it on large, expensive items but who will be mean to the extreme when it comes to the smaller essentials.

For example, I knew a man who would willingly spend up to £100 on a pair of shoes, but when the laces broke, he would not buy a new pair. He would tie knots in the broken laces or even made do with old laces from discarded shoes. Thus he walked around in beautiful shoes with tatty, odd-coloured laces.

In one of the moorland farms above Aidensfield was a lady whose actions puzzled me. She was called Betty Barton and I could never make up my mind whether she was mean or just lazy because she rarely emptied the teapot. She employed a massive metal pot, the kind one used to see on railway stations, in transport cafes and during events where lots of people gathered for tea, like agricultural shows or garden parties. It was one of those pots that could fill dozens of cups without being replenished and that's how Betty operated.

Her massive teapot would permanently sit on the hearth, very close to the warmth of the blazing fire even in the height of summer, and whenever she wanted a cup of tea, she simply poured in hot water from the kettle that was always on the hob. The bottom half of the teapot was always full of old tea-leaves and, if the resultant brew was rather weak, she would simply add a spoonful or two of fresh leaves – without emptying the old ones. The thick mass of brown sludge at the bottom simply grew deeper and deeper, but Betty seemed to enjoy the drink that it produced. On one occasion, I was handed a mug of such tea and it was terrible, something akin to that which might have emerged from a witch's cauldron.

Fortunately, as I tasted the first mouthful, she went outside to see why the dog was barking and I managed to pour my mugful into a pot of stew which was bubbling over the fire. I had no idea how long the base contents of her stew had been in her terrible pot, but ever afterwards, whenever I called at her farm, I refused her offers of a cup of tea by saying I'd just had a cup elsewhere.

I do not know whether she thought she was saving money or whether tea was supposed to be made in this manner.

Whether Betty was mean is open to argument, but we did get tight-fisted characters within the police force. I knew a superintendent who would never buy a newspaper; he would send the cadet out to the newsagents to fetch a *Northern Echo* and would read it in his office, then send it back to the newsagents with a message saying it was not the edition he wanted. The same fellow once invited a friend and his wife to make up a foursome for a day out in his car; he proposed they toured the countryside in the Yorkshire Dales and so they did, having a most enjoyable time – until the superintendent sent his friend a bill for half the cost of the petrol. And I knew another who calculated the cost of the week's groceries and then gave his wife that precise amount, even down to halfpennies, thus for one week's housekeeping she'd be given £8 15s 2½d and next week, for example, she received £8 12s 6d. The same fellow sold his wife the vegetables which he grew in his own garden – and they were for their own consumption!

A lady of similar mentality was Mrs Angelica Hastings-Waugh, the wife of Lt Col Pemberton Hastings-Waugh (ret.). They lived in a splendid house with splendid gardens and splendid views, and had lots of splendid friends. The splendid Mrs Hastings-Waugh liked to use the word splendid.

She drove around in a splendid old Rover motor-car, visiting friends for coffee or to play bridge, and she was a member of all the important groups in Aidensfield, such as the Parochial Church Council, the Hunt Committee and the splendid Ashfordly Ladies Luncheon Club, of which she had been chairman several times. She was never short of money and accordingly, was never short of splendid friends, so she did enjoy a busy and rather splendid social life. She was often asked to open things too, like garden fêtes, village produce shows, pet shows and a range of similarly splendid events.

There is little doubt that Mrs Hastings-Waugh regarded herself as a very splendid person, the sort that no self-respecting village should be without, and she always dressed immaculately, even when popping into the shop to buy a jar of jam – the finest and most splendid, of course, the sort one would normally purchase from Harrods. The shop had secured a supply especially for her, such was her splendid taste. And, of course, the lesser ladies bought the same jam, simply because Mrs Hastings-Waugh preferred it. In matters of such grave importance and as an arbiter of good taste, Mrs Hastings-Waugh set the standards which the others tried to emulate.

In the village, we knew this as the Hastings-Waugh Effect, a mental condition which was very like the Alexandra Limp. For those not aware of the latter trend in highly regarded social behaviour, this is the story. In the 1860s, Queen Alexandra, who was then the Princess of Wales, developed a slight limp following a minor accident. In a desire to emulate the Princess, the fashionable ladies of the time all developed a similar slight limp; it was considered very fashionable indeed to limp in an identical manner and so the court ladies, and the fashionable creatures of the time, all began to copy the royal limp. It must have been a strange sight, but this oddity became known as the Alexandra Limp.

In Aidensfield, therefore, the splendid Hastings-Waugh Effect was remarkably similar, being slavishly copied by certain village ladies. The more commercial-minded residents cultivated and nurtured the Effect because, knowing how silly some women can be, they realized they could make money from their behaviour.

For example, the shopkeepers in places like Ashfordly, Eltering and Strensford were all acutely aware of the Hastings-Waugh Effect; they knew that whenever she bought anything, her disciples would do likewise and so the stores ensured they always had sufficient stocks to supply her ardent followers. Everything from shoes to washing-up powder by way of hats, glossy magazines or lampshades, was kept for those splendid ladies who suffered from the Hastings-Waugh Effect.

If Mrs Hastings-Waugh purchased a bottle of Fairy Liquid instead of some other ordinary washing-up fluid, then twenty other ladies would do likewise; if she bought a Madeira cake instead of a plain fruit cake or jam sponge, then twenty ladies would want Madeira cakes; if she bought a purple dress with white spots on, so would twenty other ladies, even if they never dared to wear their latest fashion in public.

But Mrs Hastings-Waugh, sometimes nicknamed Wastings-Hore by the less savoury of local society, had a curious quirk to her own character, one about which few people knew.

She hoarded freebies. If she went into a restaurant, for example, she would fill her handbag with sugar-lumps because they were free. She would stuff cocktail sticks into her handbag along with paper napkins and uneaten nibbles. She would collect bars of soap from hotel bedrooms, sheets of toilet-paper from the loos, and shoe-cleaning tissues from the polishing place in smart hotels. When, in later years, hotels and restaurants adopted the practice of making use of sachets of sauce, mustard, sugar, salt and pepper, she would collect those, filling her handbag with dozens of them, and later she began to add those small thimble-sized cartons of milk or cream that are given away at motorway service areas with coffee or tea. She took books of paper matches and free samples of anything given away at promotional events, such as new soups, perfumes or soft drinks.

She practised this mania for years; from time to time long after I left Aidensfield, I would be attending an event at which she and her husband were present, and I always watched her, waiting the time her hands speedily and surreptitiously whipped the freebie from the table and into her handbag with the speed of light. She was an expert at operating unseen, a truly gifted craftsperson, an agile operator with fingers and hands whose movements were rapid enough to qualify as sleight of hand. She could have become a noted card manipulator and I formed the view that she could have been a very successful magician or pick-pocket. For this reason, I found some strange fascination in watching for the moment she struck; it was rather like a viper striking at its prey or trying to see how a conjurer performs a complicated card trick.

I learned of her passion during an event at Aidensfield. For most ladies, the occurrence would have been a social disaster but it did not appear to embarrass Mrs Hastings-Waugh.

Aidensfield Women's Institute had organized a garden fête which was held in the splendidly spacious grounds of Causey House, the home of the Hastings-Waughs. With splendid and expansive views towards the Roman road and the surrounding moorland, the house was magnificently built of local stone with splendid mullioned windows, and it was more like a manorial hall than a mere country house. Its grounds, well kept by two permanent gardeners, offered a splendid setting for the fête.

And, of course, who should be asked to open it but the splendid Mrs Angelica Hastings-Waugh herself?

Scheduled to begin at 2 p.m., a serious problem arose because Mrs Hastings-Waugh had a long-standing and very important appointment which could not be broken. It was an appointment with her hairdresser; she had arranged to have her hair restyled at Eltering at 2 p.m. that very day, and so, to accommodate her, the WI altered the time of the opening ceremony to 1.30 p.m. As a consequence, Mrs Hastings-Waugh could perform the necessary ritual with a few well-chosen words and still be in time to honour the hairdresser with her presence. I was at the fête too. I was on duty and patrolling the village to prevent cars blocking the roads; I had to ensure there was room for passage of the emergency services should something dramatic occur, something the public often forgets about when parking.

As the excited crowd assembled before the elevated stage to await words of wisdom from their goddess, Mr Hastings-Waugh brought her car to the gate, ready for a flying start upon her very important journey and I stood in front of it to prevent anyone blocking her in. One has to get one's priorities right in such splendid circumstances.

Mrs Hastings-Waugh, superbly adorned in her splendid salmon-pink outfit with a broad-brimmed hat, white blouse, matching shoes and large handbag, was fit to grace a royal occasion and, after giving a simply splendid opening address, swept away towards her car.

Her husband had the engine ticking over, I held the gate open as she swept onward like a galleon in full sail, but just as she reached the car, a little girl appeared from nowhere to present her with a bouquet of flowers. Mrs Hastings-Waugh had rushed off the podium without giving the child her own moment of glory, but the child had had the wit to chase after her and had caught her prey just as she was leaving. Mrs Hastings-Waugh, touched by the gesture, placed her handbag on the roof of the car to leave both hands free as she accepted the flowers; she kissed the child, thanked her profusely and handed the flowers to her husband, saying, 'There are absolutely splendid, Henry; do make sure they are placed in water immediately,' and then she settled behind the steering-wheel. I waved her out of the drive and on to the road as the faithful gathering of fête attenders formed behind to cheer loudly as they waved her off – but as she drew away, I realized she'd left her handbag on the roof of the car. She accelerated rapidly along the road as I shouted for her to stop, but I was too late.

As she drove away, her handbag fell into the village street and burst open to roll along the road. It was a large bag – and from it cascaded hundreds of free packets of sauce and salt, sugar-lumps, books of paper matches, cocktail sticks and bars of hotel soap . . . in seconds, there was a long and somewhat embarrassing trail of her assorted trophies.

She did stop, however; the shouting of her fans had attracted her attention and she halted the car, climbed out and retrieved her handbag, ignoring the spilt contents. With never a comment nor even a show of embarrassment, she resumed her drive as her followers rushed out to gather up the freebies.

I thought the moment would have embarrassed her, but apparently it did not. Her devoted followers all rushed out to buy equally commodious handbags and they began to emulate her, filling them with all manner of free gifts – taken from absolutely the right places, of course, all very splendid and the perfect place for ladies of quality to frequent. The Hastings-Waugh Effect was very strong in Aidensfield but for the life of me, I do not know what prompts some women to slavishly copy those whom they regard as leaders.

The new mass hobby of collecting freebies must have cost the local tradesmen, hoteliers and restaurateurs a fortune in handouts although, on reflection, the Hastings-Waugh adherents must have had to spend money in a wide range of very splendid establishments in order to obtain their splendid freebies.

Looking back upon the incident, I reckon that, hidden within the depths of the businessmen's attitude to the Hastings-Waugh Effect, there are distant flashes of rather splendid Yorkshire fiscal wisdom.

Another aspect of meanness manifests itself in certain avid collectors. They will strive to make their collection the finest in the universe even if it is considered trivia by many.

Such is their ardour, that they will never part with any item of their collection, unless it is to replace it with something of greater rarity or interest. Some collections of what seems trivia, however, do become extremely valuable – collectors of comics, magazines, autographs, photographs, toy cars, bottles, inkwells, beer mats, the work of obscure artists, old books, advertisements and other assorted objects and ephemera can provide fine examples of this. But in Aidensfield, we had a lady whose lifelong passion was her collection of photographs which, over the years, became the object of desire by many local residents and others with commercial leanings. She had collected hundreds of photographs of the Elsinby Flood.

The Elsinby Flood occurred in July 1893. On the moors behind the village, there was a cloudburst of unbelievably intense ferocity after which a deluge of water rushed from the heights towards Elsinby in the dale below. Along the route, it gathered more water until it was a roaring torrent which became channelled into a gully, ripping trees from the hillsides, moving boulders and carrying before it struggling livestock such as sheep and cattle which had been too late to avoid it. This huge wall of water, more than seven feet deep, hit the village like a tidal wave.

It demolished several cottages and barns in its path before spreading across the floor of the dale, and soon it was more than five feet deep across almost the entire ground upon which Elsinby stood. The little valley had become a lake of muddy water. Almost the entire village had been made awash beneath five feet of fluid slime; trees, shrubs, mud, boulders and dead livestock filled the village street and most of the houses had floodwater up to chest height.

This flash flood rivalled the famous floods of Langtoft in the Yorkshire Wolds but the astonishing thing was that no one was killed. A colossal amount of water had accumulated within a matter of minutes but recovery from the devastation took months – it was several days before the water subsided to leave behind a terrible wasteland of thick, stinking mud and debris. Every house in Elsinby suffered the effects; furniture was destroyed, the foundations of houses damaged and farms were ruined. One of the few places left untouched was the village school because it was perched on a piece of rising ground and so it escaped the waters. It became a place of refuge for the children until the flood subsided.

In spite of the trauma, several residents and some incoming sightseers had the foresight to take photographs of the flood, some immediately afterwards and others over the period of drying-out and during the subsequent replenishment of the village and the rehabilitation of its inhabitants.

The pictures, amateurish, faded and brown in many cases, provided a remarkable record of the disaster, but apart from an article in the local gazette and some features in various magazines, none were published.

By and large, the photographs were very personal ones and the village people had kept their own photographs as mementoes; some were in home-made frames on cottage walls while others were stored in old bureaux, wardrobes and cupboards. Over the years, as cottages were sold and the occupants moved away or died, so lots of those old photographs were dispersed or sold in auctions. Many got thrown out or handed to relatives who did not particularly treasure them; many were simply misplaced.

Thanks to the actions of a certain lady, however, many Elsinby photographs did survive. She had the foresight to begin collecting photographs of the flood.

She was Mrs Beatrice Wintergill of Penwick House, Elsinby, who was born in 1887. She was six when the flood had roared through the village and was one of the children who had witnessed its devastation from the security of the school. She was then called Beatrice Simpson. She had married Arthur Wintergill in 1907 and in 1915, when she was only twenty-eight, Arthur was killed in World War I. The young Mrs Wintergill returned to Elsinby to live with her only child, a son called Thomas who was then five years old. Her husband had left her well provided for and she had no need to earn her own living; money was never a problem.

Arthur Wintergill had come from a professional and very successful family in Bradford with interests in woollen manufacture, and so, in her new widowhood but with some wealth to her name, she had bought Penwick House. This was a large square house which she remembered as being swamped with water during the flood, and it still stands today, having never since suffered a similar fate.

Upon her return to live in Elsinby, Beatrice joined in the village life, becoming a parish councillor, a school governor and member of the parochial church council. In addition, she had started to research the flood disaster with the intention of writing an account of it for a local periodical and had to assemble some photographs.

By 1917, when she was thirty, Beatrice had become an ardent collector of flood photographs, now realizing that if she did not save them, many would be thrown out, lost or destroyed. I did learn that some unknown force compelled her to add to her collection; she seemed to be seeking an elusive picture, but the outcome was that by 1947, she had a most impressive collection, all catalogued and framed. Many of her photographs adorned the walls of her lovely home. She was then sixty but far from retired; her son had gone to Australia to run a sheep farm and she continued to haunt auction rooms, house sales, second-hand shops and other likely places in York, Harrogate, Hull and elsewhere, often locating just one more faded snapshot or photograph of the flood. She never stopped hunting them.

A comprehensive collection of photographs of the flood had

become her life's work; it had become an obsession in fact, for she scoured the entire country for pictures, having found one in a Brighton antique shop, another in a picture gallery in Birmingham and another in Keswick, tucked into the pages of a guide-book. When I became the village constable at Aidensfield, therefore, Beatrice was approaching her eighties and still hunting Elsinby Flood photographs. In 1967, she reached the age of 80 but was still a sprightly, remarkably fit and very intelligent lady.

The residents of Elsinby, in recognition of her years of work for the community, decided to honour her with a party in the village hall. The postman, Gilbert Kingston, suggested that the hall also be host to an exhibition of her photographic collection. Hitherto, she had never permitted a public exhibition of her photographs, although she did show them to visitors to her home. They could look, but not touch. She had become a jealous guardian of the collection and had a deep-seated fear that future generations might not care for it in the way that she had. But Gilbert was a persuasive character and even though she said her collection was incomplete, he managed to convince her that the villagers had a right to view these remarkable pictures. And so in July 1967, seventy-four years after the disaster, Elsinby Village Hall Committee staged a party for Beatrice which coincided with an exhibition of her huge collection.

The walls and many display stands showed the pictures to good advantage and in fact, two more pictures were presented to her at her birthday party, having been found by an old lady still living in the village. Afterwards, the exhibition remained on display for a month, with coffee and refreshments being sold and the public being charged an entrance fee to view it.

I popped in from time to time, both to inspect the pictures and to show my uniform as a means of giving some protection with the occasional piece of advice about their security, but Gilbert had done a good job. None of the photos had been harmed in any way.

On the day before the exhibition was due to close, I popped in and found he was alone. He offered me a coffee which I accepted.

'It's been a good exhibition, Nick, we've created immense interest about the village history, with the school kids doing a project. At the time, the school kids had a grandstand view of the flood, and besides, lots of visitors and locals want to know more. Beatrice's collection has worked magic for us, the hall's benefited too, the extra income's very useful.'

'So what happens to the photographs next?'

'They will be returned to Beatrice.'

'But she's not getting any younger,' I commented, echoing the thoughts of many. 'It's a pity these couldn't become a permanent exhibition, either here or somewhere else.'

'She's frightened of losing them, she's spent a lifetime gathering them and always maintains the collection is not complete. Just when we think there's no more photographs left anywhere on this globe, someone finds another and gives it to her. She's terrified that just one gets lost or damaged. She has insisted she gets them back and she agreed to us having them until tomorrow. I had a devil of a job persuading her to release them at all for this exhibition so I don't want to squeeze any more concessions out of her. The fact that she got another two photos for her collection has helped her to come to terms with this public viewing, so the chance of others being discovered might influence her to allow more exhibitions.'

'So what's their long-term future?' I pressed him.

'When she dies, they go to her son. He's in Australia, but I understand he's thinking of returning to England to retire. He'll be well on his way to sixty now and must soon be thinking of retirement.'

'So what'll he do with them?'

'Dunno, unless Beatrice imposes a condition or makes some stipulation in her will.'

'It would be a crying shame if they got lost or dispersed after all her efforts.' I sipped the coffee. 'I just hope her son knows what to do with them. They could become a permanent exhibition here, or at one of the local museums or libraries.'

'That's what we told Beatrice; we asked if she would leave them to the village, or even to a local museum, but she is determined to leave them to Thomas. She's made that abundantly clear, Nick, she seems to think that a family interest will safeguard the collection, but lots of people have been pestering her about their future. One antique dealer made a huge offer for the lot, well over a thousand pounds, but she refused. We had others in too, all making noises about buying the collection; a photographer came and he offered to reproduce them for sale, giving her a royalty on every one he sold – she refused him, too. Mind, it shows that some folks realize how valuable the whole collection is. It's unique, in fact.'

'And don't forget it's her lifetime's work,' I added.

I left Gilbert when a car-load of visitors arrived, taking a last lingering look at the photographs as I walked out.

Two days later when I popped into the hall, it was deserted as it awaited the annual Elsinby Show of Vegetable Produce and

Crafts. Beatrice had got her precious photographs back and her collection was still intact.

It would be several months later when sad news reached Elsinby. Beatrice's son, Thomas, had died suddenly in Australia and before his death, he had expressed a wish to be buried in Elsinby. His death and eventual funeral in the village resurrected all the interest in Beatrice's collection of photographs because, if her son and heir was dead and gone, who would now inherit her collection?

It bothered Gilbert Kingston who tried to talk to her about it once her period of mourning was over, but it also energized a host of antique dealers, photographers, journalists, writers and other collectors, all of whom began to visit the village in the hope of persuading Beatrice to part with her collection. But she steadfastly refused and gave no indication of her wishes for the eventual disposal of the photographs.

Before I left Aidensfield, Beatrice went into a decline and was taken to a private nursing home in York. A friend from Elsinby looked after the house and made sure that her precious collection of photographs was not harmed or removed, but within six months, Beatrice had died. None of us knew the fate of the photographs, but when her will was published, we learned she had done the right thing.

She had left them to the village school, asking that they form a permanent exhibition upon its walls in memory of her own recollection of the flood from that very place. She did add a proviso that a body of three trustees be formed to care for the collection in perpetuity and that they be given the authority to arrange external exhibitions in the village hall, or in such other place as they deemed suitable, any proceeds being shared between the village hall and the trustees, the trustees to use their share for maintenance of the collection. Reproductions could be permitted and any royalties accruing should be paid for the benefit of the school.

She wanted any income to be utilized to buy books and other educational aids. The collection was to be known as The Beatrice Wintergill Collection.

It is still providing much-needed funds for Elsinby Primary School and a further seven photographs have been added since her death. The last one to be received shows Beatrice as a 6-year-old girl; she is standing outside the school gazing at the floodwaters as they swirl around the village.

This was the one picture she never found; I think this was the missing one, the one which drove her to hunt for every possible photograph. But not a single other photograph has been discovered since that time.

With the picture of Beatrice, aged six, gazing upon the floodwaters from the school, the Beatrice Wintergill Collection is now complete. She would be pleased about that.

6 Men of Dubious Ability

'Tis God gives skill,
But not without men's hands:
He could not make Antonio Stradivari's violins
Without Antonio.

Mary Ann Evans (George Eliot) 1819–80

One fine spring morning as I was walking down the village
street in Aidensfield in full uniform, I heard a strange sound. It
was rather like a stone hitting metal, something akin to a pebble
being propelled with great force at a tin can or even thrown up
by the tyre of a passing car to strike a roadside direction sign.

Puzzled, I looked around and almost immediately noticed
that the weather-vane on the tower of the parish church was
spinning wildly. Something had struck it with considerable
force and I wondered if it was one of the village youths testing
his skills with an air rifle – the vane, in the shape of a cockerel,
was far too high and far too remote from the road to have been
hit by a pebble thrown up by a passing car. I saw no one and
heard nothing further; the weather-vane was still intact and
from my vantage point did not appear to have suffered any
damage, so I resumed my patrolling.

Although puzzled by this, I did not consider it worthy of further investigation until a couple of days later.

A similar incident happened when I was talking to George Ward outside his pub. Before our very eyes, a starling suddenly toppled from its perch on the rim of a chimney-pot just along the street.

'Somebody's shot it!' cried George as the stricken bird landed on the pavement with a thud.

'I didn't hear any shots,' I commented as I went forward for a closer look. The bird was dead and a trickle of blood oozed from its nostrils and beak, but there was no outward sign of injury. It hadn't been shot. There was no indication that it had been struck by either air-gun pellets, shotgun pellets or a rifle bullet; it looked as if it had been stunned.

'That's bloody funny,' said George, and I then told him about the weather-vane. Standing where I was, it was easy to see that if someone had been responsible for both actions, the missiles had come from roughly the same area. I popped the dead starling into a waste-bin and went on my way.

In the days that followed, I heard of several similar incidents, all minor in their own way while collectively they presented a puzzle. It was not something with which to exercise my official mind, however. None the less, I was curious about other reports. People in the village had seen a beer bottle, left on a wall by a drinker, suddenly shatter for no apparent reason. Old Mr Harker had his trilby hat knocked off by an unknown force and a garden gnome had his nose removed.

A pair of Miss Fogarty's red silk knickers had suddenly soared from her washing-line when there was not a breath of wind and a tom cat, wooing his heart's desire from a outhouse roof, suddenly fled with a piercing yowl. A ripe tomato was reported to have splattered against the window of a woman who persistently complained about rubbish littering the Greengrass ranch while one notoriously bad local driver ran into a rotten egg which sailed on to his car from behind a hedge. It splattered across his windscreen to make a ghastly mess.

It was around that time that I realized Claude Jeremiah Greengrass had a house guest. This is a polite way of saying someone was dossing down with him and, at that time, I did not link that character with the mysterious events of the village. On occasions, I saw them together in the pub and once or twice spotted them striding across the moors outside the village, or roaming the fields nearer to habitation with the faithful lurcher, Alfred, in attendance. Claude's companion was smaller than his host, but equally scruffy and readily identifiable by a mop of thick ginger hair, rather like the well-used spikes of a wire brush. He would be in his mid-forties and had a round, impish face with several days' growth of gingerish-grey beard. He had arrived in an old van and had all the appearance of an itinerant scrap-dealer.

'Who's the fellow with Claude Jeremiah?' I asked George in the pub one morning.

'It's his cousin,' George told me. 'He comes to stay with Claude Jeremiah from time to time.'

'Not another Greengrass!' I cried.

'There's quite a clan of them scattered about the moors,' he laughed. 'This is just one of them, he's called Zachariah Solomon Knapweed. You've not met him?'

'Never,' I said. 'Is that his real name?'

'The family was a great one for finding unusual names, Nick.

How about Anastasia Fabiola Greengrass – that was Claude's mother and there was his aunt, Anastasia's sister, who was Matilda Dymphna Knapweed – she was Zachariah Solomon's mum.'

'What's he do, this cousin?' I asked.

'Not a lot, scrap-dealing generally, a bit of potato picking or hay-timing, general labouring.'

'General lay-abouting you mean!' I'd met characters like this on previous occasions. 'So what's he doing here?'

'If I know the pair of them, it'll be a spot of poaching supplemented by a bit of wheeler-dealing in dodgy goods, Nick.'

'I'll keep my eye on the pair of them,' I assured him.

The first intimation that there was any link between the arrival of Zachariah Solomon and the mysterious shootings was when Ted Barnes, one of Lord Ashfordly's gamekeepers, called at the office of my hilltop police house in Aidensfield. He was carrying a brace of dead pheasants.

'We've had a bashing, Nick.' He dumped the dead birds on the floor. 'Last night. Umpteen pheasants have been taken with never a sound. My dogs would have barked if there'd been guns but they left those two behind, missed 'em in the pick-up.'

'Shot, are they?' I asked.

'No, that's why I brought 'em along. There's no shot in 'em, Nick, no pellet from an air-gun nor lead from a shotgun. They've not been netted either, nor given boozy raisins to make 'em dizzy enough to fall off their perches. No, Nick, they were stunned, look. Knocked cold while roosting up aloft.'

He pointed to the head of each bird and I noticed the trickle of blood from their nostrils and beaks. I touched their heads and found that one of the skulls was definitely smashed.

'You can keep these, with Lord Ashfordly's compliments,' said Ted.

'Thanks, they'll make a nice meal. You know, Ted, I saw a starling like this the other day,' and I told him about the other occurrences that had happened locally.

'If it wasn't for that peculiar cause of death, I'd swear it was Claude Jeremiah,' said Ted. 'But this is more like a catapult wound. He never uses a catapult.'

'He's got a cousin staying with him right now,' I commented.

'Cousin? Not Zachariah Solomon?' There was a shocked tone in Ted's voice. 'One of those bloody Knapweeds?'

'The very same, Ted. You know him?'

'There's your villain, Nick. Zachariah Solomon Knapweed, the finest shot anywhere with a catapult. He can hit a flying sparrow with one of his clay marbles.'

I was then treated to an account of the dubious skills of Claude Jeremiah's cousin; whatever an expert could achieve with a firearm, Zachariah Solomon could match with his catapult. He used small clay marbles as his ammunition. They were rounded and precise in size and shape, and thus far more accurate and reliable than mere misshapen pebbles. We called them clayies for they were made from clay and had the fragile texture of something like a clay plant-pot. Glass marbles would have been just as effective, but they were far more expensive – and clayies often shattered into tiny fragments on impact, thus destroying themselves whilst virtually removing any evidence of their use.

With his clayies, Zachariah Solomon could hit a halfpenny thrown into the air; he could knock the drawer out of a matchbox held endwise in someone's hand, pushing it from its casing, yet leaving the casing intact; he could fire into the opening of a jam jar laid on its side at fifty yards and make his clayie come to rest without smashing the glass. He could hit birds in flight and was extremely accurate even at long distance. Ted told me he'd even competed in a clay-pigeon contest and had beaten many of the guns with his catapult. The fellow was a catapult wizard.

I knew that this was the character who could send weather-vanes whirring, knickers flying and sleeping pheasants to their sudden death.

After listening to Ted's account, which contained a good deal of grudging admiration for Zachariah Solomon's skills, I decided to pay a visit to the Greengrass establishment. When I arrived, the cousins were changing the spark-plugs on Zachariah's old van, apparently because it was spluttering a lot.

'Now then, Claude,' I greeted him as I tried to avoid the mud and sludge which adorned his approach road.

'Hello, Mr Rhea.' He looked up from the dirty engine. 'Just doing some repairs, she's missing when she's pulling, it's a duff plug if you ask me.'

'I was just passing and thought I'd pop in,' I said, walking around the old vehicle. Pieces of its bodywork hung off and there were holes where it had lost the battle against rust and rot. And it was not taxed.

'I haven't done owt, Mr Rhea.' He jerked his head. 'Not me, I'm behaving these days.'

'You've got a cousin staying, I'm told,' I smiled at him as he emerged from beneath the bonnet, rubbing his hands with an oily rag. 'Zachariah Solomon.'

'Aye, he's stopping over for a few days, we get on well.'

'I hear he's a dab hand with a catapult,' I said.

'Oh aye, he can hit a sparrow in flight at fifty yards, Mr Rhea – not that he would, mind, sparrows being nice chirpy little things.'

'And I bet he could send a weather-vane whirring, or knock hats off old gentlemen . . .'

'You'd better ask him to show you, Mr Rhea,' said Claude, who then put his fingers to his mouth and whistled through them. At the sound, Alfred the lurcher appeared with a puzzled frown on his narrow face, but likewise a ginger-headed fellow poked his head around a barn door and shouted, 'Is it 'lowance time?'

'Aye, if you make t'tea,' laughed Claude.

Zachariah did make the tea and emerged with a plate of cakes and three mugs on a tray; I felt quite surprised to find he had arranged 'lowance for a constable and waited with considerable interest as Zachariah placed the plate of cakes and the mugs on top of an old oil drum.

'This is Mr Rhea, our local constable,' Claude Jeremiah made the introductions. 'He's been hearing about you.'

'Now then, Zachariah,' I nodded a greeting as I accepted a chipped and stained mug full of tea, risking a sip before making any further move. It was quite tasty and refreshing, to be honest.

'What's he been hearing?' Zachariah asked as he lifted his mug from the oil drum. I was not sure whether to help myself to one of the scones just yet, or wait to be offered one.

'He's heard about you and your catapult,' Claude told his cousin before we had our scones. 'Show the constable what you can do, Zachariah.'

Unable to resist the challenge, Zachariah placed an egg in an eggcup and asked me to hold it high at arm's length. With some reservation I did so and Zachariah then walked away, about the length of a cricket pitch, then pulled an enormous wooden catapult from his inside pocket. With the speed of light, he took aim and shot at the egg; the top was sliced off as cleanly as if I'd done it with a spoon. He followed with a bewildering demonstration of accuracy and speed. He hit coins thrown in the air, sent tins flying from a wall, each being struck before its predecessor hit the ground and then he fired one shot high into the air, waiting for it to return and it did – straight down a fallpipe at the end of the house. It was an astonishing display, and all done with tiny clayies. I applauded Zachariah and congratulated him, asking if he'd ever thought of giving exhibitions of his skills, but he shook his head. 'I don't like crowds,' was all he said.

But while we had been watching Zachariah, two of the three scones had vanished.

'That bloody Alfred!' cursed Claude Jeremiah. 'That dog has no manners, eating guests' food . . . Alfred!' and he went off to remonstrate with the thieving dog which had had the sense to hide itself.

One scone remained on the oil drum, but even as Claude vanished, an amazing thing happened. A cheeky and very determined grey squirrel had sneaked from the surrounding trees. It had apparently seen the scone, for it leapt on to the drum and picked up the delicacy in its forelegs, using its tiny hands to grip the food. And then, with the utmost cheek, it began to eat it. Had it also taken the others? I wondered if Alfred was being falsely accused of a crime, then Zachariah acted like lightning. In a split second, he whirled around with his catapult, loosed a clayie at the squirrel and hit it somewhere in its midrib area. The animal screeched in agony, dropped the scone and scuttled away.

Zachariah laughed. 'Bloody thing,' he said. 'It got my boiled egg yesterday, little varmints they are.'

I knew that grey squirrels were considerably adept at stealing, being one of our more persistent pests, but I noted that Zachariah did not kill it. He had aimed to bruise, not to kill.

'You didn't kill him?' I said.

'Nay, Constable, I like the little sods! Just taught him a lesson, bruised his ribs, but he'll be back. He nicked a bit of my roast beef from my Sunday dinner last time I was here . . .'

He launched into a hilarious account of coping with thieving squirrels at the Greengrass abode, but I had my duty to do.

'Claude,' I said when he returned without finding Alfred. 'I think Alfred's innocent, just ask Zachariah.'

'I'm not so sure, Mr Rhea, I know Alfred, you see . . .'

'Well, anyway, thanks for the tea, very nice – and thanks to Zachariah for making it. But I'm here on duty . . .'

'I didn't think it was a social call, Mr Rhea, not that you're not welcome here any time, of course, but . . .'

'Ted Barnes called this morning,' I told the cousins. 'Lord Ashfordly's gamekeeper. He said somebody had given his pheasants a bashing last night.'

'I've no idea who that could be, Mr Rhea,' said Claude.

'A catapult was used to kill the birds as they roosted in the trees,' I said. 'No shots were fired from guns, no other devices used. Just the silence of a catapult, Zachariah. The skill of a top-rate catapult expert, it was the epitome of marksmanship combined with the stealth of a natural poacher . . .' I watched their faces as I rambled on.

Zachariah looked at Claude and Claude looked at Zachariah.

'We'd never do anything like that, Mr Rhea,' they chorused in unison.

'If I decide to examine each of your vans for feathers or blood, do you reckon I'll find any?' I asked, looking across the yard towards the two battered vehicles.

They said nothing, so I continued, 'Or if I search the house, might I find a plucked pheasant or two, or some nice specimens hanging for later consumption?'

'One pheasant is just like any other pheasant, Mr Rhea.' Claude Jeremiah spoke with confidence, knowing how difficult it was to identify such creatures to the satisfaction of a court.

He was saying that if there was pheasant in the house, no one could prove it was precisely the one which had come from Lord Ashfordly's estate.

'In this case you're wrong, Claude,' I told him. 'Because if you have any pheasants which were killed last night, they'll all have broken skulls, injuries caused by a catapulted clay marble and not a gun of any sort. So they will be identifiable, you see, no other pheasants will have those injuries, Claude . . .'

'Aye, well, there's none like that here, Mr Rhea, honest, you can look.'

'Thanks, I will,' and I did, but found nothing. They had clearly sold their ill-gotten gains very quickly and thus there was no evidence of their activities. I could not proceed with a charge of poaching.

'Now,' I said, turning to Zachariah. 'Your van. It's not taxed, I see . . .'

'It's not on the road, Constable,' beamed Zachariah Solomon. 'It doesn't need to be taxed when it's not on the road . . .'

'But it will have to go on to the road to leave here,' I said. 'And I'll be waiting, then I can check its insurance and your driving licence, and test it for faults in its brakes, lights, steering. In fact, in its present condition, with all that rust, it looks as if it might have dangerous parts and accessories too . . .'

I turned to leave and as a parting shot, said, 'Claude, I'm going to visit the hotels and cafés in the area, just to see if they've bought any pheasants from you lately, pheasants with broken skulls and free from gunshot. If they have, I'll know where they came from, won't I?'

The veiled threat was enough. Early next morning, Zachariah Solomon Knapweed left his cousin's house and I did not catch him driving his old van because I was on late duty. But there was no more catapult vandalism in and around Aidensfield, nor did Ashfordly estate lose any more pheasants to the doubtful skills of Claude Jeremiah's catapult-wielding cousin.

But the family's legacy lived on – I think it was probably Alfred who baffled the vicar during a garden party. The reverend gentleman had obtained a plate of sandwiches and buns but had been interrupted before he could devour them. Being a good-mannered cove, he held the plate low and to one side while engaged in a riveting conversation with a lady parishioner about family bias in the cleaning rota. By the time she'd gone, so had his sandwiches and buns.

They had simply vanished from the plate and had not been spilled on to the ground; there is every reason to suspect it was the action of Alfred who was seen, at the material time, licking his lips and wagging his tail at the unsuspecting vicar.

But proof of his guilt would be difficult to obtain. Greengrass had trained the dog well.

One of the major events in Aidensfield was the annual show.

It was held in a field behind the church and consisted of livestock displays, pony classes, competitions involving flowers, fruit, vegetables, home-made produce, knitting and assorted crafts, showjumping demonstrations, music from the Aidensfield and District String Orchestra, sports for the children with tests of strength for the menfolk such as tossing the sheaf or racing with a sack of potatoes upon their shoulders. In addition, there was a whole panoply of associated events and the gathering was held on the last Saturday of August.

In general, the morning session, which began at 10 a.m. was utilized for the judging of all competition entries and while this was being done, there were livestock classes, jumping and pony events. Members of the public were permitted entry from noon and, as usual, a large crowd was expected.

For several years, the opening ceremony had been a rather unusual one. It consisted of a remarkable demonstration of sheep-shearing by the renowned Hodgson brothers. Each was a sheep-shearing champion in his own right and they had the memorable names of Matthew, Mark, Luke and John. Their father had been Peter Hodgson, himself a noted sheep farmer from the moors, and he had trained and encouraged his sons to emulate and improve upon his own skills. It was the boast of each man that he could completely shear one sheep by hand in the time it took for Aidensfield parish church clock to strike twelve. It was a demonstration of speed and skill which was hard to beat and exciting to watch.

To illustrate the speed of his achievement, a world record for hand-shearing sheep was set by a New Zealander in 1976, when, using a solo blade, he hand-sheared 353 lambs in nine hours which is just over thirty-nine animals every hour, or one sheep at roughly every minute and a half. That is a magnificent example of speed, skill and, above all, stamina. I never used a stop-watch to calculate how long it took Aidensfield church clock to strike twelve but I reckon it was around one minute.

On the occasion of show day, therefore, I was on duty at the entrance to the showfield, making sure the gathering traffic did not obstruct the village street, when I learned that Matthew, Mark, Luke and John were about to perform the opening ceremony.

Traffic was light and I decided to abandon my post to watch them. Everyone wanted to watch because, sooner or later, one of the brothers would fail this very public test; their ages ranged from forty-two (Matthew), forty (Mark), thirty-eight (Luke) to thirty-five (John), and it was felt that age would soon slow them down, especially Matthew. The entire village wondered when one or other would fail to shear his animal in the allotted time. In some ways, it was like watching a motor race in the hope one of the cars would crash . . .

The brothers were arranged on an elevated platform, each with a sheep held ready for shearing as everyone awaited the first strike of the clock. Each man had his shearer plugged in and switched on, the blades purring like the shears in a gents' hairdressers. As the tension mounted, I found myself standing next to Jonathan Newbould, a new member of the show committee. I would hear from him afterwards, but meanwhile people were looking at their watches and checking them against the large clock which overlooked the ground. The pointers inched their way towards noon and then we heard the first strike. Instantly the brothers set to work cheered on by the crowd and, once again, as the final stroke sounded there were four expertly and cleanly shaven ewes. Everyone applauded and the show was formally declared open by the President.

But it was Jonathan Newbould who said to me, 'I could make those men an automatic set of shears; with them, one man could then shear all four sheep at the same time.'

'Really?' I said.

'I'm an inventor you know, just moved to the village, Newbould's the name, Jonathan.'

'PC Rhea.' I introduced myself and shook his hand. 'The village constable. So what do you invent?'

'Anything,' he said. 'Machinery, kitchen utensils, tools, labour-saving gadgets, gardening equipment . . .'

'Is there a living in that?' I asked, turning to face my new contact. He was a mild-looking, rather slightly-built man in rather formal clothes, a dark suit, white shirt and dark tie, and would be in his mid-forties. Balding with dark hair above his ears and around his neck, he wore round spectacles and had a small, trim moustache.

'Not at the moment,' he said. 'I work for the district council, in the accounts department, but I invent things in my spare time. I'm hoping, of course, for the big one, something I can patent and which will then earn me a fortune and make me secure for life. I almost did it with a self-clean windscreen wiper . . .'

'What happened to it?' I asked out of curiosity.

'It was too heavy for the wiper arms of most cars and kept falling off. I'm working on a lighter version now and some of the car manufacturers have expressed an interest. The snag is that the self-cleaning mechanism is so heavy, you see . . .'

'Doesn't the action of rainwater clean them anyway?' I asked him.

'Well, yes, to a point, but I'm sure that standards could be improved. I'd like one that would clean greasy screens, you see, and remove dead flies in summer . . . that's my aim, Mr Rhea. What a boon to motorists!'

'And the idea you've just come up with, the mechanized multi-sheep-shearer. That won't be easy to construct, surely, because all sheep are different shapes, if only slightly so?'

'Challenges are there to be overcome, Mr Rhea. I'm sure it will work, and if it does, it might sell in Australia and New Zealand, and other sheep rearing countries, Mr Rhea. You must look beyond the shores of our island, you know, when aiming for the top. Yes, I must work on that idea.' And off he went.

I was to discover that Jonathan Newbould lived in a neat semi-detached house overlooking Aidensfield village green and he had a shed at the bottom of the garden. There, each night, he worked on his inventions and tested them on his friends or wife, sometimes even creating interest in mass manufacturers. I was also to learn, however, that none of them worked. Jonathan invented the kind of thing that one sees advertised in cheap magazines and some Sunday papers, as well as free catalogues. They are gadgets which promise to make life easier and which gullible folks buy, only to find that there is nowhere to store the thing when it is not being used, or that it is simpler to continue in older, well-tested routines.

In spite of his long record of making utterly useless things, his wife thought he was a genius. Daisy Newbould firmly believed in his ideas and provided every possible support for Jonathan and his inventions; she knew that, one day, he would break into the big time and would become a renowned inventor, a household name like Hoover or Biro.

But I had my doubts. One of his ideas was a mechanical scraper for new potatoes. You placed the potato inside, pressed a button and an electric motor set in motion some whirling wire brushes which, so Jonathan believed, would speedily and effectively remove the light skin from any size of new potato. It did – but it also removed most of the flesh too, so you ended with a potato the size of a pea. Also, it would only clean one at a time, so it would take ages to clean a panful.

Fluorescent bedroom slippers were another idea, so you could find them in the dark, but people complained that the light perpetually emitted from the slippers kept them awake. He applied the same logic to a chamberpot, for lots of older country folk still kept a pot under the bed for night-time use. But his idea did not catch on – the potential users had no desire to pee into something that shone up at them from the darkness like a large green eye. Another Jonathan gem was a spirit level which clipped to the shaft of a golf club to inform the player of the gradient of a slope. Several tests showed that it adversely affected one's swing and besides, it was difficult to read while preparing a shot.

Jonathan produced a toothbrush that would clean the top and lower sets of teeth back and front simultaneously, an idea he reckoned would speed up teeth cleaning, and he made a stomach muscle toner too. This was a round clock-shaped device aimed at people who had no time to exercise. It was fitted with an internal large spring which operated a rubber buffer. When wound up like a clock, it had to be strapped to the stomach and when the catch was released, the buffer pummelled the stomach muscles. The idea was that it toned up soft and flabby bellies, but it only served to produce lots of bruises and stomach-ache. Similar contraptions to pound one's arms, legs, thighs and buttocks produced yet more bruises.

He made toe-nail-cutting scissors for left-handed people, a portable deckchair for hikers, a perforated tablespoon which would lift peas from the pan and drain them at the same time, a chopper which would cut and dice carrots in one movement and a cutting device for clipping to a violin bow so that broken strands could be quickly removed by the player.

He made a tray for carrying pot-plants in cars, a spring-handled wash-leather for cleaning high windows, a device to aid one-handed people to wring out dishcloths and face flannels, a circular polisher for cleaning the insides of teapots, a folding walking-stick with umbrella combined, a crumb catcher for people who ate biscuits in bed and an outdoor doormat which switched on a light whenever anyone trod on it.

He produced fitments to fasten to vacuum cleaners so they would clean drains, remove dog hairs from carpets and blow-dry ladies' hairstyles, and a cutting tool for men aged thirty-six and over to clear hairs from their noses and ears.

He made the world's biggest fountain-pen which could write in red, blue, black, green and purple ink, the world's smallest umbrella, a hammock for cats and an expanding ring for holding open paper bags. Spring-loaded clothes-lines, battery-operated salt and pepper shakers and a smoke-free ash-tray were among his inventions. Overboots for keeping wellingtons clean, a pedometer for housewives and musical cricket stumps were projects currently in action as was a self-watering hanging basket. I liked his toilet-paper sheet counter, a device which had to be fixed to a toilet-roll with the counting mechanism being set to monitor the use of every sheet. It told you when the roll was about to run out, something most of us can do with our eyes, and he suggested to me that my police whistle might include an automatic dog whistle so that each time I blew for assistance, I'd be surrounded by a lot of dogs which would warn off any villains who might attack me.

For years after I left Aidensfield, I scrutinized the Sunday papers, magazines and catalogues of innovations, wondering which of the bizarre range of 'useful' gadgets had been invented by Jonathan. So far as I know, he never did invent anything which was genuinely useful, nor, to my knowledge, did he ever complete his multi-sheep-shearer.

In spite of his failure, I did contribute to one of his prototype inventions and my part in his career came when he asked if he could borrow my old police bicycle.

'What do you want it for?' was my first question.

'I've invented an automatic gear-changing mechanism for pedal cycles,' he said with pride. 'It means there will be no more gear changing by hand – as you climb an incline, so the gears will change automatically to suit the gradient. And when you cruise or go down a hill, it will select the correct gear, automatically. Just like the automatic gear-box on expensive cars.'

'It sounds fascinating,' I said. 'But why do you want to use my old bike?'

'Prestige,' he beamed. 'If I fit my gear to your bike and give demonstrations to people like Raleigh or Hercules, they might be willing to build the system into special cycles for police officers. That will be a good advertisement for my idea – you know how people buy the same cars that the police use, well, that logic would apply to my automatic cycle gear.'

'But the police have stopped using pedal cycles,' I told him. 'We're motorized now.'

'Some officers still use them to travel to work.' He was undaunted. 'And I thought, as you don't often use your official cycle now, I might be allowed to fit it with my gear system. I'd test it on your bike. I haven't got a bike of my own, you see, and Daisy is sure this will be a world-beater.'

And so I agreed. After all, I hadn't ridden the old black upright for some time and felt it was time to put it to some good use. I let Jonathan take it away and settled back to await being the owner of the world's first fully automatic gear-changing pedal cycle.

In the weeks that followed, Jonathan kept me informed of his progress, inviting me into his shed to examine highly confusing plans which included exploded diagrams containing gear wheels, cogs, ratchets and wires, along with mathematical calculations about stress, gradients and gear ratios. He tried to explain the theory to my numbed mind and I simply nodded and accepted what he told me. I gained the impression that the system would entail something like a conventional three-speed gear of the kind fitted into the hubs of cycle rear wheels, with an added mechanism established in the bottom bracket of the frame, where the pedal spindle passes between each crank. The pressure upon the pedals and thence upon the chain and rear-wheel sprocket would determine the gear to be automatically selected; the steeper the hill, the higher the pressure upon the pedals and thus the lower the gear that would be selected. If this theory worked, the gears would automatically change to suit the climb. Certainly, the theory seemed to point to a feasible invention.

The first breakthrough in his quest for acceptance came with a letter from Raleigh, the cycle manufacturers in Nottingham.

Jonathan had sent them detailed plans of his gears and the experts' response was that, in theory, his system was feasible. It looked as if Jonathan had produced a winner and Raleigh asked him to construct and test a prototype; if that was successful they would examine it with a view to production. Matters like patents and royalties would be discussed if the new gear system was functional. Jonathan was delighted, Daisy was ecstatic and my old bike was to be the test machine.

For several months afterwards, Jonathan would explain that it wasn't quite working properly just yet; things kept jamming, the gear refused to change when necessary, the internal springs did not disengage bottom gear when he reached a flat or downhill run, the pedals sometimes whizzed around without engaging anything but all these problems were, said Jonathan, minor difficulties along the route to building a world-beater.

Eventually, he asked me to witness his first test run. There would be no one else to share in his triumph, apart from the loving and supportive Daisy. Jonathan had selected a short route on the outskirts of Aidensfield. One of the routes in from the moors is via an area known as Ewe Wath, ewe referring to the moorland sheep and wath being a word meaning a ford or foot crossing-place over a beck or stream. Here, years ago, sheep descended from the moors and waded the beck to gain access to the grassy village green in Aidensfield.

Their arrival from the moors was a sign of impending bad weather, but now there is a narrow bridge which accommodates all traffic. The approach to the village comprises a narrow, steeply dropping lane which levels out to cross the stream via that narrow bridge, and after a short flat run, the road twists and then rises gently to cross the railway, followed by a steep climb into the village. George Ward's pub stands at the left of the hilltop, like a sentinel.

From a vantage point on the moorward side of Ewe Wath, it is possible to view the entire route, which is less than a mile, and so it was that on a brisk spring morning, Daisy and I stood at that place to witness Jonathan's journey into the annals of the greats in the history of the pedal cycle. She was armed with a camera and I was simply there to observe. It was my day off, so I was in civilian clothes.

He climbed aboard my old bike and I must say it did not look much different from normal, although he did say he had removed the internal workings of the rear wheel hub to accommodate his own invention. The bottom bracket had changed too, appearing to be more bulky, but the bike itself was my old faithful friend. As he busied himself with the final preparations such as checking the brakes, spinning each pedal, testing the tyres for pressures and so forth, we heard the hoot of an approaching train. 'It's shouting that this is a momentous day in the history of transport,' laughed Jonathan.

'And in our lives, darling,' beamed the proud Daisy.

'I'm ready,' he said, taking a deep breath. I shook his hand and Daisy took his picture astride the machine. And as the oncoming train pulled out of Aidensfield station on its journey across the moors, Jonathan pushed off, raised his leg to the pedal and began to propel the bike towards the first downward incline – it was the steep drop towards the bridge across the beck.

'It's working, she's moved into top!' he yelled as he sailed down the slope. 'Smooth as satin . . .'

He was travelling at a very fast speed indeed but his legs were moving slowly, as if he was in a gigantic top gear, and in this manner, he hurtled across the narrow bridge and began the short climb to the railway bridge. He must have been travelling at sixty miles an hour but the true testing time was to come – the bike must now change gear automatically to cope with the steep climb at the other side, a leg-aching ascent which led into the village. I watched, willing him to succeed and then something unexpected and terrible happened.

Something seized up. There was a shout, the bike was brought to a sudden and slithering halt and Jonathan was catapulted from it into the middle of the road. The bike flew across the narrow verge and hit the low parapet of the bridge, then toppled over it – right into the path of the oncoming train. It hooted, there was a screech of iron wheels on metal rails and the entire train shuddered to a halt, but not before it had run over and destroyed my bike.

Daisy was in tears as she ran to the aid of her husband as he struggled to his feet and I went to have words with the engine-driver.

'What bloody fool threw that bike on to the line?' he yelled from his cab. 'It could have gone through a carriage window and killed somebody . . .'

'An accident,' I shouted back as passengers lowered their

windows to watch the drama. 'But he's OK, no bones broken.'

'There'll be hell on if my train's damaged,' he said, climbing on to the track to examine the engine and coaches. 'I've got to submit reports . . .'

'How's the bike?' I yelled from the bridge.

'Flattened,' he said with undisguised pleasure. 'You'll never ride that again.'

He couldn't have spoken a truer word. It was a mangled mess of metal and wire and Jonathan was weeping with his arm about his wife. All his work had been ruined. It looked irretrievable. I doubted whether he would ever make another prototype of a fully automatic pedal cycle gear-changing mechanism.

'I'll collect it when you've gone,'' I told the engine-driver, giving him my name. 'No one's hurt . . .'

'And my engine's not damaged either. Blood stupid people, what the hell was he doing?'

'Trying to make history,' I said limply.

But Jonathan did not make history.

I said I did not want any cash for my ruined machine, he could keep it if he wished, so that he could continue his work on the automatic cycle gear system, but he said the damage was so great that repair was impossible. To reconstruct it to the details he had originally incorporated was beyond even him – he could not remember the necessary detail and his plans would not help, so he said, but I think he just gave up that idea.

The last time I saw him, he was working on a type of side-saddle for ladies who wished to ride bikes while wearing skirts. He believed the age of elegance had not yet passed and in honour of his faithful wife, he would call it a Daisy Newbould; Daisy thought it was a wonderful idea.

I said he was welcome to use the remains of my old bike for that prototype too, and said he could help himself to the bits from the village tip, and I even offered to come and observe the first testing of the new side-saddle cycle.

But I never saw that invention in action.

7 Ain't Misbehaving

> Conduct is three-fourths of our life and its
> largest concern.
>
> *Matthew Arnold (1822–88)*

The way we behave in public has long been subjected to rules
and regulations; the church has issued its guidance, the law has
imposed additional restrictions and society itself has created its
own manners and modes of acceptable conduct.

In the privacy of our own homes, however, we can virtually
do as we like, albeit with some exceptions such as making too
much noise or keeping dangerous animals. At home, for example,
we can drop litter on the floor and leave it there; we needn't
clean the windows or polish the brasses if we don't want to and
we needn't clean ourselves either. We can wear what clothes we
want, or dress in nothing at all if we so desire. We can be
awkward or even downright nasty with our family and friends,
we can use filthy language towards them, the sort that might
result in a fine if used in a public place, and we need never
wash the crockery or dust the interior. In other words, we can
live like pigs if we want to.

There is no law to say we must buy furniture, make our beds

every morning or clean out the bath after using it. There is nothing to say we must flush our toilets, sweep the carpets or refrain from keeping coal in the kitchen. There is nothing to say we must house-train our pets or wash our sweaty armpits.

As a consequence of this freedom there are, in this lovely country of ours, a lot of very filthy, smelly and horrible house interiors which are occupied by equally filthy, smelly and horrible people. But who is to say that such conduct is wrong? Who may criticize those who live in such conditions if that is their wish, even if those conditions are worse than those endured by many animals? There would be a terrible fuss if some of our zoos or kennels were as filthy as some Englishmen's homes.

Every police officer, doctor, nurse, welfare officer and other person who enters private houses can tell their own horror stories. I've entered houses where the stench made my stomach turn; I've seen filthy living-rooms devoid of all furnishings, other than a massive colour TV set; I've seen cases where repairs were never done and dirt never cleaned away – and most of these miserable homes were due only to idleness. Many of the menfolk earned good money, but spent it in the pub or on the horses, many of the women spent all morning in bed asleep instead of caring for the family home . . . rarely was there any social deprivation in such cases, just plain stupidity aided by mammoth attacks of idleness. Lack of money is no excuse for low-class living standards. It costs nowt to keep one's home or oneself clean.

One strange example I came across involved an old man who stored his own urine in milk bottles. He kept pint bottles of old urine all over the house. They lined the stairs, filled the floors of all five bedrooms save for a narrow path to his own bed, covered the floors of all rooms on the ground floor, occupied every shelf in the place, every corner and every cupboard.

There must have been hundreds of gallons of the stuff and the place stank, of course; it was nauseating but so far as I know, he was not breaking any criminal law. If he wanted to keep his own precious pee in an open-topped milk bottle, why shouldn't he?

I'm not sure the milkman would have approved, but I never did discover why he adopted this course. I did wonder if his ancestors had sold their urine to the local alum industry – years ago, men could sell a barrel of human urine for eight pence, a considerable sum at that time, for it was one of the raw ingredients used in the manufacture of alum crystals, along with alum shale and ash from burnt seaweed. Barrels of urine were collected locally or even brought from as far as London. Perhaps that old man's long-dead family had once been major suppliers and he, like them, had been reared to conserve all his natural water?

Private behaviour of the sort which would be unsocial if conducted in public, is not always a surprise or a shock when one knows the people involved. None the less, there can be surprises. The poorest and untidiest old woman can keep an immaculate house, or the most sophisticated of people can live in the midst of ordure.

During one's duty when dealing with the public in their own homes, therefore, there are always surprises and any police officer can experience a rather unexpected jolt when entering another person's house. Quite often, the exterior of the house, or the standing of the person in the community, bears no relation to their secret life indoors. It was a shock of this kind that greeted me when I paid a visit to the home of Mr Greville Beecham.

Greville lived alone in a large roomy country house set in its own grounds along the Elsinby road, about half a mile outside Aidensfield. It was called Beecham Hall and had been the family home for generations, Greville being descended from the aristocracy, but during this century most of the land had been sold to neighbouring farmers which had left Greville with some two acres, in the middle of which was the magnificent house on its lofty site. He enjoyed a private income from the past investments of his ancestors and had interests in several large department stores in Leeds, York and Hull. He was a director of several companies and was regarded as an expert share dealer by members of the Stock Exchange.

Greville had never married and lived a somewhat solitary home life, although he did seem to have a fairly active public life. On regular occasions, he would drive out of the village in his old Bentley car to attend to business and social matters.

In addition to being a member of the county council, he was chairman of various local organizations, such as the British Legion, the Aidensfield Historical Society and the parish council. Greville was considered a useful fellow to have on a committee and was a member of several. He was also very generous towards local and national charities.

Intelligent, charming and popular, he was respected and liked by everyone who knew him, including myself. An impressive figure in his middle forties, he was some six feet three inches tall with powerful shoulders and a handsome, slender figure. He had a very healthy looking clean-shaven face with clear pink skin, blue eyes and a head of thinning fair hair; he was, I suppose, a modern example of what a Viking warrior might have looked like and I was surprised he had never been captured by a good-looking woman. He was always smartly dressed in expensive clothes which had a rural appearance – tweedy suits or checked sports jackets and cavalry twill trousers, brogue shoes and thick, woollen socks. He was a stylish man, the sort who would turn heads at any gathering.

I had met him at various village events and had always found him courteous, charming and warm but, as the months passed, I realized he never invited people into his home. On the other hand, Greville received plenty of invitations to dinner, often in the homes of the local aristocracy but also to the homes of local business and professional people.

But, being a bachelor, he never returned their hospitality by inviting them to Beecham Hall. If he wanted to entertain anyone, he booked a table in one or other of the best local hotels or restaurants. People were not surprised – after all, Greville was a man, he had no wife or resident cook, and so they understood. Or they thought they understood.

That was my understanding of his life style until I made an unannounced visit to Beecham Hall. I had had no cause to visit Greville until the locality suffered a spate of night-time attacks on local licensed premises. A team was touring the north-east of England and raiding village pubs by gaining entry through the cellar flaps. They were stealing large quantities of spirits, cigarettes and, in some cases, cash from the tills in those establishments where the landlords had not emptied the drawers after the night's business. A vehicle was being used – no one could carry off heavy cases of whisky or brandy or large cartons of cigarettes without some form of transport and so we circulated warnings to all the local pubs. The means of entry was usually the cellar flap, this being prized open with a crowbar or similar tool, although in some cases the back door had been forced.

I warned the landlords and proprietors of all the inns on my beat, including George Ward, and asked them if I might inspect their cellars, rear doors and windows to offer security advice. In George's case, the cellar flap was practically useless.

When the twin coverings were closed, they were bolted from the inside, but the wood surrounds into which the bolts slotted were old and rotten. It was possible to move them by hand – thus it was an easy matter to force open the cellar flap from the outside and enter via the short wooden ladder. I advised George to replace the old woodwork and make the flap more secure. He assured me that he would.

But he didn't. One night, someone forced open the flap and removed several crates of whisky, brandy and gin, six crates of beer, ten cartons of cigarettes, umpteen boxes of potato crisps and £87 cash from the till. George was furious and so was I.

'I thought you'd warned your landlords, Rhea?' snapped Sergeant Blaketon down the telephone when I reported the crime to him. 'This one sounds easy pickings to me.'

'I did warn George, Sergeant, I inspected his cellar and his doors and windows and advised him to make them more secure . . .'

'We want this lot caught, Rhea,' he said. 'Making fools of us, raiding our pubs at night, you should have been alert to this possibility . . .'

'Yes, Sergeant.' I listened as he rambled on and promised I would do my best to trace the culprits. Later that morning, a farmer rang my home and left a message with my wife. He had found some discarded whisky and brandy cartons on his land, and I got the message at lunch-time.

When I inspected the boxes, I asked George to have a look at them and he nodded.

'They're from my cellar,' he said. 'I recognize them, that's got my mark on it, after I'd checked it over on receipt. See? G.W. My initials. I wrote it. It means I checked the contents and found everything correct. So why dump the empty boxes here?'

'To get rid of the evidence, George. One bottle of whisky's just like another and they know that. So having got rid of this evidence, if they'd got stopped after leaving here, who could say they'd stolen the booze they carried in the car? There's nothing to say where their whisky came from, is there? If it had still been in those cartons, though, and we'd stopped them for a check, we would have known where it had come from. We could have proved they'd done it. They're professionals, they must have spotted your initials on the boxes and decided to get rid of the evidence.'

'Bastards,' said George.

As I looked around, I realized that, to reach this out-of-the-way dumping place, the vehicle must have driven along a lane which ran below Beecham Hall; the Hall was perched on the hilltop and the lane skirted the hill directly beneath it to emerge in Thackerston. I decided to ask the householders along the route if they had heard or seen any activity during the night. And the most obvious house at which to begin was Beecham Hall.

When I rang the bell, Greville answered. He was dressed in casual slacks, a T-shirt and sandals and smiled a welcome.

'Hello, PC Rhea, come in,' and he held the huge door open as I stepped into the rather dark entrance hall. As I followed him into the depths of the building in very dim light, I was vaguely aware of a cluttered route, but he said, 'In there,' and pointed to a door on my right.

'Excuse the mess,' he said as he pushed open the door. 'Find a chair if you can. I'll make some coffee. You've time for one?'

'Yes,' I said, realizing he'd not given me time to explain the purpose of my visit, then as he went off to the kitchen, I entered the room, conscious only of its overwhelming darkness. The thick curtains were drawn across the bay window to omit most of the day's sunshine, but as my eyes grew accustomed to the gloom, I saw the room was piled high with rubbish which had all the appearances of being dumped and not arranged in any way. It was like a tatty second-hand dealer's junk-shop – cheap old furniture, tables, picture-frames, mangles, curtains, rugs and clothing, chairs, beds and old mattresses . . . there was a total lack of order in the room, everything was piled high, one thing being thrown on top of another without any attempt to stack it neatly. There were old cardboard boxes full of cracked crockery, mirrors, books galore, old newspapers and magazines. But this was not good stuff, it was rubbish, junk, cheap cast-offs.

As I stood in the midst of this offal, I looked around for a chair, but the only ones were battered old dining-chairs which had seen better days in some small kitchen. I dragged one from beneath a table, removed a pile of old newspapers from it, dusted the seat with an old sweater I found on the floor, and sat upon it to examine the room with more care. As I waited, Greville came in with two mugs of coffee, handed me one and pulled himself a chair from the mess.

'Sorry about the mess,' he said. 'I keep meaning to tidy up but, well, you know how it is.'

I murmured something which I hoped was a show of understanding but he made no attempt to explain the reason for this room full of junk.

'So what brings the constabulary here?' he smiled. Unlike his house, he was clean and well groomed, even when relaxing.

I told him about the raid on the pub and how I thought the thieves had driven along the lane below his house sometime during the night, then asked if he'd heard anything.

'Come through to the dining-room,' he said. 'It overlooks that lane. Bring your coffee. Yes, I did hear a car last night, or in the early hours.'

The dining-room, at the other side of the dusty, cramped hall, was just as bad as the lounge, littered almost to the ceiling with further loads of utter junk.

The heavy curtains were drawn too but I could distinguish the piles of clutter, a repetition of what was stored in the lounge. He drew back a curtain and pointed.

'Down there, Mr Rhea, you see the old barn? The track comes past it, well, I can see that view from my bedroom, directly above this room. And in the early hours, three o'clock I'd say, I did see car lights down there. I was awake, I'd got indigestion, I dined with friends last night, so I got up to take something to ease it and noticed the lights.'

'Can you give me any idea what sort of car it was? Who was with it? Anything?'

'Sorry, no. I heard doors banging but that's all, then it drove off, towards Thackerston. Sorry I can't be more precise.'

'Thanks, Mr Beecham,' I said. 'It's a start. I'm visiting all the houses along here, to see if anyone can describe the car.'

'I hope you find the crooks,' he said, leading me from the

room. I left my coffee mug on a dusty old table in the hall, thanked him and left. Outside, the mansion looked splendid, a fine house some 250 years old with mullioned windows, a fine portico and superb views. But inside, it was no better furnished than an itinerant scrap-dealer's caravan.

We never traced those who had broken into the pub and I never did find out why such a wealthy, personable and generous character like Greville Beecham lived in such utter squalor.

Many of us have heard the old joke about Queen Elizabeth I who said she made sure she had a bath at least once a month, whether or not she needed one. There were people like that in and around Aidensfield. One was an old fellow who always wore his flat cap, even when sitting in the bath and even when washing his face at other times. In fact, his wife swore he never actually washed his face – he just rubbed it with dry hands and made appropriate washing noises with his mouth.

Another was a fish seller who operated a weekly stall in Ashfordly on market day but who, for the rest of the week, was a chimney-sweep. He spent his week getting blacker and blacker and looked an oddity when serving fresh fish from behind his stall, for he never seemed to be clean and the combination of smells which surrounded him were extremely pungent, especially in high summer.

It was his boast that he was so busy that he had only one night out – that was the last Saturday of every month when he attended a working men's club in Eltering. And, in preparation, he got a bath on the Wednesday previous to that.

But it was a bathing problem that brought hilarity, with some later sadness, to Elsinby early one summer. A lady called Sybil Cornforth lived in a bungalow behind the high street. In her late sixties, she was the widow of a former fireman and had returned to live in the village upon the death of her husband, having been born and reared here in childhood; she'd been educated in Elsinby primary school.

She was a jolly woman, the life and soul of any party and she had a wonderful and infectious sense of humour. She took a very active part in Elsinby WI, the parochial church council and a wide range of village hall fund-raising events. She was also a leading member of the parish church choir, for she had a beautiful contralto voice and could move an audience to tears by the quality of her singing.

Everyone loved Sybil, and she had lots of visitors and friends, including an army of nieces and nephews who lived nearby. Sybil was a very distinctive lady, however, for she must have weighed some 22 stone. She was truly enormous, with a multitude of chins, a back as wide as that of a carthorse, a waist the size of a fully grown cow and legs like the trunk of a centuries-old oak tree.

She fairly waddled down the street but was always laughing and joking, making fun of her own size and chuckling at her lack of mobility. She had tired to slim but all her efforts had failed, and she made light of the fact that she could not sit in a conventional single cinema seat and that her own chairs were specially built to accommodate her broad backside and huge weight.

Sybil's daily routine in Elsinby was fairly well known. She would rise around 7.30 a.m., take in her milk and prepare her own breakfast. Then, around 9.30 a.m., she would potter down to the shop for her morning paper, her daily groceries and other requirements.

While in the village, she would sometimes call on friends for coffee or visit others to discuss parish church matters or something connected with fund-raising at the village hall. She was always active, always doing something or calling somewhere, therefore she was a very regular sight around Elsinby.

When she failed to take in her milk one morning, therefore, and then failed to appear in the shop at the expected time, there was immediate concern.

Neighbours knocked and shouted at her door, but without response, and by ten o'clock, someone rang me. I rushed down to Elsinby to find a knot of villagers hanging about outside Sybil's door. They burst into an anxious chatter at my approach – I noticed the full milk bottle on the doorstep as I sought a spokesman. John Oakley, who lived next door, came forward.

'You've tried all the doors?' I asked. 'Bedroom window?'

'Aye,' he said with sadness in his voice. 'Shouted through t'letter-box, hammered on t'doors, back and front, knocked on her bedroom window. Her curtains are still drawn, bedroom and front room, I fear she's not got out o' bed, Mr Rhea . . .'

I knew what they were thinking. They thought Sybil had died during the night and I was now faced with a decision as to whether or not to break in. If she was still in bed, having a sleep in, it would be a gross intrusion if I smashed my way in, but surely the loud knocking and persistent shouting by her neighbours would have aroused her?

'She never sleeps in, Mr Rhea,' said John as if reading my mind.

'OK, I'll go in,' I said.

The easiest way to break into a house, as any burglar will testify, is to smash a ground floor window close to the catch, reach in and open the window. It is then possible to climb through and so I found a stone in her garden, crashed it against the glass of her bedroom window, released the catch and hauled it open. It was a matter of a moment to climb in.

The others waited outside, not wishing to be confronted with death and so I did not open her curtains. I left them closed as I fought my way behind them, but when I saw her bed, it was empty. It had been slept in, however, for the sheets and blankets were turned back as if someone had climbed out.

'Sybil?' I shouted, looking on the floor beyond the bed. 'Sybil? Are you there?'

Beyond the bedroom, I heard a faint noise and went into the passage to investigate; the bathroom adjoined through one door, and there was a small toilet through another. The toilet door was open, and it was unoccupied.

'Sybil?' I hesitated at the bathroom door, not wishing to intrude upon a lady if she was bathing, and called her name. 'Sybil?'

There was a faint response from inside, a hoarse groan almost and I identified it as a call of distress. I had to go in.

Fortunately, she had not locked the door but when I pushed it open, I was confronted by a grotesque sight. Sybil was lying on her back in the bath, stark naked with both arms sticking up like flagpoles and both legs hanging over a tiny stool which lay on its side under her knees. Her mountain of flesh filled the whole bath, with colossal breasts and huge wedges of stomach and thigh seeming to dominate the scene. But she was alive and her eyes were filled with a mixture of relief and embarrassment at my arrival.

'Sybil!' I hurried to her. Her mouth was trying to tell me something but she was hoarse and no words would come. I could see what had happened. She was stuck in the bath. I was later to learn, that because of her size, she could not sit in the bath but always used a small footstool to sit upon. She filled the bath with water and sat on the stool to wash herself all over, but on this occasion she had reached for the soap behind her and the stool had overbalanced. It had slid forward to throw her off, and she had fallen backwards into the bath, causing a huge overflow onto the bathroom floor. Her huge size and enormous weight had wedged her in, and her arms had been similarly wedged skywards so that she could not lower them. The stool had remained in the bath, under her knees, and thus she was firmly wedged in place. She couldn't lower her arms or hands to lever herself out but had managed to dislodge the plug with one of her toes. The bathwater had drained out, fortunately, but she was very cold none the less.

She had lain there since seven o'clock that morning, shouting and even singing loudly until she had lost her voice – and although she had heard the knocking and shouting, she'd been unable to attract attention to her plight.

But all that information came later. The immediate problem for me was to get her out of the bath and to somehow preserve her modesty. I managed to remove the stool from beneath her tree-like legs which provided some relief, then went into the bedroom and took a couple of blankets off the bed to cover her as I decided how to tackle this weighty problem.

I unlocked the back door to tell the assembled small crowd of well-wishers that she was safe and well while explaining the problem. I then asked Jean, the wife of her neighbour John

Oakley, if she would mind staying with Sybil as a form of feminine safeguard against any accusations that others might level against John and I. People did do that sort of thing – they could create wild rumours about a man or men being alone with a naked woman, even if she was gigantic and stuck in the bath and even if we were on a rescue mission.

As Jean went into the bathroom to comfort Sybil, John and I settled down to discuss the logistics of our problem. Whatever way we examined the situation, it seemed the only way that Sybil could be extricated was by human muscle power. Mobile cranes and motor-car lifting equipment could not be utilized without knocking down the bathroom walls.

We did consider ringing the vet who had some equipment for hoisting cattle and horses out of quagmires. Then John suggested filling the bath. He reckoned the water would add some buoyancy, however small, to the bulk of female flesh which was trapped therein and so we suggested that to Sybil, exhorting her not to try to lower her arms. We didn't want to have to grapple with slippery bits and needed both arms to be kept dry – not that she could have lowered them anyway. They were still sticking upright like flagpoles.

Sybil agreed to the water treatment so long as the water was warm. Jean opened the tap and ran it until warm water emerged, fitted the plug and began to fill the bath. Sybil retained her shroud which was soaked as the water rose almost to the brim, covering her legs and bubbling around the bulk which was the cause of the problem.

'Right,' said John. 'Nick, if you stand on t'edge of t'bath, on t'rim, at one side and me at t'other, against t'wall, and then we take hold of her arms, one apiece, and lift, we might shift her. If she can push against t'tap end wiv her feet at t'same time, we might git her moving . . .'

We tried that arrangement. She was so heavy I was frightened I would pull her arm out of its socket, but she could not reach the tap end with her feet to give us extra help. We heaved, puffed and panted, shouted and hauled at those long fat arms, but she wouldn't move.

'If we replaced the stool to the tap end,' I suggested, 'she could push against that . . .'

The stool was placed in the bath, on its side, and Sybil said, by bending her knees, she could obtain a lot of leverage against it.

'If we heave on your arms as you push against that stool with your feet,' I said, 'we might win.'

It worked. With an enormous heave, Sybil thrust her weight against the stool as we heaved on her arms, and with a slushing of water, the mass of flesh shifted towards the head of the bath. She was free. Gently, she edged backwards – and then knocked John.

He tried to retain his balance in the cramped space on the edge of the bath, lost his footing and slithered into the bath, landing on top of Sybil. With a screeching of bare flesh on the enamel, Sybil shot forward again with John on board but, with legs outstretched, she halted their joint slither by planting her feet against the submerged stool. John managed to clamber off the white-shrouded, wet mass of wobbly flesh and, without any further help from us, Sybil struggled to her feet, hugging the wet sheet around her.

But she was free. The drama was over and we left the scene of our triumph, leaving Sybil to get dressed.

'Wait before you go, I'll make some coffee,' she called to us, and so we went into the kitchen.

As we waited, I thought about Jonathan Newbould (see chapter 6), the village inventor and wondered if he could make a non-slip stool which would make a secure perch for Sybil when coping with her bath. Perhaps he could fit rubber suckers to its feet? Or perhaps manufacturers of baths could produce a device for aiding large or even handicapped people to sit in comfort and safety while washing? Or would a showerbath be more feasible for Sybil?

Afterwards, Sybil laughed and joked with everyone about her experience, telling her friends in the village how she'd been stuck in the bath with John Oakley. It was John who blushed when being reminded of the incident, not Sybil.

She enjoyed a total lack of embarrassment about her predicament, making fun of her experience wherever she went, and everyone loved her a little more just for that.

Another example of a curious way of living involved a pair of maidenly twin sisters, the Misses Mandeville, Audrey and Rosemary. They had reached that stage of life where they did not wish anyone to know their ages but those of us with reasonable powers of observation would realize that, between them they had scored a century and perhaps a little extra.

They were not identical in appearance, Miss Audrey being taller and slightly more slender than her sister. Each had neat greyish-brown hair, spectacles and a rather pale complexion with brown eyes and a rounded, pleasant face.

They dressed smartly in good quality clothes, although their outfits were perhaps a little old-fashioned, and they favoured the more subdued colours such as browns, greens and greys.

They lived in identical bungalows which had been built by their father especially for them; their neat homes stood next to each other and overlooked the village green at Slemmington. Both bungalows were built of local stone with red pantile roofs and they enjoyed delightful gardens behind beech hedges and white gates. Both bungalows were neatly painted with white woodwork and were beautifully maintained; each sister had a small Morris mini car and each enjoyed a private, if modest income as directors of the family's ceramics business.

Each had, in her younger days, worked for a living, Audrey being a solicitor's clerk while Rosemary worked for the civil service. Each had retired early shortly before the death of their father because he had wanted them to become involved with the business he had founded; they were now involved in his business, although a brother was managing director, but they did live quite well, thanks to the legacy provided by their father. He had died some four or five years before my arrival at Aidensfield.

The sisters were quite charming although some considered them rather aloof; various people interpreted their aloofness as an indication of their pretended superiority, but I think it came from their natural reticence, each being rather shy.

Possibly because of their natural reserve, they did not take a very active part in village affairs, although they could be relied upon to give prizes for raffles or jars of honey and jam for garden fêtes, or to provide bunches of flowers for the parish church and useful work for bob-a-job boy scouts. Unlike so many spinsterish sisters, they were not antagonistic towards one another and did spend a good deal of their spare time together, perhaps on a shopping expedition or even on a weekend holiday to the Lake District or in the Scottish Highlands.

But underneath this aura of respectability and family rapport, there was some rivalry. It was a long time before I became aware of this.

England is rich with tales of sisterly rivalry, my own county of Yorkshire boasting two wealthy and warring sisters who could not agree where to build a church for the village, and so each built a church of her own. The village thereafter was embarrassed by having two fine churches. In another case, one sister built a church on the site she had chosen while her sister built the tower on her selected site – the result being that the tower was a long way from the church.

But the Mandeville sisters had not fallen out in such a silly and public way; their rivalry was of a very domestic and private nature. Upon reflection, I suspect that few villagers were aware of any domestic undercurrent between them for it was not the sort of rivalry that would become public knowledge.

I learned about it when Miss Rosemary received a clandestine visit from a housebreaker.

One Monday afternoon, Rosemary had driven into Eltering to visit her bank manager and when she returned at four o'clock, she found she had had an uninvited guest. He had broken a glass panel of the kitchen door at the back of the house, turned the key which she'd left in the lock and had then let himself in to ransack the bungalow, stealing precious ceramics, glassware, some portable antiques such as figurines, vases and candlesticks, some original watercolours and some miniature oil paintings of South American birdlife. A vehicle must have been employed to carry off the loot for it was a daring daylight raid. And no one saw anything suspicious.

It was her sister, Audrey, who rang me and I promised immediate attention, exhorting the women not to touch anything and to leave things exactly as they were until the arrival of our Scenes of Crime Officers. Some victims of burglars and housebreakers would tidy up the house and dust the surfaces before the arrival of the CID – thus destroying any evidence that might have lingered. Before leaving for Slemmington, I rang the divisional officer to arrange a visit by SOCO and then hurried to the scene. I found them both in Audrey's bungalow, Rosemary being comforted by her sister with a cup of tea. They assured me that nothing had been touched or moved, and that they had not cleaned the house prior to my visit.

Then I asked them to show me the damage. I added that I'd need a list of everything that had been stolen with detailed descriptions of the missing items. At that early stage, Rosemary was unable to provide such a list and I asked her to wait until SOCO had examined the bungalow for fingerprints and other evidence; I also felt that after waiting for that couple of hours or so she would have recovered her composure sufficiently to cope with making a comprehensive list. Once I had that list, I could circulate descriptions of the stolen goods to all police forces, and local antique dealers could be alerted to the fact that the thief might try to dispose of his ill-gotten gains.

When Detective Sergeant Thornton and his SOCO team had concluded their work, I asked Miss Rosemary to compile that list for me, asking her to be as accurate as possible because the sooner we circulated the list, the better were the chances of locating the thief. I knew she would not be able to make a comprehensive list because, in the days and weeks which followed, she would begin to realize that other objects had vanished. People would never miss a certain object until many weeks later when they wanted it for a particular purpose. But we did urgently need a working list with which to begin our circulation and so Rosemary, with Audrey in close attendance, began to examine her invaded home. It was then that I began to appreciate the sisterly rivalry.

'Two brass candlesticks have gone,' Rosemary's sadness was evident in her voice. 'From the hall, they were on the piano.'

'What size?' I was making a list in my pocket-book, later to be typed and itemized.

'Ten inches tall,' she said without hesitation.

'No,' sister Audrey butted in. 'I've got the ten-inch ones, yours were the smaller ones, eight inches tall, less valuable, of course. Father gave me the better ones. Rosemary's weren't worth a lot – perhaps £15.'

'But I got the original of Pott's painting of Rievaulx Abbey and that's been taken. It's in oil, in a gilt frame and shows the abbey in springtime, with bluebells in the foreground,' Rosemary beamed at me.

I was surprised at the fierce glow of pride in her face as she added, 'Audrey only got a print of it. No discerning thief would steal a print.'

'Was it valuable, the painting?' I asked.

'Yes, I'd estimate it at around £200,' she smiled. 'The print is only worth a few pounds.'

'If the print is an exact copy of the same picture, our photographic department might reproduce it for circulation,' I said.

And so we went through her home, listing all the items

known to be missing and I began to smile to myself as the sisters vied for ownership of the most valuable items.

As I worked, I gained the impression that their father had tried very hard to make them equal, even to the extent of giving copies of pictures to one while giving the original to the other. Thus Rosemary had some originals, Audrey had others; I reckoned they had roughly the same proportion of each. Some of Rosemary's china ornaments were larger or more valuable than Audrey's and some were not, but as I progressed about my work, I found it quite hilarious listening to each woman trying to claim the better ornaments and furnishings. Rosemary kept trying to say that the objects stolen from her home were of far better quality than their counterparts in Audrey's possession. As we progressed through the bungalow, the claims grew stronger and the sisters grew more agitated as each new loss was discovered, each trying to claim they owned the most valuable example.

It was inevitable that Rosemary should come to the conclusion that the burglar must have first examined the contents of Audrey's house before deciding to ignore them in favour of her far superior belongings. She even reached the stage when she was beginning to grow proud of her experience, pleased that the housebreaker had selected her property.

'He's clearly a man of knowledge and discernment,' Rosemary told her sister. 'I think he rejected your stuff because mine was far more valuable. Consider the objects he's taken, not one of them is cheap rubbish. It's all top quality antiques and ceramics.'

'That's being silly!' was the retort.

'No it's not. Really, Audrey, I can't see any self-respecting burglar even thinking of robbing you.'

Audrey responded, 'The man's a moron, Rosemary, and you know it. He's gone for kitsch, he'll sell your stuff on seaside junk stalls and in flea markets, the fellow lacks knowledge of real quality, otherwise he'd have raided my home.'

I let them ramble on, each trying to score points over the other as I made my notes, marking those items which were duplicated in Audrey's home and which we could photograph for police circulars, and I tried not to make any remarks which would allow the women to score points over one another. But it was a strange experience, hearing a woman boasting that her burglar was a man of superior quality.

A week later, Audrey's bungalow was raided and the MO suggested the culprit was the same man. I was pleased that Phil Bellamy was available to deal with that case.

Then I wondered whether they'd each claim to have been visited by the best policeman!

8 Of Creatures Beloved

I think I could turn and live with animals,
they are so placid and self contain'd.

Walt Whitman (1819–92)

From time to time during my constabulary duties at Aidensfield,
I had trouble with a succession of donkeys that lived upon the
dubious generosity of Claude Jeremiah Greengrass. He seemed
to assemble a menagerie of assorted mokes with personality
defects or emotional problems; many had been abandoned or
were unwanted by other carers. They were sometimes aged and
infirm donkeys whose duties on Strensford Beach were over,
although many were young ones who seemed to have moods
varying between outright anger and sheer stupidity.

I was never quite sure why he took them into shelter. He
maintained it was his love of animals combined with a natural
streak of generosity; he said he did not want to see hard-worked
donkeys end their lives in misery and, to be fair to Claude, he
did care for them and did show them love and compassion. They
were well fed when in his care, their hooves and coats were
tended and there was shelter of sorts in one or other of his
tumbledown outbuildings. I must admit that most of his donkeys

appeared to be quite happy but I was never sure what happened to them when their contented Greengrass days were over. They just seemed to fade from the landscape.

From time to time, however, he would gather a younger and very frisky animal into his care. Quite often, this was a stallion with a strong sense of desire to breed with anything on four legs. This did not please the neighbours because one source of annoyance was the stallions' habit of braying extremely loudly. Their terrible din, a sort of hee-hawing mixed with massive intakes of air and bouts of wheezing like a farrier's bellows, was said by some to be a means of communication with other neighbourhood donkeys and said by others to be an amorous love-song, a sort of donkey serenade. It might have been nothing more than a means of letting people know the donkeys were there and in need of companionship, because donkeys are sociable animals and love the companionship of their own kind, as well as that of humans, horses or other animals. Their habit of braying loudly, as in the case of the Greengrass stallions, might have been their way of protesting about the behaviour of their wily master or his lurcher dog, Alfred; Alfred would sometimes hitch a lift on the back of an unwilling donkey. The dog would stand astride the cross-marked back of the donkey and would defy all attempts by the donkey to throw him off. In some ways, Alfred was quite a showman – some reckoned he had a touch of the circus in his blood.

The most recent addition to the Greengrass stable, a lively stallion called Basil, caused further disturbance in and around Aidensfield because he constantly and noisily fell in love with lady ponies.

He appeared to prefer them to female donkeys and lost no

opportunity in making his odd desire known far and wide. It was fortunate for him, but unfortunate for the ponies and their riders, that there were lots of pony mares in the district upon whom Basil could lavish his unrequited love. It is known, of course, that donkeys and horses will cross breed to produce hybrids called mules but this riveting piece of natural history was of little consequence to the pony owners and riders with whose mounts Basil fell headlong and helplessly in love.

He had found a way of escaping from the Greengrass ranch, apparently through a piece of loose fencing, and once free would pursue the object of his lust through the lanes, woods, fields and villages until he had achieved his purpose. He would ignore the whips, feet and shouts of the riders as he tried, from time to time, to consummate his passion with the pony rider still in the saddle. Little girls received stern warnings about Basil's activities and were told that if Basil appeared on the scene with a glint in his eye, the girl and her pony should gallop for shelter in the nearest donkey-proof building. Some did wonder why, if Alfred the lurcher could ride upon a donkey, why couldn't a donkey try to ride upon a pony? Parents did not have an easy time explaining Basil's public passion to girls of tender years, although it was evident that some did quickly learn the facts of life, even if it was through regularly witnessing the unashamed actions of a lovesick and very lusty donkey.

Because he could be a confounded nuisance to pony riders as well as a danger to motor traffic, I found myself repeatedly warning Claude Jeremiah Greengrass that he faced prosecution for allowing livestock (i.e. the donkey) to stray upon the highway, or that I might even book him for obstructing the highway and that he might find Basil impounded. Claude did make an effort of sorts, but Basil could defy everyone – when he wanted love and adventure, no one could stop him. If his passion was aroused, no compound could detain him and he was quite capable of leaping a five-bar gate if a desirable pony chanced to wander by.

A fine example of Basil's precociousness occurred one Wednesday morning when I received a call of desperation from the vicar, the Reverend Roger Clifton.

'Nick,' he panted. 'I've just dashed in from the street, I'm ringing from the vicarage, there's rather an embarrassing, er, well, demonstration going on down here. It involves that donkey of Mr Greengrass's.'

I groaned.

'Have you rung him?' was my first question.

'Yes, but there's no reply.'

'So what's the donkey doing now?'

'It's got a pony, a female I suspect, cornered in the lychgate of my church and, well, not to put too fine a point on it, it's trying to mount the pony. The donkey is in, well a high and well advanced stage of passion, if you understand.'

'It always is,' I groaned.

'Yes, but this time it's especially embarrassing . . .'

'You've tried chasing it off?'

'It bares its teeth at me or anyone else who approaches, and, well, it is in a very rampant state. It could be dangerous, Nick, the donkey gets very angry when anyone tries to chase it away from its desired intention, but this situation is rather worse than normal, actually . . .'

'Worse? Why?'

'That funeral of Mr Tomlinson, he died at Strensford earlier this week and expressed a desire to be buried here. Well, the cortège has just arrived and we can't get the coffin or the mourners into the church or even into the churchyard. The donkey's in the gateway, you see, and it's got a pony cornered there; it is all so very embarrassing with its massive private parts on display, and panting all over the pony as the mourners don't know where to look . . .'

'Who does the pony belong to?'

'Fiona Lambton. She had hired it to a young girl called Molly Forster, but when the donkey made its overtures, Molly ran home and left the pony to its fate. The pony's not saddled up although it has a halter on . . . I've rung Miss Lambton too, she's not at home either and, well, the mourners are getting a bit restless and the donkey won't stop, it just keeps trying, Nick, and failing, I might add. The more it fails, the more determined it becomes. The poor pony doesn't like it either.'

I promised I would attend immediately and decided to walk down to the church rather than drive; at least that would give me a few minutes longer to try and think of a suitable course of action. I must admit that, as I paraded down the village street in my police uniform, I did not think that the image of the constabulary in action was enhanced by having to cope with a rampant and shameless donkey whose lustful intention was so blatantly obvious.

When I arrived, the cortège was stationary and all the mourners were still seated in the shining black cars with suitably glum expressions on their faces while trying not to look at the romantic natural scene being played out before their very eyes. The undertaker had left his place in the passenger seat of the hearse and was wiping his perspiring brow with a huge white handkerchief, while the vicar stood within the safety of the churchyard. And, tucked beneath the sheltering archway of the lychgate was Basil, as rampant as ever as he tried to mount the whinnying pony which he had managed to detain within the confines of the enclosed gateway. As Basil moved around in a circle, sometimes mounting the pony for the merest of moments before slipping off to try again, the vicar blushed and the undertaker, Josh Durbridge, shouted at the copulators and tried to shoo them away. But Basil bared his teeth at anyone who dared to interrupt his ardour and so no one dared even to attempt to drag him away.

'Thoo'll etti deea summat, Mr Rhea,' Josh wiped his brow again. 'There's some varry straight ladies in yon cars, maiden ladies who've nivver knawn where babies came from let alone how donkey stallions get their kicks, and Ah can't say Ah knaw what effect this'll have on 'em, seeing summat that size. T'vicar might have some bother on his hands when this carry-on's all ovver.'

'One way of treating a man who's a bit rampant, Josh, is to chuck a bucket of cold water over him,' I suggested.

'Or mak him tak a cold shower!' chuckled the undertaker.

'Would it work with a rutting donkey?' I asked. 'A hosepipe? Cold water directed at his tender bits . . .'

'It's worth a try,' he said.

I went towards Roger Clifton and asked, 'Have you a hosepipe and a water supply? Cold Water?'

'Yes, we use it in the churchyard,' he smiled.

'Let's see if we can dampen Basil's ardour,' I suggested.

As Basil continued to exercise his cupidity, we connected a

length of hosepipe to a tap in the corner of the churchyard and Josh examined the nozzle.

'We need ti git a fair pressure up,' he said, twisting the nozzle until he seemed satisfied. 'A bit o' power's needed . . . right, Vicar, ton t'tap full on, give it some welly.'

As Josh directed the hose towards the donkey, Roger Clifton turned on the tap and we all waited.

There was a hissing somewhere, the hose wriggled as the water surged through and suddenly a stream of ice-cold water burst from it. Josh aimed it at Basil. But Basil was not going to be deflected from his lasciviousness by a drop of water and as the stream hit him, he ignored it. I knew that Josh was aiming for a certain part of the donkey's anatomy but that was not so easy to achieve in the circumstances and so Josh played the hosepipe over the donkey's back and head, moving it around as he tried to find the centre of Basil's desire and lust.

'It's not makking onny difference!' shouted Josh. 'By, he's a randy awd fussack is yon . . .'

Then, as Basil slipped off the now soaking object of his passion, the stream of cold water hit the pony in her most sensitive and delicate area. With a sudden whinnying of surprise, she lashed out with hind legs, kicking Basil in the stomach and knocking him back a few feet, and then she bucked and kicked until she was free. Then, whinnying with embarrassment as Josh continued to play the cold water upon her rear end, the pony twisted like a struggling cat, emerged from the lychgate and galloped away down the village street.

'Well, Ah'll be capped,' said Josh. 'Water off now, Vicar, we've done t'trick.'

But Basil was not going to be undone. With a deep-throated

hee-haw, he set off in pursuit of the pony, his passion not in the least diminished.

I watched in some alarm as the two animals tore headlong down Aidensfield village street, with cars swerving to avoid them. My only consolation was that the funeral was free to go ahead.

'Thanks, Josh,' I said with some gratitude.

Josh beamed at the vicar, 'I reckon that's some kind of baptism, eh?' and then, adopting his solemn funereal mask, turned to the waiting cortège and said, 'We can now convey the departed into the church.'

My problem was the departed pony and donkey. If Basil got his way, he would corner that pony in some other place to continue his interrupted fornication and so I walked briskly away to try and locate the pair of them. But I needn't have worried. The pony managed to find its way into its own stable and Fiona Lambton arrived just in time to slam the door against the advancing Basil.

'What on earth's happened to Sunbeam? She's all wet!' asked Fiona as Basil frothed at the mouth while head-butting the stable door in the urge to reach the pony.

'She's been rescued from a fate worse than death.' I explained the situation. 'So, can you keep this donkey here until Claude Jeremiah comes for him?'

'He won't go away, I can tell you that,' Fiona said. 'He'll hang about that stable until he's dragged away . . . he'll tackle anything, will that Basil. What a libido! I wish I could find a man like that. Does Claude know he's here?'

'No,' I said. 'Perhaps you'd ring him and ask him to collect his donkey?'

And before she could refuse my request I walked away, relieved to leave the problem in her capable hands.

One of the reasons I left Fiona to cope with Basil was that I had had lots of occasions to threaten legal action against Fiona due to the behaviour of her own horses and ponies. They seemed to cause as much bother as Claude Jeremiah's donkeys and I thought this was one way of repaying her for past bother. (See *Constable on the Hill*.)

Her horses were a fascinating collection. One of them was always ridden to Ashfordly market by Johnny Brown, a local character, and it then found its own way back to Aidensfield. Johnny would return by bus later in the day. This was an example of the ability of some horses to operate without riders and, in the past, many milkmen would rely on the horse to find its way around the village delivery route. The milkman would deliver on foot as the horse took the cart of milk from house to house. There are lots of similar tales about horses carrying drunken owners home, or finding their own way home when their rider had had an accident.

But even in the 1960s, it was not wise to have an unattended horse wandering the country lanes. There were traffic hazards which had not been in existence even forty years earlier, and so a free-ranging horse was a problem.

I was faced with such a worry by one of Fiona Lambton's horses. It was a delightful gelding called Treacle due to his wonderful golden colouring. He was a superb animal who was loved by all who met him, but he had a curious weakness.

Treacle had a passion for fox hunting. On the morning of a hunt meeting, he would begin to shiver with excitement, growing restless and agitated and whinnying for his mistress to come and saddle him up. In the horsebox *en route* to the meet, he continued in this state of high excitement, rattling his hooves on the floor of the trailer or neighing loudly as he approached the meet. And then, when he and Fiona were galloping across the countryside among dozens of other horses and riders, Treacle was in his seventh heaven. For Treacle the horse, hunting was like a drug; he could not exist without his regular dose.

The snag was that Fiona did not attend every meet. Somehow, Treacle knew when there was a local meeting, perhaps due to other horses from Aidensfield being taken there or maybe due to a deep-seated sixth sense. When there was a meet in the district, he would become highly irritable and restless, kicking his stable door or chewing the wood from doors and gates in his frustration. Then one day, he decided that if Fiona would not take him hunting, he would go by himself.

And so he did. He leapt the fences of his home ground to escape just as he leapt the fences when hunting with the other horses.

On the first occasion he hunted alone, no one paid much immediate attention to the unattended horse. The regulars knew it belonged to Fiona Lambton and the fact it bore no harness or saddlery probably meant she was about to correct that defect. But when it galloped off without a rider and followed the hunt to its conclusion with never a sight of Fiona, the master of foxhounds realized he must do something about it.

I was told that he rang Fiona to inform her that her horse had somehow attended the meet, but she did not seem to be very perturbed about it. But when it happened on several further occasions, the MFH decided to take action.

'Look here, Fiona,' Mr Gregory Stanleigh-Prowd telephoned her one Saturday morning. 'This bloody horse of yours has turned up again, we can't have riderless horses going hunting, you know, damned dangerous if you ask me.'

She said he had come to no harm and knew how to conduct himself in the field; if someone would tether him when the hunt was over, she would arrange to collect him.

I was blissfully unaware of Treacle's regular truancy until I received a call from a motorist. A travelling salesman had been driving past Whemmelby Lane end when he'd seen a riderless horse heading into the dale. He called me because he thought the rider might have been thrown off and was perhaps lying injured somewhere. I drove down to Whemmelby only to find the place swarming with huntsmen and women in their finery.

Horse boxes were parked along the verges and there, among the lively horses, I saw Treacle and recognized him instantly. I located Stanleigh-Prowd and asked, 'Mr Stanleigh-Prowd, isn't that Fiona Lambton's horse?'

'Yes, it is, damned thing. It gets out and follows local horses to the meets. See, no saddle, no halter. It follows us everywhere we go.'

'Isn't it dangerous, having a loose horse among you?'

'Normally I'd agree with that, Mr Rhea, but old Treacle is wonderful, he's no bother really, but, well, a riderless horse on the highway isn't exactly a sound idea.'

'It could cause a nasty accident,' I said. 'So after a day's hunting, how does he got home?' I asked.

'He doesn't. He can find his way here all right, by tracking horse boxes, I reckon, but he can't find his way home again. So once the hunt is over, he will hang around near a horse box until someone tethers him. We all know him, fortunately, he's no real trouble.'

'And then Fiona is called?'

'Exactly. She will come to collect him. Bloody thing . . . he's hooked on hunting, you see, Mr Rhea. Very well trained, mind, a fine animal really.'

'Can we tie him up now? Before you ride off? You can leave without him. I'll ring her and ask her to collect him.'

'He would go berserk, Mr Rhea. No, either she rides him or he comes with us now. I'll see to him, between us we'll care for him, the others know him well enough. But we mustn't tie up old Treacle while the others are hunting, God, no!'

'That's a risk, is it?'

'God, yes. He'd do everything in his power to free himself, might even strangle himself while trying to get loose. We couldn't have that, I couldn't take that risk. Imagine, leaving him here, tied up all day while we're riding to hounds within his earshot? He'd go mad.'

'It seems we need to find a rider for him when Fiona can't make it?' I suggested.

'Yes, we tried to suggest that to Fiona, some of our members need a mount from time to time, but she doesn't seem to worry about him. But she'll have to do something, he'll go mad if he's not allowed to hunt with us. Between us, we make sure he doesn't go on any roads.'

I was conscious of the illegality of allowing a horse to stray on the highway and I was equally aware of the dangers of a riderless horse trotting along the country lanes, even if it was as calm and lovely as dear old Treacle. The drivers of cars, lorries and motor cycles might not realize that Treacle was trained to cope with traffic but irrespective of all the arguments in his favour, Treacle could not be allowed to roam by himself.

In spite of Stanleigh-Prowd's assurance, I knew there would be risks and there would be times when Treacle would be on the public roads without a rider.

I called to see Fiona Lambton later that day.

'He's liable to be impounded,' I warned her. 'If our motor patrol comes across him while he's riderless, they'll follow standard procedures. He could be locked up, Miss Lambton.'

'Poor old pet,' she mused. 'He does so love hunting, Mr Rhea, he really does. But I can't go to every meet and, well, he insists, you see. I've tried keeping him back . . . he'll kick the stable doors and might injure himself if I keep him in.'

'Couldn't one of your riding pupils go hunting on him if you can't make it?'

'Not really, not if they're not members. And it is expensive, you know, joining the hunt. Few young people can afford it.'

'Can't they join just for the day? Just for one particular outing?'

'Yes, they can, there are day subscriptions. But, well, I seldom know in advance whether or not I can go, you see. Getting a rider at the last minute, with the necessary funds, well, it's not as simple as it sounds, Mr Rhea.'

'It's your problem, Miss Lambton,' I said. 'And you could be fined or your horse could be impounded or worse still, injured. You must do something to curb his lone wanderings.'

'Yes, of course, Mr Rhea.'

It would be some four or five weeks later when I came across Mr Stanleigh-Prowd in Brantsford. He had been entertaining a business friend to lunch and took the opportunity to stop for a chat. 'You've seen Fiona about that confounded horse?' he put to me.

I explained what I'd done and he nodded. 'Well, she's been out with us since, so there's been no problem, but it will arise again, Mr Rhea, the bloody woman doesn't care, you know. She is a bit blasé about it all.'

'The rule about only members riding with the hunt is a stumbling-block,' I said. 'She has some pupils who could take Treacle hunting otherwise. Some can't afford to join the hunt nor even fork out for single-day subscriptions.'

'We can't have every Tom, Dick and Harriet turning up at our official hunts, you know. There's insurance to consider, the use of farmers' lands, club rules and so on. We do have standards to keep, Mr Rhea; we are reluctant to encourage non-members to ride with us. I agree she couldn't let just any pupil ride Treacle during a hunt.'

Then I had a brain-wave.

'Why not make Treacle a member?' I said. 'In his own right. Then he could hunt, couldn't he? If he was a member, he could hunt with someone other than Fiona Lambton up?'

'Hah!' he chortled. 'What a bloody scheme, Officer! Trust a policeman to find a way around the bloody rule book!'

'It might save the life of a neurotic horse,' I laughed with him. 'And Fiona Lambton can afford his subscription.'

'Bloody hell, whatever next! All right, I'll put it to our committee. A horse a member! Honorary membership perhaps . . . with no voting rights . . . I'll have to see what the rule book says . . .' and he strode off, chortling to himself.

But a week later, Treacle became a member of the Slemmington Hunt, with Fiona paying his annual fee and thus, in theory, anyone could ride him. Fiona made sure that the youngsters who did ride to hounds with him were very capable and thus the Slemmington Hunt had its first four-legged member.

I wondered how he could cope if he was invited to the annual Hunt Ball.

Rather like a rural veterinary surgeon, a country police officer has to deal with many animals, albeit not in a medical sense. More often than not, we are concerned with creatures who are involved with problems or whose owners are involved with problems.

On one occasion, I found myself in Elsinby churchyard because I received a telephone call late one summer evening to say there were suspicious noises coming from the corner under the yew trees. The caller, who'd rung from a kiosk, rang off before I could obtain a name and address, but I felt it sounded like a genuine call.

For some weeks prior to that call, it had been suspected that drunks were using the silence of the graves for an after-hours drinking session and also that vandals were damaging tombstones and memorials. So off I went to investigate the report, fully armed with my trusty torch and truncheon.

When I arrived, everything was in silence. There was not a murmur of wind nor any other sound among the tombstones and although it was not totally dark, it was difficult to see into the deeper recesses of the vegetation or beneath the thick yew trees. I entered the churchyard as quietly as I could, walking on the grass instead of the footpaths, as I began my tour of the tombstones.

I looked behind each headstone, for such memorials did

provide an effective hiding place for drinkers and lovers, but I found nothing. There was no one lurking behind the stones, no signs of empty beer bottles or litter and neither did I discover any recent signs of vandalism. But as I made my way towards the darkness of the shadows beneath the yews, I did discern some faint sounds. It was like heavy breathing, a gentle and almost rhythmic noise. I halted and listened. In some ways, it reminded me of slumbering cows. When patrolling at night, the calm sound of the breathing of sleeping cows was one of the noises of the darkness, one which could frighten anyone not accustomed to rural sounds. But this was not a meadow – it was a churchyard, and there should be no cows here.

If it was not a cow, it was probably a drunk sleeping off a heavy session or, of course, it might be a pair of lovers resting after the evening's activities. I crept forward and stooped to peer into the darkness . . . there was something! I halted, hair bristling on the nape of my neck as I tried to see what was lurking there – then I shone my torch.

Two massive eyes blinked back at me . . . a huge beast lumbered to its feet, white face shining in the light of my torch and nostrils extending as it fumed at my stupidity in disturbing its slumbers. It was a bull – and a big one. With the speed of light, it rose to its feet and within seconds was lumbering towards me.

I did not lumber towards the exit. I fled. I galloped. I raced across the churchyard, weaving between the tombstones and sometimes leap-frogging over them as I tried to put distance between myself and the bull. He followed, panting and making curiously frightening noises as I leapt, galloped and fled towards the gate.

The oncoming bull knocked over some tombstones, demolished several vases of flowers and trampled over some shrubbery as it lumbered after me. But I won. I raced out of the gate and locked it behind me, panting like a broken-winded gallower. The bull halted at the other side, gazing at me but unable to follow.

'You bloody vandal!' I shouted at it. Then I wondered who it belonged to.

I'd not seen the bull around the village and so I went to The Hopbind Inn which was still serving and told them of my discovery.

'It'll be Awd Jesse's,' said one of the regulars.

Jesse was Mr Jesse Ramsay of High Farm so I drove there immediately and told him the story. When we searched the field for his bull, it had gone; some hikers had apparently left the gate open and the bull had gone for walkies. Fortunately, the churchyard gate must also have been open and so the bull had wandered in for a rest and a meal of lush grass. I do not know who telephoned me, although I suspect it was one of the careless hikers.

'He's as gentle as a kitten, Mr Rhea,' he told me. 'He wouldn't have hurt you.'

'Tell that to the vicar,' I said. 'He's knocked over a few items of graveyard furniture.'

After daylight next morning, the village was full of rumours about vandals rampaging around the churchyard with the damage being claimed as firm evidence of their activities. But I told the villagers that the rumours were just a load of bull.

Among the other animals which caused problems were Bushy

the Border collie, an exploding pig and a kidnapped bufflehead.

Bushy was a lovely dog owned by an Aidensfield lady. He was a Border collie and should have been employed tending sheep, but he was in fact a domestic dog and a much-loved pet. He had a lovely nature and everyone liked him. But he had a curious hobby – he chased aeroplanes.

Other dogs had a propensity for chasing cars or motor-cycles, but Bushy preferred aeroplanes. Just as the car or motor-cycle chasers would run after a passing vehicle, barking at its back wheel for a couple of hundred yards, so Bushy would run along beneath the flight path of a passing plane, barking at it and snarling. There is no doubt he thought he was chasing the intruder away from the village because, having been barked and growled at in a ferocious manner, the plane did escape over the moors to leave the village in peace. There is no doubt that Bushy saw himself as the guardian of Aidensfield.

In his self-imposed role of protector, he could hear the distant approach of the aircraft long before we could, and long before it appeared, and so he prepared himself for the chase by standing in the village street at Aidensfield, bushy tail and sharp ears erect, eyes to the skies and nose pointing towards the oncoming noise. And as the plane flew overhead, Bushy would bark at it and chase it away. He never failed to rid us of a trespassing aircraft – every one of them fled from his strong teeth and loud barking.

The snag was, of course, that aeroplanes did not follow the routes of roads or footpaths. Unlike motor vehicle chasers, Bushy did not confine himself to accepted highways but tore across gardens, through farmyards and over hedges in his efforts to save Aidensfield from aeroplanes.

He demolished several cloches, ruined umpteen newly planted seedbeds, damaged crops of outdoor tomatoes, potatoes, peas, beans and carrots, knocked over pedal cycles, ladders and tins of paint and sent old ladies' shopping baskets flying. Most of the offended humans did not appreciate his gallant efforts to prevent aircraft landing in Aidensfield and so I began to receive complaints about his activities.

I went to see his owner, Mrs Cecily Carter, and told her of the complaints.

'I have written to the RAF,' she said coyly. 'I've asked them not to direct flights over the village but they said they could not divert their flight paths because of a dog. I wrote to the Minister of Aviation too, and he said the same.'

'That's understandable,' I said. 'But if Bushy continues to cause damage in his pursuit of aeroplanes, you're going to receive some hefty bills for compensation or repairs. And, worse still, he could cause an accident to a cyclist or a driver of any kind. He has no road sense when he's chasing his planes away.'

'I really don't know what to do, Mr Rhea, I have had complaints already, he knocked a bucket of whitewash all over someone's front step one day, and another time caused a cyclist to swerve and fall off his bike into a manure heap.'

She recounted several hilarious tales of Bushy's activities and it seems he disliked jets more than planes with propellers. But we had to halt his recklessness.

'What about one of those long leads?' I suggested. 'You might have seen them – they are two posts with a line between them, rather like a clothes-line, and the dog's lead runs along that line. The longer the gap between the posts, the more running space the dog has. If Bushy was given that kind of freedom, he could still chase his planes without causing much havoc. He'd be limited in his gallops and he'd still be happy that he was saving the village from attack.'

And so the deed was done. Bushy had a new run in Mrs Carter's back garden and spent his days protecting us all from advancing aircraft. He did a wonderful job – not one plane has ever landed in Aidensfield.

Some of us wondered what he would have done if one had landed.

Claude Jeremiah Greengrass caused a minor panic when he decided to kill and clean his own pig. In some rural areas, cottagers continued to rear and kill their own pigs, a relic of earlier times, and if there was a spot of easy cash to be made in this way, then Claude Jeremiah would adopt the system. And so he did.

One offshoot of killing and curing one's own pig was the bladder – farm lads would blow up the bladder and use it as a football, and having seen this, Claude decided that the best way to clean the hairs off his dead pig was to inflate it.

He reasoned that if he inflated the pig so that its belly and body were firm and rounded, he could then clean off the surplus hair in a very swift and easy manner. Shaving a man's cheek when it was puffed out with wind was far easier than attempting to clean a sunken cheek. That was his logic.

Having killed the unfortunate animal, therefore, Claude set about sealing all its natural openings and then decided to inflate it. In the corner of one of his outbuildings he had a cylinder of gas; he wasn't quite sure what sort of gas was contained therein but he reckoned it would be perfect for inflating the pig. Later, we thought it might have been propane but no one was quite sure. However, having connected the hose to a suitable place on the pig's anatomy, he proceeded to open the nozzle on the cylinder and allow the escaping gas to change the pig into a very rounded carcass.

Once it was tightly blown up, Claude detached the gas pipe and was about to begin shaving the pig's skin with a cut-throat razor, when he spotted a blowlamp in the shed. Why not singe off the hairs as all good butchers did?

According to his account of events, he lit the blowlamp and began to apply its flame to the body of the porker, very efficiently removing all the surplus hairs. But suddenly there was an almighty explosion. Claude Jeremiah was enveloped by pieces of flying pig and the noise alerted a neighbour who was hoeing in a nearby field.

He rang the fire brigade because he saw a cloud of smoke emerging from the outbuilding rapidly followed by Claude Jeremiah who was covered in some indescribable mess. The fire brigade was not needed and Claude survived, but the experience put him off smoked bacon for a long, long time. We wrote off the fire as 'false alarm with good intent' and a senior fire officer warned Claude about using canisters containing unknown fluids and gases.

But another dead animal found in Claude's possession caused a minor flap. A special constable had been coming home from the pub one evening when he noticed Claude's old van leaving the grounds of Lord Ashfordly's estate with a dead stag on the roof. It had a fine set of antlers and seemed in prime condition, according to the witness.

Suspecting a poaching expedition, the special had telephoned Eltering police office and I received a radio call to proceed immediately to the scene. As I was on patrol at the time, it was easy to divert to Ashfordly, but as I reached the road in question, there was no sign of my quarry. This was not surprising as he'd had a few minutes start but, being aware that the special would be well acquainted with Claude, I set off towards his home and arrived in time to see his battered old van being unloaded. Sure enough, as my headlights illuminated the scene, he was lifting the carcass of a deer from his roof-rack.

'Now then, Claude,' I said, going towards him. 'It looks as though we've got you red-handed this time.'

'Red-handed, Mr Rhea? What for?' He looked at me in amazement.

'Poaching,' I said. 'Deer poaching in fact. From Lord Ashfordly's estate . . . you were seen leaving and I have found you in possession of a dead stag, a fallow deer by the look of it. So, what's your story about this one?'

He burst out laughing.

'Nay, lad,' he said. 'This is dead all right, but it's been dead a long time. It's stuffed. Ashfordly threw it out and said I could have it if I would take it away. See, it's moth-eaten and worn out, but I'll sell it somewhere . . . you can't have me for poaching stuffed deer, Mr Rhea. Can you?'

'No,' I said. 'Sorry about this . . .'

'No problem, Mr Rhea, you're only doing your job,' he chuckled as I crept away. He'd live on that story for years!

A similar incident happened during the summer after the village schoolchildren had been taken on an outing to the zoo. Some of my own youngsters went along and so did the little lad whose parents lived in a cottage close to the police house in Aidensfield. He was called Simon Westhouse and he was six.

Gillian Westhouse was friendly with Mary and asked if Simon could join our children for the trip; Mary wasn't going for the teachers were looking after all the children.

But Gillian had to visit the optician in York that very day and would not return until 5 p.m. So Mary said that, after the trip, Simon could come to our house to play with our children until she returned.

When Elizabeth came home without Simon, Mary asked, 'Where's Simon?'

'He fell in the pond, he's gone straight home to get changed,' she said. 'His shoes and trousers are wet. He knows where the key is, it's under a brick outside the back door.'

'Fell in?' Mary was horrified.

'Only a little.' Elizabeth was not in the least concerned. 'He got his socks wet, that's all. Teacher said to get changed the minute he got home and have a bath before he caught cold.'

Mary went round to the Westhouse cottage and found the door open. She called upstairs to ask if Simon was all right and he shouted that he was.

'I'm getting my wet things off,' he said.

'Come round when you've finished then,' Mary called upstairs to him. 'And have some tea with us.'

But Mrs Westhouse returned home early; Mary had just come back from speaking to Simon when Gillian came to our front door, saying she'd met a friend and had got a lift home. Mary explained about Simon, at which Gillian rushed to attend to him.

But within minutes, she was back at our front door looking worried.

'Nick,' she said. 'Can you come? Simon's locked himself in the bathroom he says he's got a friend with him, he won't let me in.'

'A friend?' I puzzled.

'He was alone when he came home,' said Elizabeth who was hovering nearby. 'Definitely, no one came with him.'

'I'm sure he was talking to someone, I could hear him chattering in the bathroom . . .'

As Simon was an only child, and as his father was working in York until about eight o'clock, I could understand Gillian's concern. There had been a recent case where a man had entered a child's bedroom to assault the youngster in bed, and it had created a lot of publicity and alarm. So I went around to the house.

As I tapped on the bathroom door, I could hear water splashing in the bath; I repeated my knock and heard Simon saying, 'Don't make a noise, you are my friend. I will look after you . . .'

'He's got somebody in there,' I said. 'A friend . . . Simon!' I called. 'It's Mr Rhea, can you let me in?'

There was no response.

'Have you a ladder?' I asked Gillian. 'And is the bathroom window open?'

'Yes,' she answered to both questions.

I went outside, placed the ladder against the wall and climbed up to the bathroom window.

It was ajar, and it was an easy task to remove the catch and open it wide. And as I peered inside, I saw Simon sitting in the bath, quite naked, and he was washing a duck.

'Simon!' I called. 'Where on earth did you get that duck?'

'He's my new friend,' he said. 'I brought him home from the zoo . . .'

It seemed that Simon had taken a fancy to the duck, which was a very tame ornamental specimen, known as a bufflehead. It was a beautiful duck, chiefly white, with black wings and a large black head with purple, blue and green highlights. There was a large white patch on the back of its head. The bird, which is quite a rare species in this country, was just over a foot in length.

Simon had waded into the pond, picked up the bird and stuffed it inside his windcheater. In the darkness of his clothing, the bird had never struggled or cried out and he had brought it home literally under the eye of his teacher. His clothes were wet and dirty but neither he nor the bird was harmed.

'We'll have to take him back,' I said. 'He needs proper food and we have none here, besides he's not yours . . .'

The zoo officials were very nice about it; in fact, they hadn't noticed the duck's absence and said that Simon could adopt it, although he must leave it at the zoo. And so Simon found himself the adopted father of a bufflehead duck.

He called it Meredith for reasons I shall never know and paid periodic visits to feed and talk to his new friend.

But after their initial meeting, they never again bathed together.

9 Say That Again?

Egad! I think the interpreter is the hardest
to be understood of the two!
Richard Brinsley Sheridan (1751–1816)

The English are noted for their failure to learn the languages of others. We travel the globe to find that our language is both spoken and understood by a huge proportion of the world's population, and consequently we do not trouble to master the tongues even of our continental neighbours.

Even more astonishing is that we do not truly master our own language; the grammar of many English people is awful and one of my pet hates is the wide and annoying use of the double negative. Quite educated people will say 'I don't want none of that' or 'I haven't got no more money' or 'I don't want no more to drink.' Perhaps I am fortunate in having a good primary school teacher who made sure her pupils did not fall into that lazy way of speech – she made sure that we understood that if we hadn't got nothing, it meant we must have something!

Here in Yorkshire, of course, we are bilingual. We proudly speak the so-called Queen's English, albeit with a distinctive accent, but many of us also speak Yorkshire dialect. Dialect is not mere accent, however. Dialect is the use of ancient and very local words and phrases.

I have highlighted this aspect of Yorkshire life in earlier 'Constable' books, mentioning that in Yorkshire there are well over 100 dialects. The language of the West Riding differs immensely from that of the North Riding which in turn can be distinguished from that of the East Riding. In North Yorkshire alone there is a huge difference between the speech of the dales and the speech of the coastline. Perhaps it takes a keen ear to distinguish such differences, but I thought I would include a handful of words now, just to show that Yorkshire folk do speak a different language and do not merely speak with a distinctive accent.

Here are a few dialect words: bautering, betwaddled, bounderstoops, brummelneeased, canthrif, caumbrils, chalter-heeaded, clocker, crambazzled, gallowers, gammerstang, glishy, goulders, grouty, jaggins, jotherum, ket, lagged, loppered, parlous, parsling, reeafshafts, rudsteeaks, scalderings, scran, semmanty, shackles, sieves, skelbeeasts, skimmer, spawldering, swingletrees, theeaking, tivvying, yamley and yows. There are thousands of such words which pepper the conversation of country folk, particularly those in the more remote parts of the Yorkshire Dales and the North York Moors.

Many older folk do not know any other word for the object in question, consequently there are bound to be misunderstandings. On the moors near my home, a visitor asked the purpose of a small enclosure and the farmer said, 'Why, it's where t'yowes are heeafed.'

A yow is a ewe, the moorland sheep roaming free upon our moors, but the youngsters remain enclosed with their mums until they know their unmarked boundaries. When released, they will then remain upon that stretch of moorland without being fenced in. Heeaf is the local word for that procedure; heaf or heeaf means abode or habitat. Ewes that are heeafed are those which know their boundaries. My moorland friend explained that in a handful of words, but his listener still failed to understand.

Fortunately, I was brought up to speak my native North Riding dialect and consequently had no trouble understanding the conversations of true Yorkshire folk, but even so many misunderstandings did arise.

For example, a lady motorist stopped in Aidensfield to seek directions from me. She asked if there was a bank in the village, so I sent her along to the outskirts where a steep hill climbs to the moors. I thought she wanted to park the car somewhere with wide open views of the countryside, and there was a lovely position at the top of that bank. She returned and said she could not find the bank – all she had found was a very steep hill with moorland around it. In Yorkshire, a bank is a steep hill – it seems she was seeking a place to draw out some cash.

A clear case of misunderstanding which could have had fatal consequences occurred in the West Riding, a county with its own distinctive mode of speech.

When British Rail installed its early automatic level-crossing barriers, there were advance warnings upon our roads in the form of flashing lights and large written signs.

The signs told motorists to 'Stop while lights flash'. Those of us outside the West Riding, which includes the rest of the world, would have halted our vehicles and waited when the lights were flashing because that flashing indicated the coming of a train. But in the West Riding, 'while' means 'until'. A West Yorkshire person will say 'wait while I return', which in their case means 'wait until I return'. Thus, when our friends from West Yorkshire first encountered those new signs, they halted their cars to wait *until* the lights flashed – and then set off! For them, the sign's message was exactly the opposite of that which was intended. The confusion was quickly rectified with no fatalities. Now, the signs clearly tell us to stop when the lights show.

During my service at Aidensfield, I did encounter some minor embarrassments because of my Yorkshire manner of speech. One which bears repeating occurred at a garden fête where the lady of the manor asked me to instruct one of her members of staff to fetch the white Jag. I found him and said that her ladyship wanted the white Jaguar, whereupon he said they didn't have a white Jaguar. It transpired she wanted a drink of orange squash which was in a white jug on one of the stalls. She'd asked for the white jug, not the white Jag.

Here in Yorkshire, a jug is jug, not a jag; a bus is a bus and not a bass, grass is grass and not grarse, bath is bath and not barth, and we also pronounce 'fat' correctly.

Similarly, when it was suggested that Lady Ashfordly be asked to open a garden fête and remain as guest of honour, the posh-speaking secretary of the organizers, at whose meeting I was present, made it clear that three chairs would have to be arranged for her. I could not understand why she needed three chairs, unless she was bringing friends, and the same puzzle baffled the chairman.

'What's she want three chairs for?' he asked the secretary.

'Cheers, you silly man,' she said. 'Hip, hip, hoorays. Cheers, not chairs. We need to arrange three cheers for her ladyship after her opening speech.'

It was this kind of misunderstanding that caused something of a flap due to some visiting, trouble-seeking students overhearing a discussion about a lorry accident.

A loaded lorry ran away down the hill leading into Aidensfield. Its driver managed to steer it off the road and it ran on to the moor but continued several yards down a slope and overturned into a gully, spilling its load. The driver was not injured and managed to climb out of the passenger side window to seek assistance. The lorry was carrying five tons of gravel; this spilt into a narrow gully which, in winter, was the course of a fast-running moorland stream.

In summer, the time of the accident, the gully was dry but the local people knew that the heap of gravel must be cleared away as soon as possible; if there was a thunder-storm or a cloudburst, floodwater from the moors would normally flow safely down that gully and into the river, but if the water's route was blocked, it would overflow on to the road and could cause flood damage to houses and farm buildings. The heap of gravel was causing that kind of blockage and although there was no immediate urgency to remove it, it should be done as soon as possible. The hot, dry conditions could quickly give rise to thunder-storms and sudden heavy rainfall.

In the pub that day, some university students, on an expedition of the surrounding moors to gather information about a future campaign against grouse shooting overheard part of a conversation relating to that accident. They heard only a few words but as they were animal activists of rather a militant frame of mind, they felt they had stumbled upon an awful plot against the animal kingdom and decided to take positive action.

What they heard was a man, who was in fact a member of the county council's highway maintenance section, saying,

'We'll have to get rid o' them chimps as soon as possible. Ah've had words with our gaffer, Ah managed ti catch him just as he was leaving t'zoo after we'd finished that last job, and he reckons they can be left on t'moor overnight. They won't be in anybody's way up there but we'll have to get rid of 'em as soon as we can. There'll be trouble if they're left there.'

His pal had said, 'We could allus chuck some of 'em down t'cliff into that awd quarry, that'd get rid o' some.'

'We can't leave 'em blocking that gully; a pile o' chimps in that spot'll send t'flood watter down inti Aidensfield.'

'We could allus flatten some wi' shovels and spades,' said another.

'We'll need a wagon handy ti cart 'em off,' was another suggestion. 'They're quite heavy, too heavy and too many to shift by hand. Mebbe we should fetch an excavator?'

What the students did not know was that 'chimps' is a local word for pieces of gravel. When small piles of gravel are placed at intervals along the verges for use on the roads in winter conditions, we always call them 'chimp heaps'. Chimpings is an old word which, I believe, originally meant husked, unground oats, these pieces also being known as grits. In recent years, however, chimps has come to be used to describe small pieces of gravel or road grit. For the people of the moors a pile of chimps means a pile of gravel or grit.

Those students, however, in eavesdropping upon part of that conversation, assumed that the men were going to secretly and cruelly dispose of some chimpanzees which lived in the local zoo. They thought the men were part of a conspiracy to kill the chimps by battering them with shovels and spades; the men would carry their bodies on to the moors in a lorry, and then get rid of them by throwing the corpses into a quarry. It had the elements of a fiendish plot by uncaring country folk.

The students decided to halt the slaughter; they would create publicity for their new-found cause by organizing a protest at the gates of the zoo. It was with some surprise, therefore, that early the following morning the proprietor of the zoo found two dozen students outside his front entrance, all waving banners saying 'Save the Chimps'.

Mr Lawrence went out to talk to them with the intention of finding the reason for their presence.

'We want to stop the slaughter of the chimpanzees,' said the student leader.

'What chimpanzees?' asked the puzzled Mr Lawrence.

'Your chimpanzees. We've overheard a plot to kill them by inhumane methods, and to dispose of their bodies on the moor,' was the answer. 'It smacks of Fascism and capitalist cruelty.'

'You must be joking!' he laughed. 'Now look, there is no such plan, I assure you. Our chimps are healthy and well cared for; we have no plans to dispose of any of them and if one is ill, we always secure the services of a vet. We've never had to kill one, and have no such intentions. If we did want to get rid of any of our animals, it would always be done with compassion and by experts.'

'That's exactly what you would say,' shouted one of the protesters. 'It's a cover-up, and we've heard the plotters . . . we have called the press and we intend to draw the attention of the public to this gross act of Fascist cruelty to animals and to the uncaring attitudes of capitalist zoo-keepers . . .'

'I have no idea what you are talking about,' responded Mr Lawrence. But after speaking to the protesters for several minutes without convincing them of his innocence, he rang Sergeant Blaketon. Blaketon rang me.

'Rhea,' he said. 'I'll pick you up in quarter of an hour. We're going to the zoo.'

'That'll be nice,' I joked. 'I could do with a day out.'

'Don't be facetious, Rhea. It's work. There's a protest of some kind. Lefty students waving banners and shouting slogans.'

I groaned. At that time, left-wing students and their rent-a-mob pals were protesting about almost everything and as we drove to the zoo, Sergeant Blaketon explained our mission.

'They are blocking the road, Rhea, they've congregated outside the main entrance but have the sense not to trespass inside. They're asking visitors to join them in their protest. The press has been called by the student leader too, so we'll have to tread warily. We don't want our pictures in the papers; you know how some students throw red paint over themselves to make it appear we've clobbered them, or spread marbles on the road to make it impossible for police horses to stand upright.'

'Have the mounted section been called out?' I asked with some surprise.

'No, they have not. I'm just warning you about the dirty tricks some left-wingers play to gain public sympathy.'

'What are they protesting about?' I asked. 'Did Mr Lawrence give you any idea?'

'Something about slaughtering monkeys,' said Sergeant Blaketon. 'They're objecting to that.'

'Is the zoo slaughtering monkeys?' I asked.

'How should I know what they do with their old monkeys?' Blaketon shrugged his shoulders and we drove on. When we arrived, we were greeted by catcalls and jeers from the scruffy bunch of layabouts which had gathered at the entrance, but Blaketon ignored them as we drove into the zoo and parked before the office block. Mr Lawrence came out to meet us.

'Thanks for coming,' he said. 'That lot's upsetting our visitors. I've had the press on to me as well, about slaughtering chimpanzees by inhumane methods. Sergeant, I've no idea what they are talking about or who sent them here.'

'You do have monkeys here?' asked Blaketon.

'Yes, a wide variety of them, all well cared for. It's chimps they're talking about, they say they overheard a plot to kill our chimps and dispose of their carcasses on the moors.'

'And you have no such plans?' asked Blaketon.

'No, of course not. If we do dispose of any of our sick or dead animals, we would never dump their bodies on the moors anyway. That lot out there are puddled, Sergeant; God knows what rumours they've heard.'

'Show me your chimps, Mr Lawrence,' said Blaketon. 'And Rhea, you go and have a word with the student leader. Find out just what he has heard and why he's brought this scruffy mob here.'

I walked out of the main gate and called for the leader to come to me. His companions were shouting abuse at my uniform but a small, bearded youth with granny specs and ten days' growth of unwashed dirt about his face and clothes, now stepped forward with a swagger.

'You're on his side, mate,' he spat on the ground. 'You'll make us clear off and those animals will die . . .'

'I want you to tell me what you heard,' I said quietly, ignoring their behaviour.

A girl said, 'They're going to get rid of the chimps . . .'

Another butted in, 'And dump them down a quarry after flattening them with spades and shovels . . .'

'And leave them on the moor all night, then get a wagon to cart them away . . .'

'Where did you hear this?' I asked.

'In the pub at Aidensfield,' said the leader. 'Last night, a bunch of Fascists talking about it, we overhead them.'

'And they were talking about getting rid of the chimps?' I asked, having now gained their attention.

'Yep, they were. One of the men had been to the zoo . . .'

As they outlined their version of the conversation they'd overheard, I thought quickly. Now I knew what they were talking about, I knew about the pile of chimps in the gully and the worries about moving them, because I had dealt with the lorry accident. And I also reckoned these protesters needed to be taught a gentle lesson.

'I know where you mean,' I said. 'I saw the chimps there myself, but they're not from this zoo.'

'Not from this zoo? Then where are they from? And what are you doing about it then?' The words came from a smelly face which leered into mine. 'Bloody capitalists, making capital out of captive animals, getting rid of them in this cruel manner when they've earned filthy money to line their pockets . . .'

'I've made a report, they're coming to move them today,' I said, looking at my watch. 'About now, in fact. Now, I'm a believer in kindness to dumb animals, so if you like, I could take you there . . .'

'With the press?' The leader did not entirely trust me.

'With the press,' I agreed. 'They can come too. But I must first have words with my sergeant and Mr Lawrence. And I reckon you owe an apology to Mr Lawrence. You've picked the wrong target this time, lads.'

At that moment, Sergeant Blaketon reappeared and called the leader to him. 'I have inspected the chimpanzees and they are all present and in good health,' he said. 'If you, the leader that is, would care to accompany me, I will show you the chimpanzees, with the approval of Mr Lawrence. You can inspect them yourself, you don't have to take my word.'

The leader looked at me and shook his head. 'No, no need, not now. We want to go with the constable to see the ones that we really ought to be looking at. It's not those at this zoo.'

Sergeant Blaketon looked at me. 'What's all this, Constable Rhea?'

'These people have made a mistake, Sergeant, and they accept it. The chimps they are protesting about are out on the moors above Aidensfield, they're there now, I saw them myself.'

'You did? Where, Rhea?' The expression on Sergeant Blaketon's face was a joy to behold and none of the protesters missed it. His reaction confirmed my story and I had them on my side now, they trusted me.

'I've promised to show these people the place and the chimps, Sergeant. Most of the chimps will still be there, council workmen are planning to move them this morning.'

'Why didn't I know about this?' bellowed Blaketon.

'It was your day off yesterday,' I reminded him. 'Perhaps you hadn't time to read the Occurrence Book before you were called out here?'

'Rhea, I don't know what's going on but . . .'

'Trust me, Sergeant,' I hoped he wasn't going to make a mess of my plot. 'I think this gentleman wishes to apologize to Mr Lawrence, and when he's done so, I shall be happy to guide him and his friends to the site on the moors. It is only fair, after all, these people have made a legitimate protest but at the wrong place, and I can only be fair to them by showing them the chimps in question. These are the chimps referred to in the pub last night. What action they take is then up to them, so long as it is lawful. And I'll show the press too.'

'I don't know what you're up to, Rhea, but I'll need a full report of this when it's all over!'

The students cheered at him and I smiled at them conspiratorially.

'Yes, Sergeant,' I concurred.

Minutes later, watched by a puzzled Mr Lawrence, we prepared to drive off in convoy. I called to him, 'I'll ring you later Mr Lawrence, to explain things.'

The convoy of scruffy old vans and scooters, with two press cars in attendance, then followed us from the zoo. As Blaketon drove along, he was silent and then he said,

'We're going to look real fools over this, Rhea, you showing this mob some chimps that have been dumped on the moor. It'll only make them protest more . . . where the hell have those chimps come from? And who dumped them on our moorland?'

'They're from an accident involving a lorry,' I explained. 'Chimps is our local word for gravel, Sergeant. I'm going to show them a pile of gravel that's being cleared away right now.

And I'm going to get the press to take a picture of them looking at chimps but looking like chumps.'

'You mean they got it all wrong?' he chuckled.

'Yes,' I said. 'They overheard some chaps in the pub and got the wrong end of the stick. It serves them right for eavesdropping and for interfering in the business of others. Now we can teach them a lesson.'

'I'm going to enjoy this,' smiled Oscar Blaketon.

But when we arrived at the scene of the crash, the damaged lorry had been removed with heavy lifting gear, and a replacement had been manoeuvred into the gully so that it was in position to be loaded with gravel. Then things took another startling turn.

The highway department's lorry was parked with a plank leading from its rear down to the ground at the base of the huge pile of gravel and several wheelbarrows and shovels stood by. The council workmen, three of them, were sitting in a canvas hut on the moor having their mid-morning break. As Blaketon and I eased to a halt, the convoy of battered vehicles and scruffy protesters pulled up.

'Down there!' I waited until everyone had joined me, including the press reporters and photographers, then pointed to the heap of chimps in the gully. 'The chimps are down there. I'm going to have words with the foreman first!'

My intention was to explain the course of events to him and to let the press take their pictures as I explained that the pile of gravel was the 'chimps' about which they were protesting, but as I walked across to the canvas hut, I heard the leader shout,

'You mean down there? Under that pile of grit?'

'Yes, I said. 'I'll explain in a minute . . .'

'Right lads,' said the leader. 'Grab some shovels, shovel all that grit back into that bloody wagon! They've buried the bodies under this pile of grit . . . the bastards . . .'

'Rhea,' said Sergeant Blaketon. 'They're going to shovel that grit away . . .'

'Which is exactly what we want, Sergeant, isn't it?'

When I told the foreman what was happening, he chuckled and said his men could have a longer break with more time to play cards, while the volunteers shovelled away the huge pile of gravel. I had words with the journalists who were standing aside and suggested they take pictures of the action.

'I want to see them uncover the chimps,' said one photographer.

'That's just what they're doing. In this part of Yorkshire, chimps means gravel. That is a pile of chimps, that's what these idiots are protesting about – we were going to get rid of this pile of chimps, not kill chimpanzees in the zoo.'

'Really?' beamed the photographer who then told his colleagues, and so they secured some excellent shots of the protesters shovelling away the pile of gravel. As the energetic shovelling reached the bottom of the heap, it was gratifying to see the wagon fully loaded; as the foreman, beaming at his good fortune, secured the tailboard, the leader came across to me and Sergeant Blaketon.

'There's no sign of the chimps,' he was angry now and sweating profusely from his actions, 'Are you sure they were buried here?'

'Absolutely,' beamed Sergeant Blaketon. 'Five tons of 'em. You've done right well for the highways department by shifting those chimps.'

'I've not seen any chimps,' he said, frowning.

'Between you, you've shovelled the best part of five tons of them,' I laughed. 'Perhaps it will teach you a lesson about good behaviour – and a lesson in local language. The chimps that were going to be got rid of are those – the gravel. Chimps is our local word for gravel . . . the few bits you've left will be thrown down the quarry, as you overheard, or washed away by the next heavy rainfall.'

'You bastards . . .' he cursed. 'You've taken us for a ride . . .'

The press men were rapidly taking pictures of the departing council wagon, into which someone had stuck one of the banners. The lorry departed with the slogan 'Save Our Chimps' waving from the heap of gravel in the rear.

The photographers hurried off with their pictures and I wondered what the rabble would do. Would they become violent? But they turned their anger towards their leader and began to curse him as they all trooped back to their old vehicles and scooters before disappearing over the horizon.

Later that week, the local paper had a lovely photograph of them removing the pile of gravel beneath the slogan, MONKEY BUSINESS AMONG THE CHIMPS.

Mr Lawrence was delighted when I told him the story and I learned that the publicity had also helped the zoo. The highways department enjoyed it too – they sent a gift of a load of chimps to be spread upon the path outside the chimpanzee enclosure.

Misunderstandings of a more elementary type also occur, often through one party misinterpreting the instructions of another. There are lots of humorous examples, such as the question from a rail passenger who asks, 'How long will the next train be?'

whereupon the porter answers, 'An engine and five coaches.' There are many examples where people have placed a precise meaning upon the words of others and Mary, my wife, encountered an example when she was working in Brantsford Orthopaedic Hospital.

She was helping in the wing that specialized in old folks' problems when a new auxiliary nurse arrived. She would be about seventeen and was anxious to make herself useful.

Mary was busy with the old folks, perhaps too busy to give the nurse the guidance or help that she needed, but the youngster asked,

'Is there anything I can do?'

Mary thought fast. 'Yes, there is, Sandra,' she said. 'You can clean the old folks' teeth.'

'Right,' said the girl, full of enthusiasm.

But Mary was too occupied to supervise the girl as she went about her task. Unknown to Mary, Sandra had visited every one of the old folks in the various wards, about twenty-five in total, and had extracted their false teeth. These she had placed in a bucket which she had then taken to a washroom; she had then set about scrubbing all the teeth with a nail-brush.

When Mary went into the room, she found Sandra with the bucket and the sets of cleaned teeth grinning from the draining-board. Those awaiting attention were still in the bucket, like a lot of grinning pink lobsters.

'What's happening, Sandra?' Mary asked.

'I'm cleaning the old folks' teeth, like you said,' was the innocent response.

'And how do you know which teeth belong to which person?' smiled Mary.

The expression on the girl's face said everything. Sandra hadn't a clue where to replace each of the sets of gnashers but Mary thought she should learn a lesson. She made Sandra take the cleaned teeth back to the wards to try to find the owners. Some of the patients might recognize their own, but many would not and so the task would be one of trial and error, of fitting and testing, of chewing and whistling.

It took ages. But when Sandra had finished, and when the old folks were wondering why their teeth weren't quite so comfortable as they had been, Sandra had a set left over.

'I've got a set left, Mrs Rhea.' She looked bewildered. 'I'm so sorry . . . I just didn't think.'

'Have they all got a set of teeth?' Mary asked.

'Yes, I've been round them all again and again, they've all got teeth in.'

At that moment, Dr Brownlee, the consultant, came into the ward. 'Mary,' he called to my wife. 'Do a check will you? Somebody's removed a set of dentures from the corpse in the mortuary. We're doing an inventory of his personal belongings. See if you can find them, will you?'

'Sandra?' called Mary.

10 Out of the Frying Pan
and into the Fire

Kindled a flame I still deplore
(Words from a riddle in
Lady's Magazine, *June 1762)*

Throughout history, there have been people whose activities upon this earth have left overwhelming disaster in their wake – we can mention modern ones such as Hitler, Stalin, Lenin and Robert Maxwell as well as umpteen socialist heads of state and would-be financial wizards. Lower down the scale there have been several incompetent do-it-yourself fanatics of personal acquaintance whose efforts to repair houses have succeeded only in damaging them, and others of lesser fame such as the holidaymaker on a canal boat who left open the lock-gates which caused the escaping waters to flood a village, and those who leave cars parked on hills without setting the hand-brake.

The activities of some disaster-merchants rarely reach the headlines, however, and I'm sure that some do sincerely try to do well in their span on this earth – it's just that they fail in their grandiose plans and leave others to pick up the proverbial pieces or clean up the resultant mess. Many try only to please themselves as they pursue a selfish life of leisure and financial trickery and leave behind a trail of suffering victims. In some cases, the police become aware of the problems thus created.

John George Crossfield was such a disaster-merchant. I had never met him until I came across him late one afternoon on the moors above Aidensfield, and it is the background circumstances of that meeting that I shall now relate. I learned of his past activities after my first meeting with him – his life and crimes were well documented in the files of several police forces.

John George was a womanizer of considerable talent. Smooth-tongued, well-dressed, with expensive tastes and a flair for showmanship, he could charm the pants off any lady with his stories of life in exotic places, his relationships with famous people and the massive wealth he had at this disposal. But it was all talk – he had no wealth, he did not even own a house or a car and lived expensively on borrowed money which was never repaid. He 'bought' cars without ever paying for them, he lived in expensive hotels and left without paying his bills, he charmed money out of gullible women with whom he went on holiday under the pretext of marrying them upon their return and he tried several times to start businesses, all of which failed miserably after incurring colossal debts. But he had what is known as a silver tongue and could talk his way out of most predicaments. There were times, it seemed, that he actually believed his own claims.

From the viewpoint of his lady victims, there is no doubt he was handsome in appearance and a worthy companion at socially acceptable events.

In his late thirties, John George kept himself very fit by lots of exercise and he maintained his good looks by persuading rich ladies to accompany him (and to pay for him) on regular trips to the Mediterranean where he acquired fine tans and expensive clothes at their expense.

Not quite six feet tall, he was well-built with an athletic body and had a splendid head of beautifully groomed jet-black hair, splendid white teeth and velvety dark brown eyes which could charm a woman off her bar stool in a matter of seconds. When God had issued good looks, John George must have been first in the queue. He had the lithe form of a Spanish matador, but the morals of a tom-cat and the expensive tastes of an Arabian sheikh.

John George drove fast cars (which he never paid for) and even claimed to have a yacht moored near Southampton which he used for cruising around the Greek islands. We were to learn that he had 'hired' the yacht from a very wealthy friend who had fallen for his charms and believed his stories. He had followed this life style for many years, usually avoiding prosecution for fraud because none of his lady companions wished to make a formal complaint. Some even paid off his debts but his method of thanking them was to leave them alone as he concentrated upon yet another female conquest or dubious business deal.

Then he met Yvonne Patricia Carlton-Kinross, a lady of aristocratic background with financial interests in several Texan oil wells and property on Manhattan Island, New York. She was tall and lithe, a honey blonde in her early thirties with an exquisite figure and a penchant for fast cars and expensive jewels. She was, in fact, a qualified doctor who travelled the world lecturing on feminine medical problems. It was while staying at one of Harrogate's finest hotels that she encountered John George who, after buying her an expensive cocktail at the bar, promptly launched into his lady-killing playboy routine.

He displayed his gold-plated cigarette-case, his expensive cuff-links and said he had just come home after concluding a successful business deal in Sydney, Australia, hinting that he had bought a top Australian newspaper group.

But Yvonne was oblivious to his charm. She studiously ignored all his attempts to woo her, albeit letting him buy her drinks and dinner, and the outcome was that, before the week was out, John George fell helplessly in love with Yvonne. He had never fallen truly in love before; it was a new experience for him which was aggravated by the fact that Yvonne was not in the least impressed by his bravura or extravagant claims.

The effect was devastating. John George tried to woo her, he tried to get her into bed, he later tried to follow her around the country on her English tour, but she refused to succumb to his considerable charm. She agreed to be friends, but nothing more.

John George worked very hard upon this new challenge; he bought her meals, he took her to the theatre, he even took her to Ascot, Wimbledon and Henley and, more unusually, he actually paid for all their outings. But as a reward for all his efforts, he received nothing more than a polite 'thank you', some light praise for giving her a lovely outing, followed by a tiny peck on the cheek.

At long last, it seemed, John George had met his match. Here was a woman whose wealth, charm and overwhelming beauty was finer than anything he had ever encountered, and yet here was one who utterly refused to be swayed by his pretentious claims. In truth, her own background was far more glittering than anything he could conjure from his imagination. She had the style, whereas, he had to admit, he had nothing but the figments of his own imagination.

Finally, on her last night in England, he did receive an invitation to her suite at a splendid hotel in Bristol. Full of joy and romantic vision, he rushed off to buy two dozen red roses and a bottle of champagne, and duly presented himself at Room 109. Here was a promise of bliss. In the happy but preliminary moments that followed, and with the promise of yet more happiness before she left for America, Yvonne had explored his body with her sensitive hands and had then reacted with shock.

'John George!' she had shrieked. 'You'll have to see a specialist . . .'

'Why?' he had spluttered.

'Your heart . . . it sounds terrible, irregular, fighting to push your blood around . . . you must never strain yourself again . . . I'm a doctor, remember; look, I've got a good friend in Harley Street. I'll make an appointment . . .'

And so the night from which he had expected so much had ended in disaster. John George Crossfield found himself taking a taxi across London to an address in Harley Street where a pompous specialist had pronounced that John George, at the early age of thirty-six, appeared to have prematurely hardening arteries with more than a hint of something amiss with his liver. A lifespan of no more than six months awaited those with such an advanced form of arteriosclerosis and in addition, cancer of the liver or cancer of some other internal organ was hinted at. A further appointment was made at great expense for John George, and so he found himself being prodded and poked by another doctor in Hull who said he ought to be admitted to hospital for a barium meal followed by a rigorous examination by a cancer specialist. The doctor would write to John George the moment a vacancy occurred.

All these dramas occurred within days of the departure of Yvonne to the States; she had certainly made things happen for his welfare, and all these tests and worries were crowded into the life of John George Crossfield before he arrived on the North York Moors above Aidensfield.

As he was undergoing his various tests and medical examinations, there is little doubt he felt very much alone and very vulnerable. Dr Yvonne had returned to America but before leaving, had promised she would keep in touch. And she was as good as her word. As he waited for a date for his barium meal, he received a telegram from the USA it was signed by Yvonne and it said she would not be returning to England. She had decided to settle in America because she had been offered a teaching post at a famous medical university and, besides, she had had an offer of marriage from a professor of obstetrics. John George was devastated. With death imminent and the threat of cancer hovering as an additional death-warrant, and with his only true lady-love deserting him, John George decided to end it all. He would commit suicide.

He managed to buy an old Ford Consul from a scrap-yard and motored to the North York Moors, to a place where he had spent an idyllic childhood. It was a pretty place high on the moors above Aidensfield where an uncle had once lived, and now, in the heat of summer, it was perfect. In the boot he had a small green tent with which to hide his shame from the world, and so he arrived at the scene of his demise, pitched his tent on an elevated patch of moorland and prepared his last supper.

As he'd done so many times as a child, he had cooked

himself some sausages and bacon over an open fire made with pieces of wood and old stalks of heather, and, having enjoyed his final meal, settled down to die.

To speed him on his way to the happy hereafter, he had taken a large quantity of sleeping tablets; having taken what he thought was sufficient to send him into oblivion, he crept into his tent to shield his dying body from the sight of passers-by, then lay down in his sleeping-bag, zipped it up and waited for the end. He reckoned that if anyone did pass by this lonely place, they would not invade the privacy of the small green tent and so he would be allowed to die in peace and his body would remain upon the moors for a long, long time. As he crept inside, the evening sun was setting in the west.

In fact, John George, had chosen well. The location was a place that few, if any, people would pass during the average course of a year of two. It was remote, it was hidden in the depths of a cleft in the moors and it was well away from all the more popular footpaths. His body might lie there, undiscovered, for years.

But in preparing so well for his departure, John George had forgotten to put out his fire. It was some distance from his tent and as the sticks were reduced to glowing embers, a stiff north-easterly breeze arose while the sun was setting. As John George lay down to pass from this world to the next, so the breeze strengthened and it began to fan the dying embers into tiny flames. Some pieces of burning ash were blown from the fire and settled in the tinder-dry heather and bracken until the inevitable happened. A potentially devastating moor fire was ignited.

The keen breeze fanned the tiny flames into larger ones

which, in seconds, gained a hold on the dry grass, heather and bracken and within minutes, a patch of moorland close to John George's tent was ablaze. But the breeze was blowing from behind the tent, carrying the fire away from it; within twenty minutes, the flames were racing through the heather and bracken as they were fanned by the stiffening breeze, and a huge pall of black, grey and white smoke began to gather in the sky.

Had the wind been a westerly, John George would have been roasted alive, but because it was blowing off the sea, his inert body knew nothing of the inferno being created only yards away. But every puff of wind created the blaze further from the silent tent and within half an hour the tent was out of danger but the sky above was filled with thick dark smoke.

A moorland gamekeeper, checking the season's grouse chicks, noticed the pall of smoke over Whinbush Moor and instantly assessed the danger. He hurried to a telephone and raised the alarm, and very soon a host of practised beaters and volunteers, plus the fire brigade from Strensford, turned out to fight the flames. They knew that if the fire burned deep into the peat which carpeted the moors, it would burn for months. The peat is up to thirty feet deep in places, and a fire can smoulder in those depths for months before breaking out again to sweep across the dry moorland. In fighting a moorland fire, speed is vital, but the volunteers knew their job.

Like the others, I received the alarm call and hurried to the location in my mini-van, parking it among the other emergency vehicles in a safe place. I found myself on the southern edge of the fire and, after arming myself with a beater, a long shaft with a flat blade at the end, I began to beat the advancing flames in an attempt to put them out. It was a hot, smelly, perspiring task and as one flame succumbed to my efforts, other tongues would break out as the fire was fanned by the ever present wind. I did not count the numbers who were trying to beat out the flames, but there were hundreds and every one of us knew that we must conquer the blaze because it was relentlessly advancing towards Gelderslack.

That remote moorland village stands literally upon the edge of the moor and if we did not extinguish the fire before it reached the village, it could destroy some of the cottages; indeed, some have thatched roofs and so, as we worked, we prayed that the breeze would drop and that the sultry summer conditions would produce a thunder-storm. A thorough soaking of thundery rain would be a true godsend.

As we tried to beat out the flames, an advance party set off across the moor to dig out a wide barrier of heather by using an earth-moving machine, thus creating a wide band of bare peat between the fire and Gelderslack. Without the surface heather and bracken, the advancing flames would have more difficulty in gaining a hold.

A dry stone wall in the path of the flames was another means of halting its advance but it was impossible to build such a wall in the time available. Likewise, there was no time to demolish any of the local walls with an earth-moving machine and to transport the stones into the path of the flames. As always, the fire brigade, well-trained in dealing with moorland fires, was at the forefront of the battle and, fortunately, able to make use of a moorland stream for its water supply. Five small tenders had managed to gain access to the advancing front and so a fine battle was being fought.

Then I saw one of the volunteers racing through the blackened moorland towards me, gesticulating and shouting. I could not hear his words due to the crackle of flames and the noise of our activity, but hurried towards him. It was Jack Lewis, a farmer from High Garth.

'Mr Rhea, Mr Rhea,' he coughed with the action of the smoke. 'There's a chap in a tent ovver t'brow, out like light, seems ti me t'fire started hard by his tent.'

'Is he dead?' I asked.

'Nay,' he tried to get his breath. 'He's unconscious, I reckon. He's in a badly way, mind, he needs attention.'

'I'll come,' I said.

And that was when I found John George Crossfield. At that moment, of course, I had no idea who he was or why he had chosen to attempt suicide, but a quick inspection showed me the awful pallor of his skin and his deep, slow breathing.

Closer examination revealed that his pulse was very slow and weak, and I found an empty bottle of sleeping tablets on the floor of his tent.

'Hospital, Jack,' I said. 'Immediately. Barbiturate overdose if I'm not mistaken. Can you help me to carry him to my van?'

Picking up the empty bottle for the hospital's reference, I gave the casualty the fireman's lift across the moor with Jack doing likewise for part of the way and between us we reached my parked van. I hoped that our jerking movements would help keep him alive – one of the first aid treatments in cases of barbiturate overdose is to try to keep the patient awake or even to make them vomit. But this fellow was in a deep stupor although not yet at coma stage.

After plonking the unconscious man in the front passenger

seat, I radioed for an ambulance and said I'd meet it on the highroad above Gelderslack, at the junction with the Rannockdale road. I stressed that the casualty looked like someone who had taken a barbiturate overdose and, as Jack went back to fight the fire, I bumped across the moor towards the rendezvous point. The ambulance arrived within quarter of an hour of my arrival, took the casualty and the empty bottle with its informative label, and sped off. I told them I had no idea who the fellow was – I would begin my enquiries once we'd got the blaze under control and would contact Strensford Hospital at the first opportunity.

It took more than four hours of concentrated effort by something like a hundred volunteers and four fire appliances and their crews, to get the fire under control. We were aided by a reduction in the strength of the breeze and, later, around two the following morning, it began to rain. Our prayers had been answered and so we mastered yet another moorland fire; even as we departed, however, the fire brigade retained a presence on the moors until well into the next day, as a precautionary measure. There had been immense damage and it would be impossible to estimate the cost of the damage, both in financial terms and in the devastation of the wildlife.

Young conifers, silver birch and hundreds of gorse bushes had been burned to the ground; acres of heather had been destroyed, as had the nests of countless grouse, skylarks and other ground-nesting birds with their young. Lizards and other mammals had perished, the insect life was devastated and many examples of rare moorland plants had been destroyed. Lots of habitats had disappeared beneath a desert of ash while much of the surface peat had been irreparably damaged.

Once I knew the fire was under control, I walked across to the

isolated tent. I saw the remains of the camp-fire and the patch of
blackened moorland which surrounded it, and it was easy to
follow the path of the fire from that point. I drew the attention of
the fire brigade to the remains of the fire, letting them decide
whether in fact the devastation had been a direct consequence of
this man's camp-fire.

I searched the tent for anything of value, but found nothing
apart from the sleeping-bag and later, the old car. I took down
the tent and stored it and the bag in my van for eventual return
to its owner. Then I went home for a late bath; Mary groaned as
I walked into the bedroom for I disturbed her sleep, but even in
her own half-wakefulness, she had enough stamina to say that I
stank of smoke and smelled as if I'd been working in a bonfire.
I got to bed at 4.30 a.m.

I telephoned the hospital at 9 a.m., having caught about four
hours sleep, to ask after the gentleman who had attempted
suicide. I was told that he'd survived; we had found him in time
and his stomach had been pumped to rid him of the residue of
the tablets. At that time, in the late 1960s, suicide was no longer
a crime. Once, it was a crime known as felo de se (felon of one's
self) although it was recognized there could be no earthly
punishment. It ceased to be a crime with the passing of the
Suicide Act of 1961 and consequently attempted suicide was no
longer a crime either. Until that time, attempted suicide had
been a crime and it did carry a penalty, although few attempted
suicides ever reached a court. Other forms of treatment were
considered far more suitable.

That fairly recent change in the law, however, meant that the
patient had not committed any criminal offence by his actions
but I still had to submit a report about the incident, particularly

as his actions seemed to have started a devastating and dangerous moorland fire.

For my report, I had to interview the fellow in hospital and waited until the doctor gave me the necessary permission. It was then that I learned the name of the patient in their care but now he was most contrite, giving me a full account of his exploits and promising to mend his ways, if only for the few months of life that remained. He told me everything about his heart trouble, his supposed cancer of the liver and his ill-fated romance. His happy world had come to a sudden and very abrupt end and so he had decided to conclude his useless life in a place which he had offered everlasting happy memories. I felt touched by his frankness.

'What does the hospital say about your heart condition?' I asked him after we'd had a cup of tea together and after I'd got the necessary information for my report.

'I daren't ask,' he said. 'No, I got the hard word from Harley Street . . . I won't try to end things now, Constable, I'll battle on . . . after all, life is very precious, isn't it?'

'It is,' I said, thinking of those acres of destroyed moorland and the devastated wildlife. 'But surely you've told the doctors here? About the Harley Street verdict, your heart, your forthcoming cancer tests?'

'No,' he said. 'They saved me from myself. I've been a bloody fool, Constable, I'll try to do some good for someone before I do leave this world.'

As there was no question of him having deliberately set fire to the moorland, I felt sure that my superintendent would not authorize a prosecution under the Malicious Damage Act and told him that my recommendation would be 'no proceedings'.

He thanked me, shook my hand and thanked me for saving his life. I told him I had not done so – for that, he must thank Jack Lewis and I gave him Jack's address.

On the way out, I saw John George's physician, Dr Handley, and asked for a word in private. In his office, I told him of John George's visit to Harley Street and to the doctor in Hull, whereupon Dr Handley frowned. He pulled a reference book off the shelf and asked, 'Who did he see about his heart trouble?'

I checked in my notebook and said, 'A Dr Brownlow, No. 19a.'

'There's no such person,' said Dr Handley. 'We have a list of all the Harley Street heart specialists . . . he's not there . . . see for yourself.'

'And what about the doctor in Hull?' I asked.

He made another check of his references and shook his head. 'No, no such person of that name either.'

'Have you examined him for heart or other problems?' I asked.

'Yes, we gave him a thorough medical once he'd come round. His heart's as sound as a bell, he's in real good health. And I'm sure I'd have spotted something if his liver or other organs were cancerous or causing problems.'

I then told Dr Handley about Yvonne Patricia Carlton-Kinross, the lady doctor who had come here on a specialist lecture tour and he said he knew nothing about it, but would check and ring me at home. I provided him with a list of some of the venues of her talks, as given to me by John George.

He rang me two days later.

'There's been no lecture tour by that Yvonne Patricia lady doctor,' Dr Handley told me. 'No one in our profession's heard of her; some of us would have known the name, Constable, if she was a specialist over here from the States or wherever.'

'Do you think John George Crossfield has been conned good and proper?' I ventured to ask.

'I think he has,' laughed Dr Handley. 'After you'd gone the other day, I gave him another thorough going-over, heart, lungs, kidneys, the lot. I could find absolutely nothing wrong with him, he's a very fit man. Very fit indeed.'

'I wonder if she was a relation to one of his early victims?' I smiled. 'Getting her own back perhaps, in a very clever, feminine way. Hell hath no fury like a woman spurned and all that . . .'

'He's had a fright,' Dr Handley said. 'Whatever she did to him, it's shaken his self-confidence. Now, he's over it all and I know he'll recover.'

'But will our moors recover?' I asked, realizing that some of our finest countryside had been devastated by the most recent of John George's man-made disasters.

Constable
Beneath the Trees

I Seek and Ye Shall Find

There is pleasure in the pathless woods.
Lord Byron (1788–1824)

'Times are changing, Rhea.'

Sergeant Blaketon was pensive as he sipped a mug of coffee in Ashfordly police station. We were sipping together in the spacious enquiry office. On that Monday morning, things were comparatively peaceful and he had cleared his desk before 9.30. There had been no reported crimes overnight and no fresh problems to exercise his mind. Now that his in-tray was empty and his telephone quiet, he found time to suggest that I made the coffee – which I did. Thus he joined me for a chat. I had just returned after a fortnight's leave and had driven from Aidensfield to Ashfordly to collect my mail. Ashfordly was peaceful that morning – but so was Aidensfield. As I'd had no telephone calls before nine o'clock, I had left my hill-top police house for the short drive to Ashfordly.

'Times changing, Sergeant?' I asked. 'In what way?'

'Every way, Rhea,' he sipped from his mug. 'There's going to be new procedures, new technology, new forms to be filled in, new telephone systems, changes to beat boundaries, changes to the names of things, changes in the way we do our job . . . did you know that the think-tank at Headquarters is considering the abolition of the policewomen's department?'

'No, I had no idea,' I had to admit. 'I've been away for a couple of weeks.'

'The pace of change is hotting up, Rhea. You've had two weeks away and in that time the whole concept of policing has altered. With my responsibilities, I can't go away, Rhea; I might return to find somebody else sitting at my desk. Do you realise that policewomen won't be specialists any more? They'll have to compete for promotion with the rest of us, Rhea, they'll patrol with the men, working nights, dealing with fights. Can you imagine working for a woman inspector, Rhea?'

'I've never really thought about it, Sergeant,' I had to admit. 'I would think that if a woman knew her job well enough, there'd be no problems . . .'

'You youngsters are all alike, Rhea, you've no respect for the past, for well tried and tested procedures and structures. I can't see a woman constable sorting out a fight between a bunch of drunken yobbos. If a woman is patrolling the streets at night, the male officers will spend their time worrying whether she can cope and they'll be caring for her, not the public – and don't think your cushy beat at Aidensfield will escape the eagle eyes of those at the top either!'

'They're not going to close me down, are they, Sergeant?'

'Now that you've been issued with radio-equipped minivans instead of motor bikes for patrolling, Rhea, the powers-that-be believe that beats should be larger. There's going to be amalgamations, Rhea, amalgamations of rural beats.'

'Is there?' This was news to me.

'Bigger beats will be the rule, Rhea. If a rural constable from say, Pattington, decides to retire or he is promoted, then the vacancy that occurs when he leaves might not be filled. That means his patch will disappear – it will be divided between the adjoining rural beats and the police house will be sold. That's just an example, Rhea, but that sort of thing is going to happen, mark my words. Bigger areas covered by fewer constables, that's going to be the trend.'

'Are you saying that Aidensfield rural beat might be closed down, Sergeant?'

'When you move on, Rhea, that would be a possibility, a very distinct possibility. I can't deny it. And as rural beats become larger, village constables will be expected to work in towns too. They'll do shift work, Rhea, part of which will be in the town and part of which will be on their own patch.'

'Town duties, Sergeant.' The notion was horrifying.

'If rural beats are amalgamated,' he had clearly been giving the matter some consideration or had read some documents relating to the subject, 'if rural beats are amalgamated, several constables in vehicles will patrol the area between them, working shifts. Eight-hour shifts. That would replace the present twenty-four-hour responsibility of constables like you. It would give you more time off, Rhea. Not a bad thing, perhaps?'

'But we rural bobbies like to work our own beats, Sergeant,' I said. 'We need to know all the people on the patch if we're to keep crime down. And the idea is that we live and work on the patch for twenty-four hours a day. I don't object to that, it's the best way of giving value for money, you work when the work's there and relax when it isn't.'

'That's not considered the way to do things in the new style of thinking, Rhea. Bigger beats shared between several constables is the new concept – and that's a new word in police jargon! Concept! And if you're on duty when someone else is patrolling your normal patch, you'll be drafted into town for additional urban patrols!'

'I don't think it's a good idea.' I could see that if this scheme was adopted, the rural areas would be deserted by patrolling constables. In the minds of supervisory officers, towns were always short of constables and they would always be supplemented by rural officers. The demands of town-policing would always take priority.

Blaketon went on, 'You'll be working more hours in Ashfordly, Eltering and Strensford, Rhea, supplementing the officers in those busier places. Being motorized means you can cover a bigger area in the time available and being equipped with radio means you'll be in contact with Control all the time. You must admit there isn't much crime in Aidensfield, Rhea, there's no real need for a police presence there.'

'But if the village constable is removed from Aidensfield, Sergeant, crime will break out the minute he's gone! And there'll be no one around to deal with it, or report it to. It'll start with the kids vandalizing things, then they'll rise to petty thefts and even break-ins . . . remove the constable from the streets and crime will increase, Sergeant. With no one in authority to prevent them, the kids will do as they like, and once they do as they like, they'll start to do wrong.'

'I know that, you know that and all police officers know that, but the Home Office doesn't see it our way. They never give us enough men to achieve our ideals. So we must make do with what we have and we can't halt what some regard as progress, Rhea,' he drained his mug. 'So we do as we are told. We've always done that, we police officers, even if it means being subordinate to a senior officer who is a woman. Well, I've got that off my chest so what are your plans for today?'

'I shall return to Aidensfield, Sergeant, and I'll probably do a foot patrol in the village. Meet a few people, chat to a few of the locals, make enquiries about Claude Jeremiah Greengrass to find out what he's up to these days . . .'

'Well, don't let me keep you, Rhea.' He rose from the chair and returned to his office. It was time for me to depart too. As I was leaving, Alf Ventress entered to begin his shift in the office; his first chore would be the washing-up!

'Hello, Nick. Did you have a nice leave?'

'We rented a cottage near Ullswater,' I told him. 'It was lovely, sheer peace – even with four youngsters!'

I told him about our family holiday. Then, nodding towards Blaketon's closed office door, he asked, 'And how's Mein Fuhrer?'

'He's worrying about changes,' I smiled. 'He's been chatting to me about it – something's set him off. He seems to have a chip on his shoulder about women police inspectors.'

'It'll be the arrival of that new inspector,' smiled Alf. 'Fresh from the special course at the police college. Somebody said it was Christine Pollock; Blaketon thinks it's a woman who's coming to Strensford but it's a chap, Crispin Pollock is his name. He's due to start this morning.'

'No one's told Blaketon it's a feller, then?' I smiled.

'No, not yet. We thought we'd let him sweat a bit,' grinned Alf, lighting a cigarette as he took his chair. 'It'll be interesting to see the preparations he makes for "Christine" when she makes her first official visit! So you *have* missed all the news! Strensford's divisional boundaries have been extended to include Eltering and Ashfordly, which means we are answerable to Strensford's hierarchy. And we might be doing seaside patrols too! That new inspector's been brought in to modernize the system, so they say. He's coming to implement new ideas and procedures, our division's a sort of testing ground for changes at force level. We're to be used to see if the new ideas and changed boundaries will work in practice.'

'But Pollock only joined a few years ago!' I cried. 'He's got less service than me!'

'He's got less service than most of the bloody members of this force,' grimaced Alf. 'Five years. He's still wet behind the ears! He's only twenty-six years old . . . Blaketon's old enough to be his father but he'll be telling Blaketon what to do! He'll be telling us all what to do . . . I don't know what the force is coming to, Nick, really I don't.'

I left Ashfordly police station with a sense of foreboding. Those of us with a few years' service to our credit were always conscious of our lack of promotion, but in those days it was normal to be promoted to the rank of sergeant after some twelve or fifteen years in the job. Having reached the exalted heights of being a sergeant, promotion to inspector might follow after a further five or six years – if one passed the promotion exams. But this Pollock had passed his exams with very high marks, after which he'd spent a year at the police college on a course designed especially for those selected for accelerated promotion. And now he was back . . . as a senior officer at Strensford. And he was to put into action a host of new, and probably very unpopular, changes. I shuddered.

But in spite of one's personal opinions and prejudices the job has to go on, and one of the blessings enjoyed by me was that Aidensfield was a fairly remote village. The fact meant it was well away from the constant supervision of senior officers. I was often left alone to get on with my job.

With a bit of luck and some applied ingenuity I could still work the beat in the way I thought best. At least, I hoped I could! I remembered one old constable who often said, 'Reforms are all right – so long as they don't change anything.' There were times and occasions when one could agree with that sentiment – and this was one of them!

I was mindful of the impending alterations to my mode of policing whilst going about my routine duties that summer. Working a rural beat as a police constable was a most pleasant means of earning a living, provided one was left alone to perform one's duties in one's own style. But when senior officers started to impose their own, often impracticable ideas, the routine quickly lost its appeal. Such an occasion occurred during the abnormally chilly, foggy and wet month of June that year.

I was patrolling Aidensfield on foot, enjoying the relaxed style of life in the village. I had parked the police van on the green and had spent that morning chatting to the locals, checking the homes of several old folk to see if they needed any help and visiting local businesses during the course of routine crime enquiries. Villains sometimes tried to offload their ill-gotten gains in village stores, for example, and these visits were all part of my routine enquiries. Besides, the sight of a uniformed bobby in a shop did act as a deterrent to shoplifters – and we did have shoplifters in Aidensfield!

Following these visits, I was walking towards the post office when a harassed-looking woman ran up to me. In her early thirties, she was a sturdy young woman of medium build and had neat, dark hair cut short. She wore a light plastic raincoat and carried a small umbrella to ward off the persistent drizzle. I recognized her as Mrs Shaw, Joy to her friends, and it was very evident that she was in some distress.

'Oh, Mr Rhea, I'm glad I caught you. It's our Stephanie, I can't find her. I've looked everywhere . . .'

'Shouldn't she be at school?' was my first reaction, knowing the girl to be eight or nine years old.

'Yes, but she never got there . . . they rang me. Oh, I'm so worried . . .'

'Come and sit in the van,' I said. 'We can talk there.'

In the warm shelter of the police minivan she explained how Stephanie had set off for Aidensfield primary school just after 8.30 this morning, her normal time. She'd been carrying a satchel containing some bird books because they were having a lesson about nature later in the day. Mrs Shaw had watched Stephanie walk to the end of the garden where she'd closed the gate behind herself as usual, waved and then hurried off to school. She had been wearing a yellow plastic mac with a hood. Mrs Shaw had then returned to the house to clear away the breakfast things and to do her normal household chores.

The school had telephoned at half past ten to say Stephanie had not arrived. The headmistress, a Miss Blacker, had not been too concerned at first, thinking perhaps that Stephanie had been poorly, but when one of the other children said she'd seen her alone near the war memorial with her satchel, Miss Blacker had begun to experience some concern. The war memorial was not on Stephanie's direct route to school. A search of the school grounds and buildings had drawn a blank and so she'd called Stephanie's mother. Mrs Shaw explained how she had searched her own home with its bedrooms and outbuildings before going to her mother's house. Stephanie often went to visit her grandmother's cottage, especially after school, where she helped to feed the hens and geese, but granny had not seen her that morning. Joy Shaw added that she had searched all Stephanie's usual haunts but had not found any trace of the child.

Among the places she'd visited were the tennis club where Stephanie's mum often played (Mrs Shaw was secretary of the club), the village hall where she attended a junior youth club, the church hall where she went for her Brownie meetings and various other places in and around Aidensfield including the homes of her school friends. And now, having searched without success and having wept alone, she had found me. Her husband was a lorry driver and he was somewhere on the road in Northumberland well out of contact. Outside, she had put on a brave face but in the privacy of the police van she was weeping quietly to herself, a brave but very worried woman.

'Has she done this before?' I asked. 'Played truant, I mean?'

'No, never,' she said. 'She likes school, I've never had trouble getting her there. Today there was to be a nature lesson, and they were going on a walk beside the river this afternoon if it was fine. She was looking forward to that.'

'Did Miss Blacker say if any other child was missing? I mean, has she gone off with a playmate and forgotten the time, or what day it is? It can happen!'

'No. I asked. All the others are accounted for.'

'You know she was seen near the war memorial?' I put to her. 'Is there any reason why she should go that way?'

'None, I can't understand that. It's not on her way to school, I can't think why she would want to go that way.'

'She never said she was meeting anyone? A friend?'

'No, nothing,' wept Mrs Shaw.

The more I questioned Mrs Shaw about her own search for Stephanie, the more evident it was that the child's disappearance was both a mystery and a matter for concern. All the normal reasons for not attending school – bullying, a dislike of lessons, a dislike or fear of the teacher, inability to cope with reading or writing – had been considered and discounted. Stephanie was a clever child who loved school and who would never disappear like this under normal circumstances. This suggested the circumstances were not normal, which in turn demanded a fully co-ordinated search by professionals.

I drove Mrs Shaw home and together we searched the house yet again, this time with me opening the doors of wardrobes and cupboards, searching the loft, looking under beds and in outbuildings, checking the boot of the car and looking into dustbins and tea-chests plus a hundred and one other places where a child might hide but which an untrained searcher would never consider. I rang the school from Mrs Shaw's home too but the answer was still negative. Stephanie had not arrived.

The school and its buildings, along with all the other public and several private places, would have to be searched by police officers, but that demanded more officers and it would take a long time. I then decided to ring Sergeant Blaketon to ask him to mount an official search for Stephanie Shaw. By now it was just eleven o'clock in the morning and we had the whole day ahead of us, even if it was foggy, damp and dull.

From the office of my police house I rang Ashfordly police station. Alf Ventress answered. I explained the problem and he said, 'Hang on, Nick, Sergeant Blaketon's here.'

Blaketon came to the telephone and, upon hearing my account of events, said, 'Right, I'll ring Division and recruit some assistance. Police dogs will help, I'll request their attendance. We'll make a thorough search and I'm sure the villagers will help once word gets around. Meanwhile, Rhea, you take another recce around the village; check the school yourself and I'll meet you there in an hour. 12.30 at the school. Right?'

'Very good, Sergeant.'

While awaiting the sergeant and his team of searchers, I went to the school and searched the entire complex with Miss Blacker, indoors and out, and we drew a blank. Miss Blacker assured me that Stephanie was not a problem pupil, she enjoyed school and had lots of friends there. A little dreamy perhaps, but she was not bullied or teased by her classmates and the headmistress could think of no reason why the girl had not arrived this morning.

'You said she was a little dreamy?' I put to the teacher. 'What do you mean by that?'

'She lives in a world of her own sometimes. Day-dreaming I call it. Sometimes in class she will be concentrating on something in her head so much that she'll exclude everything that's going on around her. I just wondered if she'd wandered off in a bit of a dream this morning.'

'Has this caused problems before?' I asked.

'Not really,' smiled Miss Blacker. 'Although when she did a lesson about Jesus walking on the water, she went down to the river to try it. I think she thought she was Jesus!'

'She fell in?'

'No, the minute the cold water got into her shoes, she stopped – it was almost like snapping out of a trance. She does have a very strong imagination.'

'So what lessons did you do yesterday? Anything that might have promoted a similar reaction?'

'No, I did consider that but it was a very ordinary day of reading, writing and arithmetic.'

This snippet of information was important, I considered, and I began to wonder whether Stephanie had undergone one of her strange experiences before disappearing. It was something I must pursue and something I must put to her mother. Still at school, however, I found one of Stephanie's friends who had seen her this morning. She was called Carol Hodges. After questioning the child, she told me she'd seen Stephanie near the war memorial just after half past eight; she'd been wearing her distinctive yellow macintosh with the hood up.

'But if she was near the war memorial,' I put to her, 'Stephanie must have been walking away from the school? Did she say where she was going?'

'No,' said Carol. 'I said I would walk to school with her but she said no, she'd catch me up.'

'Catch you up?'

'I sometimes walked to school with her from her house but she was going the other way today. She just said she would catch me up.'

'Did she say anything else? Who she was going to meet, or

where she was going? Why she was at the war memorial perhaps?'

'No, she didn't say anything.'

'Was she going to the shops, maybe?'

'I don't know,' she said.

'So what did you do?'

'I went to school. When Stephanie didn't come, I told Miss Blacker where I'd seen her.'

Miss Blacker interrupted now. 'That's when I became rather concerned, Mr Rhea, and rang Joy Shaw.'

'Was anyone with her?' I had to ask Carol. 'A man or woman, another boy or girl? A car maybe?'

'No, she was all by herself.'

'Was there a car or a lorry anywhere nearby?'

'No, nothing. She was just standing there all by herself.'

'Did you see where she went from the war memorial?'

Carol shook her head. 'It was drizzly and I had my hood up, I just came to school and went straight inside.'

Having elicited as much information as I could from Carol, I then addressed the entire class of children and asked if any of them had seen Stephanie this morning. Two small boys had seen her walking towards the war memorial and their sightings confirmed Carol's version. But as all had been heading away from the distinctive stone cross, none had seen where she had gone from that point. The fact that she had walked to the war memorial was odd because it did not lie on her route from home to the school. To reach it, she had to make a considerable detour – if she had gone straight to school from there it would have added five or ten minutes to her normal journey.

I decided to ask at the nearby shops before Blaketon arrived;

surely some of the shopkeepers had seen the child in her bright yellow raincoat and carrying her satchel. All those whom I questioned said that Mrs Shaw had been asking earlier in the morning and only one of the storekeepers had seen the child; he'd not been able to recognize her but had seen a little girl in a bright yellow raincoat standing near the war memorial just after 8.30. Like the other witnesses, he had not seen her leave that point.

As I heard these stories, there was a growing dread in my mind that she had been picked up by a passing vehicle. If that had happened, then she was at great risk; we might even have a murder investigation on our hands. But even that possibility did not explain why she had walked to the war memorial, a diversion from her normal route to school. If the child had been in some kind of trance it might explain her actions, but this seemed a rather remote possibility.

Then Sergeant Blaketon's familiar little black car arrived and I went to meet him. He was alone, Alf Ventress being left in Ashfordly police office to man the telephones and radio.

'Anything further to report, Rhea?' he asked as he donned his cap and came towards me.

I provided an update on the recent information but had to say that the girl's disappearance was a total mystery. I did express the fear that she might have entered a motor vehicle although we had no description or sighting of one.

'Well,' he added, 'Division say the new inspector's coming out to lead the search. She's going to use police college techniques with maps and compasses and things.'

'Hadn't we better get started?' I asked. 'The child's been

missing for nearly four hours . . .'

'Orders are orders, Rhea, and if our new inspector says we must wait for her arrival, then wait we must.'

'Did she say that herself?' I put to him.

'No, it was Division, relaying orders. "Inspector Pollock will rendezvous with you at the village school" was what they said. "At 12.50." Twenty minutes to go, that's all. What I want to know is how these young women police inspectors can improve the way we operate, Rhea. God, it's going to be tough. I'll be glad when I reach retiring age.'

'She might not be quite what you think, Sergeant,' I ventured, allowing him to continue thinking Pollock was female.

'She could be worse,' he added. To occupy the time before the arrival of Inspector Pollock I gave Sergeant Blaketon a guided tour of the school, re-examining all the places I had searched and introducing him to Miss Blacker. He repeated all the questions I had previously asked, and assured her that we would make every effort to find the child.

Then we went outside and he stood nervously beside the school gate, awaiting his new boss. A smart black police car appeared in the distance, followed by a personnel carrier containing ten constables and another sergeant.

'Here comes the cavalry,' he grunted. 'Led by Boadicea.'

Sergeant Blaketon was clearly nervous; he fidgeted with his feet and flicked imaginary specks of dust from his uniform as the little procession approached. Eventually the leading car turned into the parking space before the school and came to a halt. Inside, the outline of a figure in police uniform could be seen collecting documents, placing a cap on its head and checking its appearance in the driving mirror.

'She looks a bit on the bloody masculine side to me,' whispered Blaketon. 'Short hair cut . . . wide shoulders . . .'

As his gaze was concentrated upon the new inspector, the personnel carrier came to rest beside the car and its assortment of constables disembarked, led by the sergeant. By this stage, news of Stephanie's disappearance had circulated among the villagers and a small knot of bystanders began to assemble. In the meantime, the school had broken for lunch and the children were in the playground, shrieking and shouting as only a playground full of children is able. Miss Blacker, the only teacher in the small school, came across to join us. She asked if the children could help in the forthcoming search, but we declined; we didn't want more of them getting lost!

But Sergeant Blaketon's eyes were upon the inspector, now leaving the car. I watched Blaketon watching the inspector; the expression on his face became a frown as he realized that this was indeed a very mannish person; short hair, sturdy walk, the frame of a man and not a woman; wearing trousers, not a skirt.

'It is a man, Rhea! That new woman inspector is a man!'

'Yes, Sergeant,' I said. 'It looks very masculine to me.'

'Who said it was a woman?' he hissed from the side of his mouth.

'You did,' I replied.

'Me?'

'Yes, Sergeant, Christine Pollock, you said. It's actually Crispin Pollock . . .'

'Crispin? What sort of name is that?'

'He's the patron saint of cobblers, Sergeant,' I replied. 'St Crispin that is, not Inspector Pollock.'

'Cobblers?' he smiled wryly.

'And the same to you, Sergeant,' I returned as the new inspector came forward. Sergeant Blaketon and I each slung a crisp and smart salute and chanted, 'Good afternoon, sir,' as Inspector Pollock approached with a large map in his hand.

He was a short, rather squat individual with a very neatly cut head of light brown hair; his uniform was immaculate and his shoes were polished so that they reflected the dull light of the day. His face was round and plump, almost childlike in the clear state of his skin; it looked as if he had not reached the stage of shaving because his skin was soft and pink and his eyes were a light blue. It was a baby-face, I realized, but when he smiled his teeth were pure white and evenly positioned, and there was a look of genuine pleasure on his features.

'Sergeant Blaketon, I presume?' were his first words. 'And PC Rhea?'

'Yes, sir,' we chanted in unison.

'Good, well, let's get moving. There is no time to waste on pleasantries. I have brought reinforcements from Strensford and the dog section is en route. Now, Sergeant, what have you discovered to date? We need a description of the missing child and then we can commence the search. We will quarter off the village and its surrounds, as per this large-scale map, and I will co-ordinate the search, using techniques I studied at the Police College. My car will be the control point; we have field radios and other equipment in the personnel carrier and loudhailers to maintain contact with any civilian volunteers who join us. Now, PC Rhea, you have made enquiries in the village? And you have made a perfunctory search?'

'It was more than that,' I had to tell him. 'It was a careful search, sir, done with the intention of examining all the likely hiding places in and around her home, the school and the key points of Aidensfield. It was thorough but it produced no results. She was last seen as the war memorial at half past eight and . . .'

'It will be repeated,' was all he said. 'Now, I will explain how I propose to search the district, including the school, her home and every building in Aidensfield, then we shall expand into the outlying fields, moors and woods.'

'It's very foggy and wet, sir,' warned Sergeant Blaketon. 'Visibility in the woods and on the moors will be extremely limited and we shall have to exercise the utmost care when despatching our searchers. We don't want them to get lost.'

'The police college system allows for such problems, Sergeant. Right, men, gather around. And any volunteers – please join in.'

Inspector Pollock was clearly enjoying the challenge; on his very first day of duty he was able to put theory into practice in a most public way. He was showing no sign of nervousness or lack of experience. He was putting on a very confident show and I must admit I was impressed by his initial action. As he was speaking to his team of men a handful of villagers had gathered, among them Mrs Shaw, and they were ushered closer by a constable. Having made the introductory remarks and explained the task that lay ahead, Inspector Pollock outlined his plan of action. As he spoke, Claude Jeremiah Greengrass and Alfred, his lurcher dog, materialized from the fog. They stood at the back to listen. I saw Claude whispering to Mrs Shaw.

Inspector Pollock suggested that each constable be accompanied by at least two volunteers from the village. Then, laying his open map on the car bonnet, he proceeded to allocate areas for each group to search. He began with the imported constables. As he was performing this task, Greengrass sidled around to my side. Mrs Shaw came with him.

He whispered, 'A minute of your time, Mr Rhea.'

'I hope it's important, Claude,' I said. 'We're about to start an urgent search.'

'Well you'll need to begin with Beckside Woods,' grunted Claude. 'I saw that lass there this morning, nine o'clockish, in her yellow mac. I've just been asking Joy about her . . .'

'What was she doing there?' I asked.

'Heading deep into t'woods,' said Claude.

I turned to Mrs Shaw. 'Joy, why would she go into the woods?'

The tearful Mrs Shaw shook her head. 'I can't say, I've no idea . . . we've been there for walks, with Stephanie, but she's never mentioned going there alone, certainly not this morning.'

I then decided to ask Mrs Shaw about Stephanie's alleged day-dreaming and her mother confirmed this. 'Oh yes, she gets so wrapped up in things. When she read *Alice in Wonderland*, she went out looking for the White Rabbit and the entrance to Wonderland, and . . .'

'Joy,' I put to her. 'What did she read last night? Or perhaps she watched television? What was on?'

'There was a repeat of that old film, *The Adventures of Robin Hood*, you know, the 1938 version with Errol Flynn. She was absorbed by that, the men in Lincoln green, their lives in the woods and so on.'

'That's it,' said Claude quietly. 'There is a Robin Hood's Cave in those woods of ours.'

'My husband said something about that!' and for the first

time there was a smile on Joy Shaw's face. 'During the film, he said he'd tried to find Robin Hood's Cave in Beckside Woods when he was a small boy, and he never did find it! He mentioned a legend about a tunnel going to Robin Hood's Bay . . . yes, I remember him saying that . . . I bet Stephanie heard him . . .'

'Where is this cave, Claude?' I asked him.

'Well,' he said, blinking his eyes rapidly. 'There's a few, six or eight caves, and all of 'em said to be where Robin Hood rested. The genuine one has an underground passage leading to Robin Hood's Bay, so they say; he used it as an escape route when the authorities were after him.'

'Do you know where they are?' I asked. 'And have you used that tunnel when the authorities have been pressing you?'

'Well, there's no tunnel, that's just a tale. But as to where the caves are, well, I might know and I might not, I mean, it's not as if I go trespassing on private land, Mr Rhea. Them woods are private, you know, they're on Lord Ashfordly's estate.'

'Come off it, Claude! Stop being so defensive – and besides, there is a public right of way through the woods. But this is serious, you're not breaching your principles to help the police, you're helping the people of Aidensfield to find a little girl.'

'Aye, well, if you put it like that. Right, well, I know where most of 'em are, they're just caves, you know, holes in the rock, nowt special about 'em.'

And so it was decided to abandon Inspector Pollock's wider plan of action in order to concentrate upon the woodland caves. His map did show the woodland and its paths, of which there were several, and he began to divide the wood into areas, each of which would be searched by a team of police and civilian volunteers. A constable would remain at the car for radio contact and the rest of us would search the four square miles or so of Beckside Wood. To search the caves, we were issued with electric torches from the personnel carrier, but it was decided that the field radios would be an encumbrance – besides, they'd probably not function over the distance between the village and the wood. Mrs Shaw asked if she could come, but we suggested not.

'You'll be far better at home,' suggested Pollock. 'If Stephanie does return home, she'll want you there, won't she? Not in the wilds of the North York Moors looking for her!'

'Yes, of course. But the moment you know something . . .'

'We'll let you know,' smiled Pollock.

And so the massive search began. Carrying a map in a waterproof cover and strung around his neck like a rambler, Inspector Pollock marshalled his troops and allocated them each a section of the wood. Sergeant Blaketon and Sergeant Lazenby from Strensford were each given half of the wood to supervise while the constables' task was to search the undergrowth as well as any caves, just in case the child had fallen and injured herself. In addition to the torches we were equipped with long sticks with which to probe the undergrowth.

Claude Jeremiah, with his unrivalled knowledge of the countryside, directed each of the groups to their positions. I found myself with two village men and we were allocated a portion of woodland beneath the towering cliffs through which the river flowed; it was on the Elsinby edge of the wood, about a mile from Aidensfield.

As we trudged towards the venue, Claude Jeremiah caught

us and said, 'I'd better show you this cave, Mr Rhea, it takes a bit of finding, it's hidden with undergrowth and the entrance is nobbut the size of a dog kennel door. But inside, it's like a ballroom . . .'

Without elaborating the detail of that search, it is sufficient to say that we found the cave and that I would never have located it without the aid of Claude Jeremiah. Even as he led us to the tiny entrance, we could see the curled-up figure of a little girl in a bright yellow raincoat. She was just inside the cave, lying asleep on a bed of dry leaves.

'Stephanie?' I touched her gently and she awoke with a smile. 'Come along, time to go home.'

'I came to find Robin Hood's Cave,' she said.

'And you've found it,' I said. 'Come along . . .'

'I wanted to look inside but it was dark,' she spoke sadly. 'I had no torch.'

I looked at Claude and the other men, then said, 'OK, I've got a torch, come along, we'll have a look inside, all of us.'

And so we crawled into the dark interior, squeezing through the tiny entrance. As I switched on the torch I realized that Claude had been right. It was massive inside; shining the light on the walls, I reckoned it was as large as the average village church and then, as the torch swept along the dusty, web-ridden walls, Stephanie shouted.

'There it is . . . look!'

I halted my action and moved the circle of light back a few yards. And there, hanging on a narrow protruding piece of rock was a quiver of arrows and a long bow. Reaching up, it was just possible to reach down the bow and the quiver; each item was smothered in dust, probably from centuries past. None of us could speak.

'I don't believe it,' I whispered.

'She does,' smiled Claude.

'Here,' I said to Stephanie. 'You can take these home – then everyone will know you were the person who found Robin Hood's Cave.'

Following the successful search, we reassembled at the school as, one by one, the searchers emerged dripping and wet from the woodland. It was still foggy but everyone had been recalled and the sergeants were ticking off the names. Mrs Shaw hurried out to greet us, somebody having telephoned her to say we were emerging from the woods with Stephanie safe and sound. Soon we were all gathered before the school; George from the pub had managed to produce some mugs of warm soup and some bread buns. Then Sergeant Blaketon asked, 'Where's the inspector?'

Sergeant Lazenby did a quick count of heads, shouting out the names of his constables. Each one responded.

'That man hasn't got himself lost, has he?' grinned Sergeant Blaketon.

'If he has, I'm not looking for him!' smirked Claude Jeremiah. 'I don't believe in helping the police!'

'Has anyone seen the inspector?' Blaketon called to the assembled officers.

'He was seen supervising the entire operation, somewhere deep in the trees,' volunteered one constable. 'He had his map . . .'

'Well, he's not come out of the trees,' Blaketon observed wryly, and added, 'Rhea! This is your patch, so it is your responsibility. You'd better go back into those woods and find the inspector! In the meantime, we will wait here and drink our soup!'

'Yes, Sergeant,' I acknowledged. The inspector had a loudhailer with him but its range was limited; I took another with me hoping I could make contact by bellowing through the thing. I could imagine myself shouting 'Inspector Pollock' in the dense woodland. But I knew the team would be waiting when I emerged – if I emerged! I hoped I didn't get lost in that dripping thick fog.

But as I trudged back into the damp and foggy woodland, I found myself forgetting about the inspector – all I could think about was that bow and the quiver of arrows which had been hanging in Robin Hood's Cave.

2 Tricks in Every Trade

That one may smile and smile and be a villain.
William Shakespeare (1564–1616)

There are very few criminals who will boast about their activities to the police but Samuel James Carson was such a man. Although he lived a long way from Aidensfield, in York to be precise, he was known to most of the officers in the police forces across the north of England. Criminal intelligence circulars warned us about his activities and although we maintained a careful watch for him during his law-breaking, he always managed to evade capture. He was a master criminal without a criminal record. We knew that. The public didn't.

In his early thirties when I was at Aidensfield, Samuel James Carson was a highly professional housebreaker and burglar. He featured in many of our sectional meetings and conferences at Ashfordly police station, and he was the topic of a good deal of gossip, but I had never met him. Even so, I felt I knew him well because his activities were such a regular feature of our crime circulars and discussions.

Although his speciality was breaking into domestic dwelling-houses, he would occasionally switch to garages, inns or shops

261

– all places where cash was kept.

At that time, prior to 1968, breaking into a house during the daytime hours (i.e. between 6am and 9pm) was called housebreaking, while breaking into a house at night (i.e. between 9pm and 6am) was known as burglary. Burglary was then considered a most serious crime, on a level with robbery and rape. At one time burglary carried the death penalty and even in the 1960s the penalty was a maximum of life imprisonment. At that time, there were very few cases of burglary! By comparison, housebreaking resulted in a maximum penalty of fourteen years' imprisonment if theft or some other crime was also committed within the premises, and seven years if the breaking was done merely with the *intention* of committing a theft or other serious crime inside the house.

A range of lesser crimes included warehouse-breaking, schoolhouse-breaking, garage-breaking, shop-breaking, office-breaking and so forth. Also regarded as a very serious crime was sacrilege: i.e. breaking into a church or other place of divine worship; this had also once carried the death penalty but during the 1960s the maximum penalty was life imprisonment.

The Theft Act 1968 altered the entire law relating to breaking into premises and all such crimes were collectively known as burglary, irrespective of the type of premises which was attacked. The penalty for burglary was reduced to a maximum of fourteen years, with life imprisonment for aggravated burglary, i.e. committing burglary while armed with a firearm, explosive or other weapon of offence.

Few burglars now receive anything like the maximum penalty – a period of probation or a fine (often paid by further burglaries) is the normal penalty. And, of course, all breaking offences have multiplied considerably during the past thirty years or so.

But neither the then severe punishment for burglary nor the tough penalties for house-breaking deterred Samuel James Carson from his chosen career. He burgled merrily in and around York and was able to afford a modest but very smart car. I think he could have purchased a very splendid model, but he seemed content with what might be described as a family saloon. Thus equipped, he travelled into the outlying towns and villages to continue his profession, burgling by night and house-breaking by day.

At that time, before the age of the computer, police stations maintained an index of criminals and their activities and we were able to identify most of those who were active. We were aware of the criminals who were operating on our patch, even if the courts refused to convict them. In the ever-present hope that, one day, we would be able to provide the villains with the punishment they deserved, we kept them under observation and noted their movements. In our efforts to secure a conviction, we relied on real evidence (i.e. being caught in possession of the stolen goods) although good circumstantial evidence would always help to secure a conviction if a defence lawyer was as crooked as the villains.

It was in this way that officers in the police forces surrounding York maintained their surveillance of Samuel James Carson. Our officers knew what he was doing; they stopped his car and searched him many many times, but not once did they produce the evidence necessary to convict him. People might ask how police officers know a person is committing a crime when such a person has never been convicted; the answer is that police officers are professionals. Just as an artist knows instinctively when a picture is right, and when a hair dresser knows a hair-style is right without being able to explain why, so a police officer knows who is committing crimes.

Proving such knowledge to the satisfaction of a modern court of law is, however, very difficult and sometimes impossible. But police officers do know who the criminals are, and they know the damage and destruction these parasites can cause to society. And one such parasite was Samuel James Carson. Certainly, he did not regard himself or his activities as offensive in any way. He regarded himself as a professional person, a man whose skills lay in taking money from others in much the same way that shops, bookmakers or dealers take money from their customers. Our intelligence system indicated that he did not think he was being sinful, wrong or even selfish even if he was breaking the law. He knew he was breaking the law, but he did not believe his activities were wrong.

House-breaking and burglary provided his livelihood and he considered himself the best in his chosen profession. In that, he was probably correct. To his credit, he never carried a firearm, he never used violence against any person or animal, he never raided the homes of the sick or the aged and he would never offer any kind of violence towards the police. He was far too much of a gentleman to lower himself to that kind of behaviour. Furthermore, he never stole jewellery or objects of sentimental value; his only objective was bank notes. Coins were too bulky and noisy to carry away, so he never stole anything but paper money. He never caused damage in the houses he raided, other than a small hole in a ground-floor window or the glass panel of a door. He did this so that he could reach inside and release the window catch or door lock, and so let himself in.

Sometimes, he would borrow a ladder from the garage of his intended target and climb through a bedroom window. One of his boasts was that his 'customers' always supplied him with the means of entry – this might include a small brick or stone to smash the glass, a ladder to gain access upstairs, a key left inside a lock or on a piece of string inside the letter box or even under the doormat, a chisel, screwdriver or some other tool in a garden shed to force a stubborn window. Garden spades were ideal for lifting patio doors from their rails, for example.

Samuel James never carried house-breaking tools because his customers were good enough to provide them. Some even helped by advertising their absence – they did this through milk deliveries not being cancelled, newspapers being delivered and left sticking out of the letter box for days on end, lights not showing during dark evenings and similar evidence of a deserted house. He always said his customers made his job that much easier. And so they did.

But to see him walking around the streets, one would never guess he was a criminal. In appearance he was like any other professional person – he might have been a doctor, a solicitor, an accountant, a bank manager or even a high-grade salesman. He was of average height, something around five feet nine inches, and was always clean and tidy. His dark brown hair was cut in the fashion of the period, he wore smart business-type suits, polished black shoes and often carried a brief-case.

Whenever the police searched him or his case, there was never any evidence of his burgling activities. The brief-case might contain a map or even his sandwiches, never any house-breaking tools or evidence of his crimes.

He drove a clean, smart but modest car which he changed

frequently – his cars were always of average appearance like a Ford Cortina, Hillman Minx or a modest Vauxhall and his only hobby was horse-racing. Through that he could, if the occasion demanded (such as an income tax investigation), explain his cash income.

Carson's confidence in his own infallibility was such that he would boast openly to the police, and even to people like shopkeepers and landlords, of his criminal activities. Even on holiday, when people quizzed him about his job, he would say he was a professional burglar. Few believed him. We knew he did this because he once told a man he met in the Lake District; the man happened to be an off-duty police officer who quietly passed on the details of Carson's whereabouts at that time.

Among his claims was that he had bought his terrace house in York with the proceeds of crime; he bought his clothes, food and furnishings with cash from the same source and in fact, every penny he spent was the proceeds of crime. But because it was all in cash, taken from houses all over the north of England, it was impossible to prove the origin of the money. Few people kept a list of their bank-note serial numbers and so there was no proof that the source of his cash was illegal.

We, the police, knew where it was coming from, but we could never prove it.

Like all local officers, I regularly received circulars about his activities; we were even treated to a black-and-white photograph of him in several police publications. But, to my knowledge, Samuel James Carson had never ventured across the moors to Aidensfield yet. I was always vigilant, knowing that one day – or more likely, one night – he might arrive.

I fully expected him to target the village for one of his raids because there were some good-quality dwelling-houses in the vicinity, many owned by people who kept a lot of cash on the premises. The one thing I did not anticipate, however, was that he would actually buy a cottage and move into the village as one of the residents. But that is precisely what he did.

At first, I did not associate the Mr Carson who bought No 2 Hilltop Terrace with Samuel James Carson, the burglar from York. The house, a neat stone-built three-bedroomed property with a nice garden and garage, had been on the market for a few weeks and it was George Ward at the pub who told me it had been sold.

'It's a businessman from York who's bought it,' he told me one morning. 'A smart-looking young chap, self-employed businessman, he said he was. He said he'd always wanted a cottage in the country and this place was ideal; quiet, off the beaten track, plenty of room inside, not overlooked, recently modernized. He paid cash, an' all, no mortgage, so he must be earning good money.'

'Do you know him at all, George?' I was always interested in newcomers to Aidensfield.

George shook his head. 'No, I can't say I do. He came in here for a drink and a sandwich once or twice when he was considering buying the cottage. He looked around it a few times with the estate agent before he made his mind up. Carson, he said his name was.'

'Decent sort of fellow, was he?' I asked.

'Yes, very. A real pleasant young chap, the sort we could do with in Aidensfield.'

Even though George had supplied me with the man's name, I must admit I did not immediately associate it with Samuel

James Carson. Then, in due course, Carson moved into the house. I saw a small removal van parked outside one morning, but no sign of the new owner. I did not intrude – after all, there was no reason. Then, about a week later, I was on patrol one morning when I saw a small green Austin car at the garage. A smart young man was buying some petrol and when he handed over the cash, I saw his face. I knew I had seen it somewhere before and when I heard the petrol pump attendant say, 'Thank you, Mr Carson,' I realized who was now living on my patch.

My heart sank. It was Samuel James Carson, the north's most successful house-breaker, burglar and full-time criminal. I must admit I was in a momentary quandary and before I could decide what action I should take, he jumped into his car and drove out of the village. I did, however, have time to note the registration number.

A check with the vehicle taxation department would confirm the name of the owner – just in case it wasn't the Carson in whom I had some professional interest! I returned to my police house and rang the taxation department at Northallerton. They supplied the name of the owner of the car.

It was indeed Samuel James Carson of 2 Hilltop Terrace, Aidensfield. A man who never overlooked the smallest detail, he had immediately registered his new address with the vehicle taxation department. That one small action by him made me realise he was a man to be reckoned with; quite clearly, he thought of everything to avoid confrontation with the law, so to convict him of a crime was never going to be easy.

My next task was to break the glad tidings to Sergeant Blaketon. I rang the office at Ashfordly. He was there.

'Good morning, Sergeant,' I greeted him. 'I've got some very interesting news for you.'

'I hope it's good news,' he sniffed. 'I could do with some good news. I think I've got the flu.'

'Well, this should clear your head,' I laughed. 'You remember those circulars about Samuel James Carson, the York burglar?'

'Yes?' There was a question in his voice.

'We're all supposed to keep a look-out for him,' I strung him along. 'To report sightings and so forth for the CID, so that the Crime Squad can monitor his movements . . .'

'Rhea, are you trying to tell me that Samuel James Carson has just driven through Aidensfield?' he sniffed.

'No, Sergeant. I'm reporting that he's just bought a house in Aidensfield. He's coming to live here, he's one of my villagers now; he's one of the residents of the village whose life and property I must protect.'

'I don't like jokes, Rhea!' he snapped.

'It's no joke, Sergeant. But as he is now resident on my patch, I thought I'd better report his presence amongst us.'

'You can't be serious, Rhea! I don't believe this . . . I can do without this right now. What makes you so sure it's him?'

'I recognized him, Sergeant. He's got a car, I've checked the registration number. He's bought a cottage at No 2 Hilltop Terrace, Aidensfield, and he paid cash for it. His car's an Austin,' and I gave him the registration number.

'And that'll mean a crime wave hereabouts, Rhea, a crime wave that never gets halted and crimes that never get solved. I can do without this . . .'

'You sound as if you're sick . . .'

'I am now!' He coughed.

'Take a few days off, Sergeant,' I suggested. 'We could always hand over this responsibility to the new inspector.'

'I can cope, Rhea, no sprog inspector's going to show me how to deal with a criminal of this kind. An inspector who gets himself lost in the woods will be no good at logging the movements of the most notorious criminal since Dick Turpin.'

'So, what do I do about it, Sergeant?' I asked him.

'Nothing for the time being, Rhea, just keep an eye on him. Make a note of his every move, dates, times and places he resorts to. Get the names and personal descriptions of anybody who calls on him, and log their car numbers.' He sniffed.

'Very good, Sergeant.'

'Note the times he leaves at night to go about his nefarious trade, list the dealers he might be visiting, anything that will nail him. We'll show those other forces how to deal with real villains, Rhea, mark my words,' and he sneezed violently.

'But what about telling CID and the Crime Squad?'

'Leave them to me, Rhea, and by the way . . .'

'Sergeant?'

'It was good work, Rhea, very observant of you. It's vital that a good country constable knows his patch and everyone who lives and works upon it. Especially the villains. Good work. I'm sure our new inspector will be impressed.'

And so the arrival of Samuel James Carson was duly recorded in the crime intelligence system of Ashfordly Section. The problem was what to do about him. I realized that I would have to meet him face-to-face sooner or later and decided that the best approach would be for me to make the first move. I would pay him a visit at his house and introduce myself.

When I made my first call that same morning, he was out. I

knew that his car number would already have been circulated to neighbouring police forces and all officers on patrol in our own area. That meant his vehicle would be stopped and searched if it was seen. I peeped through the window of the cottage. Inside it was neatly but sparsely furnished. There was a TV set in one corner, some nice vases and china ornaments, paintings on the wall and a clean rug before the fireplace. A typical home in fact. I knew none of these items would have been stolen – he was too crafty for that because some of them, like the TV set, might be identifiable by serial numbers or other marks. But all this would have been paid for with stolen money – and there was no way anyone could prove that.

Eventually, one afternoon, I did find him at home. I knocked on his door and he opened it with a smile.

'Come in, PC Rhea,' he held the door wide open. 'Nice to make your acquaintance.'

He spoke with barely a trace of a local accent and pointed to a chair. 'Drink?' he asked. 'Tea, coffee? Something stronger?'

'No thanks,' I refused, knowing that a man of this calibre could construe my acceptance of even a cup of tea as being a bribe or at least a tacit acceptance of his criminal way of life.

'So what brings the law to my humble home?' he asked.

'You are Samuel James Carson?' I tried to make my visit sound very formal.

'The very same,' he said charmingly. 'Recently arrived from York. Very happy to settle in Aidensfield. A lovely part of the country, charming place.'

'You are aware that we know how you earn your living?' I felt it unwise to accuse him outright of being a criminal.

'Of course,' the same warm smile crossed his face. 'You know your job, you are doing it very well, you are a professional which is why you are here now. I am a professional too, Mr Rhea; I know your name for a start. I know that your people are watching me, hoping to catch me as I go about my work. But they never will. I am a professional burglar, Mr Rhea, the best there is. I steal only cash and I will never break into any premises in this village. That is one of my rules – never commit crimes on my own doorstep. In York, I lived in Bootham and never burgled that part of the city. I will not harm a living thing, Mr Rhea, I will take only cash and you will never catch me. I shall live a peaceful, quiet and fulfilled life in this village; I shall never harm a hair of anyone's head and I shall not be a threat to you or to anyone here. I am a self-employed man who will leave the village to go to work, just like any other commuter.'

'If you weren't a self-confessed burglar, I should welcome you,' I told him. 'But I can't make you welcome, not when you admit to being a burglar.'

'Well, that's put the record straight,' that smile was still there. 'It's a pity we couldn't be friends, two professionals who each respect the other's skills.'

'I can never respect a criminal,' I said. 'My job is to apprehend those who commit crime.'

'And for that you need proof, eh? You will never get proof that I am a housebreaker or burglar, Mr Rhea. Never.'

'I can always try,' I said.

'Others have tried in the past,' he said. 'Senior detectives, crime squad officers, uniformed patrols, traffic police . . . I shall never be caught, Mr Rhea. You are wasting your time.'

'I came here just to let you know I am aware of your identity and your mode of life.' I stood up to leave. 'I came also to let you know that I shall not cease in my attempts to convict you of any crime you might commit.'

'Fair enough. I respect your honesty. And I shall tell you that I will continue to commit housebreakings and burglaries throughout the north of England, but not in Aidensfield. Catch me if you can, Mr Rhea.'

And on that note, I left his house.

I knew that I was to be faced with regular night patrols during which I would have to stop and search Carson or his vehicle; I would also have to ring the CID to warn of his departure from the village, knowing that if he intended going to Middlesbrough for the evening he would make us believe he was heading for Harrogate or Scarborough or even Leeds. He was clever, he was cunning. I guessed that when he stole cash, he did so in small quantities – £10 here, £5 there, small sums taken on spec from handbags left on kitchen tables, insurance money tucked into tea caddies, milk money left on doorsteps. And then he would hide it overnight, or pay it into a bank account or post office savings account so that we never caught him with large sums upon him. I guessed we never knew the extent of his crimes. If he had a day in Middlesbrough, stealing from houses with unlocked doors as neighbours gossiped, I guessed he might pick up £100 in small sums without anyone realizing he'd even paid a visit. £5 missing here, or £1 there or even a ten-shilling note might not be missed if the house bore no signs of forcible entry. The police might not even be informed of the majority of these crimes.

Over supper after my first visit, I told Mary about him and

she asked, 'But you could have accepted a cup of tea from him, surely?'

'No,' I said. 'Not from him.'

'But why?'

'Because if the tea leaves were bought with stolen money, then they also become stolen property,' I tried to explain the law. 'And if I knew the property was stolen and then received it myself, I would be guilty of receiving stolen property. I know it would never be proved, but that is the principle of the law. With a man like Carson, I must not give him one hint that I sanction his lifestyle. Not the tiniest of hints.'

'But that means that when he buys anything at all, the people who take his money are guilty of receiving stolen property.'

'Not necessarily,' I said. 'They don't *know* the money is stolen. I do.'

'But if you told them he was living by crime,' she smiled, 'then they would know. Then they would be guilty of receiving stolen property.'

And I knew she had provided me with the ideal means of making Carson's life intolerable, at least in Aidensfield. I started at the garage.

'Malcolm,' I said to the owner. 'That new chap, Carson. He gets petrol here?'

'Yes, he said he'd be using quite a lot, he travels all over, he said.'

'He's a professional burglar and house-breaker.' I told him all about Carson. 'He boasts about it. Which means his cash is stolen money – which means you are receiving stolen money, doesn't it? And if you know it's stolen, you are liable to be arrested and charged with receiving stolen money.'

'Stolen money? I had no idea it was stolen . . .'

'But you know now, Malcolm,' I smiled. 'And I want you to tell everyone else, just as I'm going to do. The shop, the butcher, the post office, George at the pub, shops, garages, pubs and post offices in Ashfordly. Elsinby, Maddleskirk, Thackerston, Briggsby, Crampton and in fact throughout the entire district. I'll stop him spending his money, Malcolm.'

I decided to emphasize my point. 'We're building a file on his activities,' I continued. 'Where he spends his cash, who his contacts are, where he goes by day and by night . . .'

By the time I had finished, I knew that Malcolm would spread the word around his own colleagues, friends and contacts. They would all be frightened of accepting money from Carson. From there, I went across to the pub for a similar chat with George and then the post office, shop, butcher . . .

Knowing how rapidly and effectively a village bush-telegraph system works, I realized that all the retailers would agree not to accept Carson's money, so I spent two or three days going around the other villages on my beat, repeating this exercise. I told Alf Ventress too, and he said he'd pass the word around Ashfordly, aided by the local constables. So we began our campaign against the charming Samuel James Carson.

It took a few days for him to realize what had happened and I was delighted one day, when he arrived at the garage while I was there, that Malcolm said he could not accept his cash. Carson looked at me.

'Every business in this area will refuse your money,' I smiled at him. 'They don't want to be charged with receiving stolen cash. You can't buy anything hereabouts, Mr Carson – no food, clothing, petrol . . .'

'Is this your way of telling me to leave Aidensfield?' he smiled, but I could see that the smile was weak now. His eyes betrayed something of his concern.

'You can stay as long as you like,' I returned his smile. 'We're not like the Wild West, we don't drum people out of town. But none of the local tradespeople will take your money.'

'So you're saying I should sell up and move?' The smile had gone.

'And who would buy a house that was bought with stolen money?' I asked him. 'Which estate agent would handle the sale of a house bought with stolen money, Mr Carson? It will be my duty to warn them, won't it? To prevent them committing a crime. And which furniture removal firm would help to remove furnishings bought with stolen cash?'

'You bastard,' he said, driving off. Now the charm had gone and so had the smile.

He moved out a week later (Malcolm actually gave him two gallons of petrol to help his departure) and he went to live in Newcastle upon Tyne, but the house remained unsold. No one would buy it and no one would rent it from him. Our efforts made sure of that. We rang the CID at Newcastle to warn them of his arrival and explained what we had done. Newcastle City Police said they would continue in a similar vein, although such action would be more difficult in a large town. But Samuel James Carson never returned to Aidensfield, not even to burgle one of our houses.

Aidensfield's best known criminal was, of course, Claude Jeremiah Greengrass and although he was not in the same league as Samuel James Carson, he was a petty nuisance.

Claude wasn't evil – but he was very devious. Typical of his activities was the time he purchased a fine chest of mahogany drawers for just £1 from old Mrs Murphy. Although I was no expert in antiques, I had seen a similar chest for sale in Strensford for £250 and reckoned that hers was worth far more than a mere one pound.

I discovered this when I paid a routine visit to Mrs Rita Murphy; she lived by herself on a smallholding which she and her husband, Ted, had run. Ted had also worked for the county highways department until his death, and now Mrs Murphy was alone with her cottage and patch of land to care for. Whenever I was passing, I would pop in for a chat, just to see that she was all right. Hers was not an easy life and she was always short of cash, and so she would occasionally sell a piece of unwanted furniture or pottery. And Claude had scored with this purchase, I discovered he had sold it to an antique shop in Strensford for £25.

'You were a bit sharp with Mrs Murphy,' I had to express my concern when I saw him in the village. 'A pound for those drawers, Claude! You could have given here £10 or even £15.'

'It's not breaking the law, Mr Rhea,' he blinked at me. 'Just a good bit of business, buy cheap and sell at a profit. That's how money is made, that's how I operate.'

'But she's a widow, Claude, she can't afford to let things go that cheap!'

'She's got a bit put by,' he was contemptuous of my concern. 'She's worth a fortune, with all that land and that house.'

'But she has no income, Claude. She'd only be well off if she sold up.'

'Aye, well, she's like me then. Existing from day to day like all us poor landowners, doing what we can to make ends meet . . .'

I realized he had no conscience and gave up my efforts to make him repent. Claude was proud of his moment of success, regarding it as nothing more than a good business deal. I could take no action because he had not broken any law.

It would be several months later, as I called one morning during a routine visit, that I found her in some distress.

'What's wrong, Mrs Murphy?' I asked.

'Oh, I shouldn't trouble you with my worries, Mr Rhea,' she sighed. 'It's that paddock of mine, I was going to have it ploughed up and had decided to plant it with potatoes. I could make a few hundred pounds selling them. I've bought the seed potatoes and Ron Lewis said he would plough it over for me – I'd pay him. Well, he's gone bankrupt, the receivers have impounded his gear and so he can't come. The others I've asked either charge too much or can't come for weeks.'

'It's urgent, is it?'

'Yes, it needs to be done soon, you see, if I'm to plant my crop, I'll have to do it within the next couple of weeks. If I don't my seed potatoes will be wasted and I've laid good money out for them, money I can ill afford.'

'It's not very large, is it? The paddock?' I asked.

'A shade over an acre.'

'If I can persuade someone to come and do it for nothing, would you agree?' In the deep recesses of my mind I was thinking about Claude Jeremiah Greengrass for I felt he had to be made to pay for his earlier deception of this lady.

'For nothing? Nobody works for nothing these days, Mr Rhea, not even for people like me!'

'Leave it with me,' I said. 'I'll be in touch – but if anyone comes to offer to plough your land for nothing, don't be surprised!'

I knew where to find Claude Jeremiah. He would be in the pub at lunchtime and so I made it my purpose to pop in, ostensibly for a casual chat with George and the regulars. These pub visits were part of our duty, not only to check on the good conduct of the premises, but also to gather crime intelligence from local gossip. We never drank on duty, however. Sure enough, as I entered the bar I saw Claude Jeremiah and his cronies playing dominoes, each with a pint at his side.

There were the usual pleasantries, combined with the usual banter from Claude, then George asked,

'Anything doing in the big world outside these walls?' He was pulling a foaming pint for Claude who now stood at my side.

'I'm swotting up the law on treasure trove,' I smiled. 'I reckon I might need to know the procedures soon.'

'Treasure?' cried George and this was enough to alert Claude.

'I've just been to see old Rita Murphy up at Hollings Intake,' I said. 'She's on about ploughing that paddock of hers and setting it down with taties.'

'Everybody's planting taties these days!' smiled George. 'They keep the crisp factories going! It must be my turnover of cheese and onion flavoureds!'

'What's this about a treasure then?' Claude could not resist.

'You'll probably know better than me,' I said to him. 'There was a tale, years ago, about a previous occupant of Hollings Intake. An old woman – she was called Hollings. She hid a hoard of gold sovereigns in a treacle tin somewhere in that

paddock; then a man came along offering to buy sovereigns at
£3 apiece – this was in the 1940s, I think, and she said she had
some but they'd take a while to find. She told him to come back.
He asked how many she had – he was thinking of buying two or
three, but she said she had three or four *hundred*. He said he'd
come back after he'd been to the bank!'

'Blimey!' exclaimed Claude. 'Four hundred sovereigns!'

'Anyway,' I continued. 'While he was away she got her
spade out and began to dig, but she'd forgotten exactly where
she'd buried the tin.'

'Get away!' George was listening intently.

'Before the chap returned she found three tins, all full of
coins! She'd buried them so long ago she'd forgotten about
them. She took four hundred out of the tins and kept them ready
for the buyer – well, he came back with the cash and paid her £3
for each one. A handsome profit. £1,200 for an outlay of £400.
And she still had several hundred left!'

'So what did she do with those she didn't sell?' asked
Claude.

'She buried them again, separating the tins this time. And
she put the money he'd paid in with the remaining sovereigns.
Then she died and the story was forgotten, but somebody
unearthed it in an old newspaper last week. I wish I'd kept the
tale – so there's some full treacle tins of gold sovereigns and
fivers somewhere under that soil, they reckon.'

'But doesn't Mrs Murphy know about it?' asked George,
with Claude listening carefully.

'She didn't mention it to me,' I said. 'I don't think she knows
the tale, it happened many years before she and her husband
bought the place. I think I must pop around there later today and

tell her. That's why I'm swotting up the law on treasure trove, just in case those tins turn up.'

'Are they likely to turn up?' asked George.

'If the field's given a good ploughing, they might,' I said. 'Or if somebody's read the story in the paper, they might turn up to start digging one night; she might lose the lot if the story gets widely publicized!'

'And if anybody found them, could they keep them?' George persisted.

'Well, it's possible,' I said. 'But the system is to report it to the police as treasure trove, then there'd be an inquest on the find.'

'Inquest?' said Claude.

'Yes, an inquiry conducted by the coroner. If he decides the money was deliberately hidden years ago, then it belongs to the state – but the finder gets the full market value. The finder, that is, not the landowner. The finder is paid the full market price and the gold coins would be handed to the British Museum.'

'So him that finds the money could be rich?' beamed Claude.

'It's a big field to dig by hand!' said George.

'Some folks have ploughs for that sort of thing!' I laughed. 'There's riches galore under our soil if only we could get at it.'

'Well,' Claude said suddenly. 'I must be off. I've work to do. Come on, Alfred,' he called to his lurcher. 'We can't sit around in this place when there's work to be done.'

When man and dog had rushed out, George asked, 'Where's he gone rushing off to? He hasn't finished his pint!'

'I think he'll be offering to plough Rita Murphy's paddock,' I smiled.

George looked at me. 'That tale about the gold,' he had a quizzical look on his face. 'Was it true?'

'It was – but it didn't happen anywhere near Mrs Murphy's paddock,' I smiled. 'It happened at Littlebeck, near Whitby, long before the First World War. A true story, George, and the hidden treacle tins full of sovereigns might still be there – in Littlebeck, that is, not under Rita Murphy's land!'

I then told George about Claude's deal with the chest of drawers and he smiled. 'Serves him right,' he said.

I went home for lunch and about an hour and a half later drove to Rita Murphy's home at Hollings Intake. An Intake, by the way, is a patch of moorland which at some time in the past has been enclosed then reclaimed as agricultural land. There are many examples throughout the North York Moors and they are usually named after the person who enclosed them. Thus there are Morgan Intake, Pearson Intake, Brown's Intake, Coates' Intake and, in this case, Hollings Intake. In the local manner of speech, this is sometimes shortened to Intak.

When I arrived, Claude Jeremiah was perched on his little rusting Ferguson tractor with Alfred sitting near his feet. He was hauling a plough through the soft earth and seemed very happy with his chore.

When he saw me approaching, he drew to a halt, but left the engine running as he came across to me. Rita Murphy also came out to meet me.

'Good afternoon, Claude,' I smiled as he came to a halt before me. 'You look busy!'

'Just helping out an old friend, aren't I Rita?' he beamed, his eyes blinking at me. 'Neighbourly gesture, like, me being a friendly sort of chap.'

'Well, I do know Rita wanted her paddock ploughing, so I know your work is needed.'

She had arrived at my side too. 'It was so good of Mr Greengrass to offer,' she was genuinely surprised. 'And out of the goodness of his heart, too. He said he wants nothing from me.'

'Is that right, Claude?' I put to him, just to clarify the situation.

'Oh, aye, well, I thought she could do with a bit of help, Mr Rhea, and me having a plough I wasn't using, well, I thought it was neighbourly to turn the ground over for her . . .'

'Well, I think it's very noble of you,' I said.

'Will you have a cup of tea, both of you?' she asked.

'Thanks, I would love one,' I accepted.

'Not for me,' said Claude. 'Work of this kind can't wait, you understand, strike while the iron's hot and all that . . .'

And so I went indoors with Rita Murphy and she produced some lovely home-made scones, a pot of strawberry jam and two mugs of hot fresh tea.

'I can't understand why Mr Greengrass is so keen to plough my ground,' she said. 'He even offered to plant the potatoes.'

'Then let him,' I said. 'And when I come again I'll explain his generosity!'

And so Rita's small piece of Aidensfield was ploughed and planted by Claude Jeremiah Greengrass, and later she had a crop of beautiful new potatoes. Claude was given a sackful – but he never did find the treacle tins full of gold sovereigns.

Later in the pub he asked me. 'Mr Rhea, that tale about those treacle tins of sovereigns. You didn't make it up, did you?'

'No, it's a true tale,' I said.

'Well, I ploughed all her land and found nowt,' he muttered.

'You might have to dig deeper next year!' I smiled.

3 By Chasing Two Hares, You'll Catch Neither

For duty, duty must be done,
The rule applies to everyone.
Sir W.G. Gilbert (1836–1911)

It was inevitable that our new sub-divisional inspector would attempt to impose his wisdom upon the rest of us. Such is the way of those new to the power of command. It seems that the police service, like any other profession, is riddled with new brooms which always want to make clean sweeps, even if the places in question have been swept clean times without number on many different occasions and in many different ways.

I am convinced that organizations like the police service, and especially departments of local authorities, keep their staff in work only because they regularly change their procedures, names or intended purposes. 'Reorganization' is the key word; in my time at Aidensfield, for example, the Civil Defence department was reorganized every two years simply because they had nothing else to do. There were very few civil people to defend! Eventually it was decided to rename it War Duties department, and as such it was reorganized even more frequently, chiefly because there were no wars to fight and thus no duties to perform. But the constant challenge of reorganization kept people in work and prevented boredom.

With the arrival of a new inspector, therefore, we felt it was inevitable that he would want to change something. Thus it was that Inspector Pollock called a meeting of all the constables of Ashfordly Section. Sergeant Blaketon was also instructed to attend. With bated breath we assembled in the muster room of Ashfordly Police Station, boots shining and hair neatly trimmed, to await his arrival and to find out what changes he intended to implement. Sharp at the appointed time, 10.30 one Thursday morning, he appeared before us like a vision – boots gleaming, trouser-seams and the front of his tunic sleeves pressed until they were like knife edges, not a fleck of dust anywhere and not a hair too long nor a whisker out of place. He stood before us, erect and stern, like a wax model of a supercop, but he was real.

'Good morning,' he said, and we duly chanted our reply.

'I am very concerned about the level of law-breaking in this sub-division,' were his first noble words. 'I know I have not been here very long but already I have been deeply disturbed by the unlawful behaviour of many local people and I have decided that we, all of us, should make a concerted effort to enforce the laws of this splendid England of ours. If law breaking becomes endemic, the whole of society will crumble,' he was in full flow now. 'The well-being of this nation has been built upon the willingness of the British people to accept the laws of the land, irrespective of class, colour and creed. We, as police officers, have been charged with the awesome responsibility of enforcing those laws, laws made by Parliament; I might add, the Mother of Parliaments. Our Parliament has set an example to the rest of the world. We should not shrink from our duty to enforce its laws.'

He paused for a moment, his eyes glistening and tiny beads of sweat appearing on his brow and cheeks. He was sensing greatness now, he was enjoying this; I got the impression he thought he was Winston Churchill stirring us into a fine and noble war effort. Then he continued,

'I have therefore conducted a detailed survey into law-breaking in this sub-division and have concluded that far too many motorists are parking without lights. Cyclists are even riding without lights during the hours of darkness. It is my intention, therefore, to conduct a campaign of effectiveness. With effect from today, each of you will endeavour to report for summons every motorist who parks without lights and every cyclist who rides without displaying obligatory lights to the front and rear of the machine. I have had a supply of special forms printed; I appreciate the difficulties of interviewing drivers who leave their cars upon the streets at night, but if you find a car without lights, you will place one of these forms upon the windscreen, directing the owner or driver to report to the nearest police station with his or her driving documents.

'They will then be interviewed by the office constable and reported for summons for whatever offences are disclosed. And this, you all know, is a fine way of checking driving licences, insurance, motor vehicle excise licences and details of vehicle registration. Many people forget to record changes of address or fail to sign their driving licence – all will be reported for process if offences are disclosed.'

It is fair to say that every man present groaned deeply within; we did not issue a loud, corporate groan, but suppressed our deepest feelings with honour. Every constable at that momentous meeting knew that this sort of purge had been done before, always with disastrous results. It seemed to be the aim of every new inspector to go around upsetting the local people. As things were, the local police used common sense when enforcing the traffic lighting regulations; we'd never dream of booking drivers who parked their vehicles unlit at night in cul-de-sacs or quiet back streets. If someone parked their unlit vehicle on a busy main road or in a dangerous position, then the law would be enforced, if only to teach the offending motorist a lesson in common sense. But to prosecute every driver who parked without lights, especially in remote rural areas, was sheer stupidity and it was guaranteed to alienate the public. In one quick burst of petty law enforcement, we could ruin years of good relations between police and public.

At that time, every motor vehicle parked on the streets during the hours of darkness had to show obligatory lights; these consisted of two white lights to the front and two red lights to the rear, with one of each for motor cycles and some other vehicles. The law applied to every public road in every town and village. Lorries, buses, cars, vans and motor cycles were all expected to obey this law, the only exceptions being tram-cars and vehicles used on railway lines. Furthermore, even at that time, those lights had to be kept properly trimmed (that was the actual word used), in a clean and efficient condition and they had to be attached to the motor vehicle in the prescribed manner.

There were special provisions for invalid carriages, horse-drawn vehicles, pedal cycles with sidecars, horses with or without riders, wheelbarrows, prams, hand-carts, lawn-mowers, agricultural implements and lorries with overhanging loads. If we were to enforce every law about the use of lights when vehicles were on the road, we should be considered persecutors who were operating a police state. But as experienced officers, we knew that the finest way to show Inspector Pollock the error of his ways was to obey his orders meticulously. It was inevitable, therefore, that his scheme should become known as Pollock's Purge. And there was no finer person to obey those instructions to the letter than Sergeant Blaketon.

One of the old school of police officers, he was the sort of policeman who, if the inspector told him to jump off a cliff in the course of duty, would do so. Having served in the army, Sergeant Blaketon would never question a lawful order. After listening to the inspector's added views on how we should go about our new law-enforcement duties, we left the office to resume our normal patrols.

Alf Ventress was fuming with suppressed anger. 'This is bloody ridiculous!' he snarled. 'I can see what's going to happen – every night, you lot will stick notices on all vehicles without lights and next morning, I'll be faced with a queue of drivers a mile long as I check documents and report them . . . they'll all be blowing their tops . . . I can see trouble brewing but if that's what he wants, that's what he'll get.'

Alf was right. That night, the patrolling constables of Ashfordly sub-division planted tickets on every car which was parked without lights. I was off duty that night, so Aidensfield escaped the first flush of Pollock's Purge, but as the night-duty constables went off duty at 6.00 a.m. another day was dawning.

And so it was that for hundreds of motorists the new working day began with the discovery on their windscreens of white pieces of paper headed 'North Riding Constabulary'; these were stuck beneath their wipers and exhorted them to pay a swift visit to Ashfordly police station, and to take along their licences and insurance.

At the station, they would be reported for summons for the offence of parking without lights. A lot of our customers would be late for work that morning and many would have stories to tell their colleagues. The police force would suffer yet another bout of canteen criticism – some victims' stories about being booked for parking without lights would make their experience seem more serious than having a hospital operation.

While a substantial proportion of the motorists of Ashfordly were trudging towards Alf Ventress and Ashfordly police station clutching their licences and insurances and at the same time wondering about the cost of a new battery for their cars, I was preparing for my morning patrol of Aidensfield. I had no intention of booking every motorist whom I discovered parking without lights – my relationship with the village people was too important to jeopardize for the sake of such a futile aspect of law enforcement – and so I decided to patrol the village and warn all the residents of the inspector's orders. Pollock's Purge would soon be hot news in Aidensfield.

Such warnings were generally appreciated. An old rural bobby once told me that the best way to ensure that people bought licences for their dogs was to walk into the post office and announce that you were going to inspect every dog licence in the village. With the speed of light, word of the constabulary intention would reach every dog owner in the district.

The effect would be that all those without licences would promptly rush to the post office to obtain the necessary document.

Thus the legal purpose was achieved with the minimum of work by the police and also without the hassle of upsetting a host of forgetful dog owners.

I reckoned the same logic would work with car lights and so I paid a visit to all the key establishments in Aidensfield, such as the pub, the garage, the shops and the post office and issued warnings, in the strictest confidence, that the new inspector had ordered a purge on all cars parked without lights.

I reinforced my news with the fact that I would be patrolling Aidensfield that evening, during the hours of darkness, to plant tickets on every car I discovered on the streets without lights. It was the confidentiality of the information I was imparting which produced the greatest impact and word of the inspector's crackdown soon reached those parts of Aidensfield which I would not normally visit. I knew that, from tonight onwards (at least for a week or two), all cars would either be parked off the road or they would display the necessary lights. The village would be aglow; it would shine like Blackpool Illuminations.

With regard to the lack of car lights, I knew, as I began that first car lighting patrol, that visitors to the pub and to evening functions in the village hall were likely to be the worst offenders. I recalled from past experience that many people would enter the premises in daylight and forget about the car they'd left outside; as the sun sank in the west in Ashfordly, so the law would approach such cars with the intention of compiling yet another offence report. But that would not happen in Aidensfield. I detested that kind of impersonal approach – if the cars were likely to cause a danger, I would walk into the premises and ask the offending owners to switch on their lights. Many would do so without a quibble. Sometimes I would switch the lights on myself because most cars were never locked – there was no need to lock them because, at that time, most people were honest and did not steal from unlocked cars. It was a simple job to reach inside and operate a light switch.

And so, that first night, as I patrolled my village beat, sometimes switching on car lights and sometimes getting car owners out of their homes, the pub or the billiards match at the village hall to put on their lights, I realized that most parts of the village were rather like a major city. There were lights everywhere. I had never seen so many cars with their sidelights blazing and I made sure my uniform was seen as I patrolled the rows of parked vehicles. I felt that the campaign was something of a success – I had achieved this result without issuing a single ticket.

It was with some surprise, therefore, that I saw a small black car creep into the village and park outside the pub. The time was nearly ten o'clock and the car was displaying lights. As I approached, I realized it was the new inspector. I went closer, chanted 'Good evening, sir,' in a fairly loud voice and slung up a smart salute.

'Good evening, PC Rhea.' He climbed from the little vehicle, returned my salute and asked, 'Everything in order?'

'Yes, sir, all correct,' I chanted in the regulation tone. 'All cars correctly parked and illuminated. No cars parked without lights.'

'Yes, I have performed a tour of inspection around Aidensfield,' he said. 'And I must admit I am impressed by the law-abiding nature of the villagers. You clearly run a very efficient beat, Rhea.'

'Thank you, sir.'

I took him into the pub and introduced him to George; Pollock's eyes scanned the assembled locals who fell into a respectful silence as he scrutinized them, doubtless seeking under-age drinkers, but nothing untoward caught his eye. Even Claude Jeremiah Greengrass, sitting with a pint in his hands, made no comment.

'A very well run establishment, Mr Ward,' said Pollock. 'An example to many others, I would suggest. Well done.'

'We do our best,' beamed George. 'We have no wish to break the law here in Aidensfield, Inspector.'

'Thank you, Mr Ward,' and he left with me at his side. He then decided upon a short foot patrol of Aidensfield, to get acquainted with the layout of the village.

As we perambulated, we discussed a few local matters such as the crime rate for Aidensfield, the lack of any special constables in the village, the overall conduct of the other licensed premises on my patch at Elsinby and Crampton and, apparently satisfied, off he went, a happy man. When I was sure he'd driven out of Aidensfield, I returned to the pub to thank George for his co-operation; he'd ensured that all his customers were on their best behaviour tonight and so that first brush with Inspector Pollock's law enforcement strategy was over. But I knew he would return. I could not relax my vigilance just yet.

I learned afterwards that it was a different story in Ashfordly. Throughout that first day of Pollock's Purge, poor Alf Ventress had been faced with a queue of very irate and upset residents; they queued out into the street, they had all received tickets and all had presented themselves as required. The determined night-duty constables had visited every nook and cranny of the town and had swamped hundreds of unlit cars with tickets.

On the morning after the first phase of Pollock's Purge, poor old Alf had been at the receiving end of a non-stop tirade of verbal abuse and complaints; there were grumbles about a police state, about the insensitivity of the purge, about the daftness of having to display lights at the end of a no-through road and about the mentality of the police who sought to persecute motorists instead of solving real crimes.

A local magistrate, a doctor, two solicitors, several dozen holiday-makers and sundry other people had been caught. The catch included several moving vehicles whose lights had been faulty, several caravan units, a hand-cart, a lorry with a load projecting more than the specified distance without the specified lights, a mechanical crane, a yacht on board a low-loader, several pedal cycles without lights and a horse-drawn agricultural implement, namely a binder.

It was not a happy day for Alf; in addition to coping with the bad-tempered customers, he had problems explaining the law on the lighting of hand-carts more than two and a half feet wide by more than six feet long and four and a half feet high; the rules about tail lights on horses, white lights on motor-cycle sidecars and whether a combine harvester travelling backwards needed red and white lights at both ends. In short, it had been a downright miserable day for Alf.

It would not be a happy day for the court officer either; Sergeant Bairstow, the man whose task it was to get these offenders to Ashfordly Magistrate's Court, would have the chore of issuing summonses and bringing all these malefactors before the bench to answer the charges against them.

When Alf had finished his miserable spell of duty at five o'clock that first day, his place had been taken by PC Alwyn

Foxton and that evening he was faced with a continuing stream of angry motorists.

As Alwyn was to say later, he had no idea there were so many car drivers in Ashfordly. The night-duty shift had certainly been active and while Alwyn had been dealing with them in a most patient and apologetic manner, Inspector Pollock had arrived. Sergeant Blaketon had been in the office, too, helping to process the non-stop stream of offenders. As the new inspector had marched past the queue to gain access to the office, some had booed him, recognizing him as the architect of their misery. Alwyn had stood briefly to attention before continuing with his work and then Pollock had said, 'Ah, Sergeant Blaketon. Still on duty, eh? That's what I like to see, a man dedicated to the work in hand, a really conscientious officer . . .'

As Blaketon had taken Pollock into his office for a discussion about the effectiveness of the purge, a large rotund man with jet black hair and dressed in a smart grey suit had entered the police station. He had pushed past the queue shouting, 'Where's that man Pollock?'

Before Alwyn could stop him, he had thrust his powerful way past everyone and had entered the police office, his face red with anger and his fists clenched.

'Just a moment, you can't come in here, this is private, please wait outside, sir, take your turn . . .'

'Turn?' the man had blustered. 'I'll give him turn. Do you know who I am?'

'No, but that is the public area, out there, you are supposed to wait in the passage,' said Alwyn.

'I am Detective Superintendent Galvin, Regional Crime Squad and I want to see Inspector Pollock. Now.'

'He's with the sergeant, sir, through there . . . I'll show you . . .'

'No need, I can find my own way. Now, who are all these people? Why are they queuing like this?'

Alwyn had explained about Pollock's Purge whereupon Galvin had thrust his head through the hatch, 'Right, I'm overruling this foolish escapade. All of you, hand in your tickets and get away home. You'll not be prosecuted. This is ridiculous. And you, Constable, take those tickets and cancel them. And cancel any more who come in. Do it on my authority. I'm pulling rank on that bloody stupid man. And I'll get the sergeant to cancel those who have come in earlier. That man Pollock has just ruined weeks of carefully planned work by the Crime Squad, we've lost a major criminal through this stupidity and I'm going to have his guts for garters, so help me.'

And he stormed along the corridor towards Sergeant Blaketon's office.

'Very good, sir,' smiled Alwyn with some relief.

It was later that we learned the full story. The voice of the angry detective had carried into the office where Alwyn had suddenly found himself alone with a pile of useless tickets. But even as Alwyn carefully cancelled each ticket, more people were entering with their slips of paper. Alwyn simply warned them to display lights next time and sent them home.

He told us later, however, that Detective Superintendent Galvin had bellowed at the inspector, making him acutely aware of the fact that he had ruined a major crime squad exercise to trap a gang of important villains. It seemed that a group of northern criminals were planning a series of armed raids on building societies and crime intelligence had alerted the Regional

Crime Squad. In the event of there being insufficient evidence to prosecute all the plotters when the actual raids occurred (the raids would use only two or three men out of a total of eight or nine plotters), the Crime Squad needed evidence sufficient to sustain a charge of conspiracy against them all. And they had learned that the group was to meet at a house in Ashfordly – on the very night of Pollock's Purge.

The CID, in several unmarked vehicles, had positioned themselves in various strategic places which provided a good view of the house and all who entered it that night. Night cameras, radio controls and an entire back-up team had been gathered for this operation, with the detectives concealed in vehicles disguised as a fruiterer's van, a plumber's van, a bread van, a caravan and car and sundry small private cars. And at the crucial moment, as four of the suspects were walking towards the house, a uniformed constable had appeared.

The four suspects simply kept on walking, they did not even attempt to enter the drive of the target house; clearly they had seen the constable and had thought he was keeping observations. Thus, in that very simple way, the exercise was ruined and months of hard and even dangerous work had been rendered useless. And to add insult to injury, all the Crime Squad vehicles had received tickets for parking without lights, that being their means of merging unobtrusively with the other cars parked nearby.

Detective Superintendent Galvin was not a happy man and spent the next half-hour shouting his anger into the shell-like ears of Inspector Pollock. It did not appear to worry him that his verbal abuse could be heard by everyone in the police station, and probably everyone in the street outside. He was determined to embarrass Inspector Crispin Pollock.

Galvin's outburst had the desired effect. Next morning, the inspector issued an instruction which cancelled his campaign of effectiveness; we said somebody had pulled the plug on Pollock's Purge. But some good did result from his idea – for a very short while, the garages in Ashfordly and district did a roaring trade in new bulbs and 12-volt batteries.

It was the poet Matthew Green (1696–1737) who wrote that

> Experience joined with common sense,
> To mortals is a providence.

What is common sense to some, however, does not necessarily appear to be common sense to others. Some unfortunates don't have much common sense and there are others who lack any semblance of this most basic of human gifts – we can all quote examples, as do-it-yourself enthusiasts who bring down portions of their houses by stupid work, motorists who set off for a strange part of England without even a map in the car, picnickers who light fires on tinder-dry moors, people who work on electrical wiring without switching off the power, people who go sailing on the sea without any previous experience. Most of us can provide many other examples of sheer idiocy. Sadly, many of these silly actions result in extra and unwelcome work for Britain's police officers and I often think the police officer's job is to tidy up the mess that others leave behind. In some ways, police officers are the salvage operatives of a very careless society.

In trying to define common sense, most of us who suffered

from Pollock's Purge considered it was something he lacked. Inspector Pollock was an academic, not a practical sort of character and it seemed he was going to go through his career making an almighty mess of most things. He seemed to possess lots of bizarre theories which could never work in practice. Furthermore, his lack of common sense was, unfortunately, compounded by a corresponding lack of experience in his job and we felt that this was not a very welcome combination in a senior officer of supervisory rank.

In spite of his shortcomings, however, we did feel he would learn from his experiences. But he did not. After getting lost in the woods at Aidensfield, and then the fiasco of his vehicle lighting purge, he decided he would organize a crackdown on local pubs.

The two aspects of pub life which upset him were those landlords who served under-age drinkers and those who did not close at the required time. After-hours drinking was a well known and very popular sport in most rural areas and most police officers tolerated this, unless it really got out of hand. Tolerance of the liquor licensing laws was one of those unwritten aspects of police work which need to be tempered with humanity, a precise understanding of the laws and, of course, common sense.

Quite a lot of us could not understand why one could sup from a pint of beer until precisely 10.30 p.m. while the same act was illegal only ten seconds later. Fortunately, that law was changed in the 1960s, allowing a ten-minute drinking-up time. But even so, the liquor licensing laws were fairly rigid. It must be stressed, however, that the police do not make the laws – that is done by Parliament and the task of the police is to enforce

them without fear or favour, however daft some of them appear
to be. And so Inspector Pollock, in his infinite wisdom, decided
to enforce the law on the sale and supply of alcoholic drinks
which were consumed after permitted hours. Under-age drinking
could be tackled at a later date.

Now, most rural police officers know that a pint of beer
supped after closing time tastes infinitely better than one
purchased within licensing hours. It would not be breaking any
confidences to report that many off-duty police officers have
enjoyed a pint or two after hours. Furthermore, it would likewise
be truthful to say that many of them were very senior officers.
For policemen to find a pub which served drinks after hours was
like finding an oasis in the desert; at the end of the permitted
drinking hours the bar curtains were drawn, the doors locked
and the assembled multitude got down to the serious task of
supping their golden nectar. This act was somehow a defiance
of the silliness of the liquor laws and there was a deep satisfaction
in beating the system.

Police officers knew that once the awful shout of 'Time
gentlemen please' rent the air, the beer assumed a delicacy of its
very own; it became like ambrosia, the mythical food of the
gods, a golden life-giving liquid which helped its supporters to
get through the tough days and weeks ahead. And so men risked
their reputations by drinking late. The landlord risked his
licence by selling alcoholic drinks after time and those who
were caught drinking risked public humiliation in the courts
and in the local newspapers. Drinking late was as exciting as
driving a racing car. It was a very risky business – but almost
every pub was prepared to take that risk for the comfort and
well-being of the customers. It was indeed a rare inn which

closed exactly on time every night of the year.

Oddly enough, many town inns did close on time, chiefly to prevent trouble from some of their more robust customers, but in rural areas there were isolated hostelries in lofty places which were meccas for the faithful. Even if the law was being bent slightly, who could honestly claim that they suffered from the cheer which flowed from their sturdy walls? There were few neighbours to complain and most of the imbibers did not have cars, preferring to walk home and so enjoy the still night air of the moors. Some even sang to themselves during the homeward journey, a sure sign of their ability to commune with nature in the bliss and solitude of the calm night hours.

It seems that Inspector Pollock, a non-drinker, did not fully appreciate these finer points. He lacked any hint of romance and had never even tasted a glass of best bitter, his drinking being restricted to a small sweet sherry at Christmas. Thus his views were biased against the most English of pastimes. Following his arrival at Strensford, we discovered that he had undertaken several missions into the countryside specifically to check up on late-opening inns.

Armed with a list of rustic hostelries, he had sallied forth in his official car, and indeed had sometimes performed the journey when he was off duty. He had toured the inns, noting the names of those whose bar lights were still shining at eleven o'clock or later, noting those with cars and bicycles parked outside after closing time and writing down the names of those with the noise of happy voices coming from within.

And he had been shocked by his findings – he discovered that every moorland inn and village pub within Ashfordly section was busy after closing time. Inspector Crispin Pollock had therefore decided to have a second purge, this time on village and moorland inns. It was to become known as Pollock's Public House Purge.

It ought to be said that the period in question was one of impending change for inns and public houses. In addition to the ten-minute drinking-up concession, many were offering bar snacks; some took advantage of changes in the licensing laws to open smart restaurants and another factor was that members of the female sex were now visiting pubs without the risk of being labelled as women of doubtful virtue. To sit in the lounge of a country inn and sip a gin and tonic was not then considered quite as sinful as some might have suggested a few years earlier.

It needs to be further added that the raiding of pubs whose landlords sell drinks after licensing hours required the extreme cunning and superb skills of those who used a wooden horse to gain access to the ancient city of Troy. If landlords decided to sell drinks after licensing hours, they did not leave their doors open so that the police could enter the premises and catch them in the act. They locked the doors, closed the windows and drew the curtains to make the place secure against any raiders, whether they were police officers or late-night drinkers who'd been ejected from other places.

Acquiring the evidence necessary to gain a conviction was therefore very difficult but this did not deter the gallant Inspector Pollock. He gathered us together for lectures on the art of raiding pubs, reminding us that we needed evidence of the sale of alcohol, that we must catch the customers with the drinks actually in front of them and that we must seal every glass and initial it with a note of its contents.

Thus we would raid licensed premises armed with sticky

labels and pens; the idea was to rush to a table of drinkers, order them not to move and then stick a label over the top of each glass saying, for example, 'Three-quarters of a pint of bitter seen before a man who gave the name of Eddie Donohue.' Logically, we had to obtain the names of the drinkers, take photographs of the scene if possible, seize all the evidence and warn the landlord or landlady of the impending prosecution. Lots of officers were needed to raid just one pub.

And so Pollock commenced his Public House Purge. What he had failed to realize was that all the landlords in the district were very aware that a new and very keen police inspector had arrived. They knew he was operating in the vicinity and they knew what he would do. Like generations of new inspectors before him, he would raid their premises and so they were prepared for whatever action he might take. Their response to a purge on after-hours drinking was very simple. All doors were locked at the end of licensing hours.

Those drinkers who were leaving would be told to simply let themselves out but make sure the latch dropped. If a police raiding party wanted to gain admission, therefore, they would have to knock or otherwise demolish the door. If they knocked, the landlord would alert the drinkers who would immediately dispose of their beer, either by drinking it quickly or pouring it down the sink. Thus by the time the police actually gained access to the bar, they would be confronted by lots of empty glasses and many happy customers playing dominoes or discussing horse racing, politics or some other topic, all of which were quite lawful.

Some police would gain entry by subterfuge, pretending to be a travelling doctor and shouting that they must use a telephone.

They resorted to various devices in the hope that the doors would be opened; other officers adopted the technique of waiting for a departing drinker to leave the door open just long enough for a large police boot to be wedged between it and the jamb, and so they would sneak in. Some even attempted to 'plant' undercover cops among the drinkers but this never worked. A stranger in the bar was a real giveaway! In any case, all these tactics were known to the landlords; Pollock's raiding parties attempted various schemes, but all failed.

Over a period of some six months, his raiding parties entered about seventy moorland inns and local pubs without finding one which was breaking any of the licensing laws.

He did find lots of men playing dominoes, lots having earnest discussions about the government, the trades unions and the state of English football, but he never found anyone who was drinking after hours nor did he catch one landlord or bartender selling alcohol after time. And yet on every occasion that he passed those same inns whilst off duty at night, the lights would be burning, there would be the sound of happy voices from within with cars and bicycles parked outside. He knew they were taking advantage of him, he knew they would be drinking late and there seemed to be nothing he could do to stop them.

The only casualty of his campaign was Sergeant Blaketon; everyone blamed him for the upset caused by the raids. He got letters from the Licensed Victuallers Association, he got stopped in the street by drinkers and landlords to be quizzed about his actions, while some thwarted drinkers even wrote critical letters to the press, claiming that the freedom of the drinking man was under threat. Poor old Oscar began to realize that he had to find a way of halting the menace which was Inspector Pollock. For all his faults, Blaketon did not rigidly enforce the liquor licensing laws – he did use common sense.

Blaketon was feeling very sore about the whole enterprise when I was in Ashfordly Police Office one morning. Then Pollock arrived. He caught Blaketon in a particularly black mood due to yet another abortive raid which had failed the previous evening.

'Sir,' began Blaketon. 'I think we should halt these pub raids.'

'Give them up, Sergeant? Why, might I ask?' There was a look of defiance on Pollock's youthful face.

'Because we're not having any success, sir, it's a waste of valuable time and a waste of manpower. It's getting us nowhere, not one pub has been found offending against the law.'

'Perhaps you feel this way because you are shouldering the blame for the raids?' smiled Pollock. 'You should not shrink from upholding the law, Sergeant, however unpleasant it may be.'

'I must say I am getting a certain amount of antagonistic feedback, sir,' grunted Blaketon. 'As the first man to enter the premises, the leader of my team as it were, I am thought responsible for the organizing of these raiding parties. I do get rude comments in the streets, and some landlords are refusing to donate any more prizes for our Christmas raffles.'

'Sergeant, you disappoint me,' said Pollock. 'You don't win wars by giving up when the first battle is lost. We shall continue. I shall pursue my policy until I am satisfied that every one of those licensed premises is operating within the law, not just upon one night or for one week, but permanently. And I have not yet reached that state of satisfaction. So I shall expect more late-night examinations of licensed premises in your next quarterly return.'

'As you say, sir,' sighed a weary Sergeant Blaketon.

Pollock continued, 'Now, I am here to examine your register of dog licence inspections, register of explosives stores and your lost and found property books. In your office please, Sergeant. Now.'

And so they disappeared into the inner sanctum which we called Sergeant Blaketon's office.

I must admit I felt sorry for Sergeant Blaketon; in spite of his approach to most aspects of police work, his relaxed attitude towards licensed premises, especially those within Ashfordly section, meant we never had any problems with the landlords. There were very few reports of drunkenness, few occasions of fights or other trouble and all the landlords ran well-conducted premises, even if they did occasionally allow late-night drinking. Not once had we had a complaint from a member of the public about late-night drinking or the general conduct of any pub; Pollock was the only person to make a fuss about it and it seemed he was going to persist with his hard-headed notion of raiding the pubs until the landlords and the customers became heartily sick of our presence. It was no way to gain the respect and co-operation of the public; if something serious occurred, we relied on the co-operation of the public but this stupidity would serve only to alienate them. I knew Blaketon was seeking some means of stopping these raids.

We all realized that Pollock's lack of experience let him down in this matter; whenever a pub was causing real problems through late drinking, the simple remedy was to park a police car outside at closing time. Then, as the customers left, at whatever time, a uniformed constable would stop and test every car and ask every driver to take a test to see if he or she was fit to drive. It was a simple but effective way of showing we meant business – and it was a fine way of emptying a pub, even during licensed hours! If Pollock had wanted to gain control over the pubs, that's how it could have been done. Easily, with no hassle, no confrontations. Just a police car parked silently outside, waiting. But if Pollock was going to continue with his purge, he must be taught a lesson. The question was, how?

As we pondered the long term ill-effects of his actions, it was Sergeant Blaketon who told Pollock he had received some prior knowledge that there was to be a late-night drinking session at the Chequer Board Inn on Cockayne Moor. Cockayne Moor was a lofty area above Rannockdale and the inn was perhaps the most isolated of all those upon the moor. Once, long ago, a drovers' road passed this way and the ancient inn had served the drovers while their long lines of foot-sore cattle rested on their way from Scotland to York. Now, the inn was popular with hikers and tourists; it stood alone surrounded by nothing but open moor, the nearest house being five miles away. Few policemen ever raided the place and so it was a true haven for serious after-time drinkers. They came from far and wide to sample the fresh moorland air and the gorgeous golden bitter which had the flavour of heather within its bouquet. The Chequer Board Inn had a large clientele from Middlesbrough, Redcar and the smaller communities around Teesside. And it did not lie within Ashfordly section, therefore it was not the responsibility of Sergeant Blaketon and his officers. It did, however, stand within Strensford sub-division and it was consequently within the jurisdiction of Inspector Pollock.

I was working in Ashfordly police station one Saturday morning, completing a road accident report, when Sergeant Blaketon came through. He was smiling. I was surprised by this: he appeared to be in a very good mood.

'Listen to this conversation, Rhea,' he said. 'I need a witness. I am about to ring Inspector Pollock at Strensford.'

With no more ado he dialled Strensford police station on the internal network and said, 'Sergeant Blaketon here, put me through to Inspector Pollock, please.'

He waited as the connection was made and then I heard him say, 'Ah, good morning, sir. Blaketon here. Yes, all's correct. Now, my reason for ringing, sir. It concerns late-night drinking. I've received a tip-off, sir, from one of my informers. There is to be a late-night drinking session at the Chequer Board Inn; no, the licensee has not applied for an extension of hours nor has he notified us of a private party.'

Blaketon beamed at me as he made that call, adding, 'Well, sir, I cannot help, it's not within Ashfordly section, sir. It's just over my boundary. It's part of Challonford section. But I thought I had better pass along the information, should you wish to take action.'

And that was it.

Blaketon could see my puzzled expression and said, 'You heard me make that call, Rhea, eh? I was not secretive, it was all done openly.'

'Can I ask why I had to witness it?'

'I am hoping that Inspector Pollock raids that pub tonight,' he beamed. 'I want him to know that I passed the information to him openly and not in a conspiratorial manner.'

And with that, he returned to his office, chuckling to himself.

The whole story emerged later. The chief constable of one of the smaller police forces in the Midlands had rented a country cottage on the moors in order to celebrate his twenty-fifth wedding anniversary. Having been born and bred in the North York Moors, he had lots of friends and relations in the vicinity, including the chief constables of Middlesbrough, Durham, the North Riding of Yorkshire and Sunderland. All had been invited to a huge party at the Chequer Board Inn. There was a total of sixty guests, and dinner had been provided in the dining room. It was a good night, highly enjoyable and highly successful.

At midnight, Inspector Pollock and his party of two sergeants and eight constables were positioned around the isolated inn, waiting and watching. The place was humming with activity; the chink of coins could be heard as money was dropped into the till. Among the cars parked outside were two coaches and one overnight camper. The inn was ablaze with lights and full of people. Pollock realized that the men had to come outside to visit the toilet and had issued instructions that the raid would commence at 12.15 a.m. precisely because he had noted that the exit door was never locked. There was the point of entry.

He had no idea that inside were five chief constables, several local dignitaries, magistrates and county councillors as well as family members of those important guests.

At 12.15, Pollock gave the order. 'Enter the premises, immobilize all the drinkers, label each glass and specify its contents . . . report the licensee for selling drinks after licensing hours and report all the drinkers for consuming intoxicating liquor otherwise than during licensing hours. Right, men. Go!'

This time, due to the certainty of his actions and the volume of customers present, he led the raiding party. Once inside, he shouted for attention; he ordered everyone to stop whatever they were doing and announced that this was a police raid. All drinks would be seized as evidence. All names would be taken . . . the licensee must not move!

A deathly hush had fallen as the army of police officers went to work with Inspector Pollock leading the action, shouting orders and demanding co-operation.

After watching him for a while, and after smiling as the constables sniffed the drinks in an attempt to identify them, a tall gentleman stood up and said,

'Inspector Pollock. I am your Chief Constable. And these gentlemen here are also chief constables . . . now, I think this little bit of fun can cease . . .'

Pollock was flustered, but only momentarily. 'Sir,' he said, 'I received information that after-hours drinking was occurring on these licensed premises and, in accordance with my statutory powers, I have entered the premises to find everyone drinking . . . sir, with due respect, the law applies to everyone and if you and the other chief constables are found to be drinking alcohol after the permitted hours, I shall have no alternative but to report this matter.'

At this, there was loud applause from the party. It seemed they all thought this was a stunt performed as entertainment for the guests but the Chief Constable raised his hands for silence and said, 'Inspector, we are celebrating the twenty-fifth wedding anniversary of Mr John Lodge, the Chief Constable of Stamfordshire. As you may know, he holds a senior post within the Salvation Army and he does not drink alcohol. It is a condition of any social gathering which he arranges that no one drinks alcohol. We are all drinking non-alcoholic drinks.'

The expression on Pollock's face changed from one of authority to one of doubt; he looked around. His sergeants and constables, one by one said, 'This is orange, sir . . .' 'This is bitter lemon . . .' 'This is lemonade . . .'

The Chief Constable went on, 'And as we are not drinking alcohol, we are not committing any offence. There is no law to say we cannot remain on licensed premises after hours, and there is no law which says the landlord cannot sell soft drinks after hours. Therefore, there was no requirement to apply for an extension of hours, nor was there any need to notify the local police of a private party.'

And at that, the entire party erupted into cheers and Inspector Pollock slunk out of the pub, followed by his smiling constables. He drove away without saying a word.

And that marked the end of Pollock's Public House Purge.

4 Poetic Justice

'Twas a thief said the last kind word to Christ;
Christ took the kindness and forgave the thief.

Robert Browning (1812–1889)

Among the many very interesting houses on my beat was one
called Poets' Corner. It occupied a splendid riverside site at
Crampton where its well kept lawns and gardens sloped gently
to the edge of the water. At the bottom of the garden, among
some thick reeds, there was a small pier which jutted into the
water where the family, called Eastwood, maintained a tiny
rowing boat which they used for trips along the river. The boat
was always moored near this jetty and I often thought its
open aspect was a security risk. A burglar could easily row his
own boat to this point, raid the house from the rear, and escape
with his loot without anyone seeing or hearing him. And yet
the house had never, to my knowledge, suffered such an
attack.

The house itself, a fine Georgian structure of dark moorland
stone with a blue slate roof, stood at the top of the garden, with
more lawns separating it from the road which twisted and
turned through the picturesque village. The main windows

overlooked the river with spectacular views across the dale beyond.

It was a house that appealed to all who had had the good fortune to visit it and the Eastwoods were regarded as friendly and welcoming people. There were two large entrance gates which opened on to the road; these led into the garden and then into a parking area in front of the house. There was lots of space before the house and the garden was occasionally open to the public for charitable purposes, such as raising money for the Red Cross or for the repair of the church roof. Thus a lot of people had visited the gardens, which were beautifully maintained and full of interesting shrubs, flowers and rock plants.

Its chief attraction, however, was the unique collection of statues of famous British poets. Mrs Judith Eastwood, a lady in her mid sixties, was widely known as a collector of such statues – over the years she had scoured salerooms, antique shops and cottage sales in her search for these statues and her collection was now regarded as the finest in Britain. Indeed, it was perhaps the only one in Britain and included some items in wood or stone; others were fashioned from a type of plaster like the statues found in many Catholic homes. One or two were even made from glass, some of them solid, others hollow. Other materials included marble, Whitby jet, brass and even concrete!

Several were very large, almost the size of human beings, while others were of a more modest size, perhaps standing two to three feet tall. Some were a mere eighteen inches high.

She had some miniatures too, these being only six inches in height. These were kept indoors, as were all the most valuable or fragile examples. Some of her statues were several centuries old, such as a wooden one of Shakespeare. The larger ones, particularly those made of stone and some of the wooden ones, stood out of doors and occupied prominent positions about the garden. During the winter months the wooden ones would be taken into an outbuilding to avoid the weather, but in summer all the more robust examples reappeared in the garden to stand like silent sentinels, surveying all before them.

I don't think Mrs Eastwood knew precisely how many statues she owned; there were umpteen Shakespeares in stone, wood, glass and plaster, countless Miltons and Bacons, several Cowpers, Swifts, Tennysons, Wordsworths, Shelleys and John Donnes and miscellaneous minor ones such as Walter Pope and Sir Thomas Wyatt. She claimed that every British poet of note, born before 1900, was represented and her knowledge of British poets was such that few doubters had the expertise to challenge her claims. It would have been a nigh impossible task to discover which were missing.

It was this collection which brought visitors to her garden on its occasional open days; in addition, various poetry societies and parties of aficionados from the poetry world would enjoy private visits by appointment. With such a diverse crowd of visitors, I must admit that I worried about the security of her statues.

I had no idea of their individual monetary value since there did not seem to be a large market for such statues – I knew of no other collector who would want to steal them. But one Monday morning in late June Mrs Eastwood rang me. Someone had stolen a wooden statue of Geoffrey Chaucer.

I drove to the house and my first task was to examine the

scene of the crime. Mrs Eastwood, a tall, very slender and rather handsome woman with dark, greying hair, led me into the garden along a maze of paths. Eventually we halted beside a bed of roses. There was an empty stone plinth on top of a small, ornamental dry stone wall.

'He was there,' she pointed to the empty place. 'He was standing right there last night, I checked. And now he's gone, Mr Rhea.'

'You've searched the garden?' I asked. 'Sheds, outhouses, places where it might have been hidden?'

'Everywhere. My husband and I searched every single hiding place, including the reeds beside the river, the boat and the compost heap at the far end of the garden. He's gone.'

I was intrigued by the way she referred to the statue as 'he', almost as if she was referring to a real person, and, after conducting my own search of the area for clues such as footprints left by the thief, I began to note the necessary details. One factor to consider was whether Geoffrey could be quite easily carried away by one moderately strong person.

Fortunately Mrs Eastwood had several colour photographs of this Geoffrey; I was able to borrow one which I would be able to reproduce and circulate via police channels to antique dealers and others to whom the statue might be offered for sale. She explained that the statue was some two feet six inches tall, carved from dark oak and clothed in Chaucer's period, the fourteenth century. Carved on the foot of the statue, upon the base where the feet were resting, was the outline of a large church, probably Canterbury Cathedral. The statue depicted Chaucer as a sharp-featured man in late middle age, sporting a white goatee beard and white hair; it was based on the portrait used by Thomas Occleve in his *De Regimine Principum*. The artist was unknown.

Mrs Eastwood was uncertain of the age of the statue, but informed me that experts had dated the wood and the style of carving as the middle seventeenth century. She reckoned it was worth about £250, but that was a very arbitrary figure. It might be worth far more to a serious collector. I then asked whether in recent weeks she'd had any suspicious visitors.

'The gardens were open yesterday,' she acknowledged. 'We had almost a thousand people looking around, for the Red Cross, and one man did ask if he could borrow that very statue.'

'Borrow it? What on earth for?'

'I have no idea, I didn't ask and he didn't explain. It was such an unusual request that I immediately turned it down.'

'Did he persist in his request? Was he a nuisance?'

'No, not at all; when I refused him, he apologized for troubling me and just wandered off to look at the others. I kept an eye on him, of course; I was worried he might be tempted to take one of my poets, but he didn't. I lost sight of him eventually and he never returned.'

'Can you describe him?' This man seemed to be a suspect, at least someone who ought to be eliminated as soon as possible.

Mrs Eastwood told me that the man was very distinctive in appearance. He had long and very scruffy dark brown hair which came down almost to his waist; he wore casual clothes – jeans and a multi-coloured shirt 'rather like those one was accustomed to seeing upon Canadian lumberjacks,' she added. He had sandals on his feet but wore no socks, and he sported a long, unkempt beard which was the same colour as his hair. She said it was difficult to estimate his age but she guessed he'd be in his late thirties or early forties, although she might be years out due to his hirsute appearance. When I quizzed her about his mode of speech, she said he was well-spoken without any discernible accent; he did not wear spectacles and she did notice that his teeth were in very good condition.

She had no idea how he'd arrived at the open day, whether he rode a bicycle or had come by car; he did not appear to have any companion and other than his asking her if he could borrow Chaucer, she'd had no contact with him.

At that time, it was fashionable among young people, especially those of artistic temperament, to live in so-called hippie communes. Regarded by many as gentle and caring people, hippies sought an alternative society which was free from the constraints of authority and tradition. They wanted to be free to live their lives as they wished. Some became known as flower people but, sadly, they did attract the more unsavoury elements from the baser levels of our society.

Drugs, promiscuity and widespread irresponsibility became associated with some of these communes, which were being utilized by those who had, in their own words, 'dropped out' of society. These drop-outs were dirty, dishonest and even violent, the very opposite of the original notion of the gentle flower people. So hippie communes began to attract an unsavoury reputation. It was sad that these well-meaning groups drew the worst elements of society into their midst; the result was that no self-respecting village or town wanted a hippie commune within its boundaries or even within a reasonable distance. One or two hippies did venture into Aidensfield and district, but they seldom remained very long. After living for a while in derelict farms or old barns, they moved on, often leaving rubbish and damage in their wake. In spite of their gentle image, the hippies' hangers-on earned them a bad reputation. Having listened to Mrs Eastwood's description of the man at the open day, I did wonder if another hippie commune had developed in the vicinity.

Her description of the visitor had all the hallmarks of the kind of person who would frequent such places and the odd request to borrow Geoffrey Chaucer was the kind of behaviour one might expect from them. I could imagine a commune of hippies sitting around a camp fire reading aloud from his *Canterbury Tales* and thinking that the life of the pilgrims somehow mirrored their own existence.

Having extracted all the necessary details needed to compile my official crime report, I set about my enquiries, beginning in Crampton. It was a compact village on the southern slopes of the dale and, like so many communities in that area, boasted a peer of the realm, a shop, a post office but no pub. This was because Lord Crampton did not wish to attract unsavoury characters to his village – and he did own most of the property. Several breweries had offered to purchase or rent suitable premises as an inn, but he constantly refused.

I started by asking Stuart Cannon, owner of the village shop, whether he had seen this character around the place and his response was immediate and positive.

'Yes, Nick. Regularly. Once a week he comes in here to buy provisions – fruit and vegetables, groceries, a magazine or two – the usual stuff any householder might purchase.'

'Who is he?' I asked.

'No idea,' he spread his hands in a gesture of defeat. 'He just comes on Thursday mornings, gets his stuff, pays in cash, and leaves. He doesn't seem to want to get into conversation.'

'Is he new to the village?' was my next question.

'Well, he's not a native,' Stuart told me. 'I should think he's around for the best part of a year or so. I never ask about his private life and he never volunteers anything.'

'Where's he live?' I asked.

'I wish I knew. So far as I know, he's not using one of the houses in Crampton. He just appears, always on foot, buys his provisions and disappears. He carries them in a rucksack on his back. I did hear he's been seen walking along the road towards Ploatby but when he leaves me he usually goes into the post office.'

When I realized I could get no further information from Stuart, I pottered across the road to the post office, which was run by Dorothy and Laurence Porteus. I explained the purpose of my visit and Dorothy smiled,

'It sounds like Mr Chatterton,' she said. 'He comes in here once a week to collect his mail. He uses us as an accommodation address. Garth Owen Chatterton is his name, we get quite a lot of letters for him, addressed care of this post office. He has a post office savings account with us too, he pays money in and draws it out from time to time.'

'Where does he live?' I asked.

'I don't know, he's never told us. I just assumed he lived somewhere nearby. He's been coming in to see us for about a year now, always on Thursday. Shall I tell him you wish to speak to him?'

'No, that might frighten him off!' I laughed. 'I'll try to arrange my duties so I'm in Crampton on Thursday. What's his usual time of arrival?'

'Mid-morning,' she said. 'He's not in any trouble, is he?'

'Not to my knowledge,' I told her. 'But I do need to have a word with him.'

And so I left the post office, knowing that news of my interest in this character would soon filter through the population. At least I had made some progress and it only remained to find out where the mysterious Garth Owen Chatterton was living. If the village post office had no idea, then Crampton estate office might be able to help. That was my next visit. But the secretary to the estate manager said that none of the estate's cottages or properties was occupied by a Mr Chatterton. They did have one or two vacant premises which were available for rent, but he had never expressed any interest.

Before returning home for lunch, I did encounter one or two other residents of Crampton as they went about their daily business. In each case, I approached them and asked if they had encountered the mysterious long-haired Mr Chatterton. The only one who could help was a young married woman called Rose Harvey. She explained that sometimes she drove from Crampton to visit her mother in Aidensfield. Usually she made the trip on Thursdays and had sometimes noticed the long-haired man walking along the road which led to Ploatby. Sometimes she'd seen him heading towards Crampton; at other times he'd been heading in the opposite direction. The description she provided made me positive it was the same man but, like the others, she had no idea where he lived.

After lunch, I checked the electoral registers for each of the villages on my beat, but none contained the name of Chatterton. Likewise, I checked with CID at Force Headquarters to see if the name had cropped up in our criminal records, but it had not. I realized I had a mystery man living on my beat. But where was his home? And what was his interest in Mrs Eastwood's statue of Geoffrey Chaucer?

As I went about my duties that Monday afternoon, and throughout the following Tuesday, I made enquiries in Aidensfield, Elsinby and several of the other tiny communities that formed my beat. But no one had seen Chatterton in those villages. Then on Wednesday, as luck would have it, I encountered Claude Jeremiah Greengrass as he was walking to the pub for his lunch-time pint. I decided to quiz him about the missing statue, not seriously thinking that he was the culprit but rather as a matter of routine. I quizzed him about every crime that happened on my patch – it was part of our on-going professional relationship.

'Morning, Claude,' I greeted him. 'Nice day.'

'It was till you showed up,' he grunted.

'So where were you on Sunday night?'

'In bed, where I should be, that's where. Why? Has somebody been nicking pheasants?'

'No, statues.'

'Statues? What sort of statues? And why would I pinch a statue?'

'To sell it and make a bit of cash.' I then decided to switch my line of questioning to confuse him. 'So who's this long-haired chap that's wandering about?'

'You're baffling me now, first asking about statues and then a long-haired chap. Are you accusing me of something?'

'You?' I laughed. 'Why should I accuse such a fine, upstanding member of the community of anything? No, Claude, I am endeavouring to solve a crime. Somebody has stolen a fine statue of Geoffrey Chaucer from a garden in Crampton and a long-haired, untidy specimen of a man is suspected.'

'Well, I'm well-dressed, neat and tidy, as you know, so it can't be me.'

'So who is this long-haired untidy chap? Fortyish, waist-length hair, scruffy, walks everywhere . . .'

'It'll be that chap in Elsinby Forest,' Claude said, trying to get himself absolved from whatever suspicions I had. 'Lives in that old lumberjacks' hut, deep in the forest. Mind, I'm not saying he took the statue! I'm no grass! And he does walk everywhere . . . I've seen him . . . when I've been walking . . .'

'When you've been poaching, you mean!'

'You blokes are never grateful for us citizens helping you with your enquiries. You'd think I'd learn a lesson and keep my mouth shut . . .'

'The only reason you're helping me is to get yourself off the hook so I'll stop asking you awkward questions, but your help is appreciated. So come into the pub, I'll buy you a pint,' I heard myself offering. 'That'll help you realize I do appreciate your help. Then I must be off.'

In the bar, I surprised the landlord, George Ward, by buying a pint of beer for Claude, but none for myself as I was in uniform and on duty. I remained a few minutes for a chat, asking Claude to describe the old huts. Eventually, I realized where they were. Deep in Elsinby Forest, which comprised rows and rows of conifers planted some forty years earlier, there was a complex of disused huts. They were far too deep within the trees for a casual visitor to discover and they had been used by forestry workers when the plantation had been first prepared; for a time, they'd used the huts as they nurtured the young conifers but over the last twenty or thirty years the complex had been deserted. I had never had any reason for visiting the buildings, and in fact they were so deep within the forest that they were almost impossible to locate. But now I had a reason for finding them.

I went to see Harry Bolton, a retired forestry worker who lived near the church and, with the aid of my own map of the area, he told me how to locate the huts.

'We built 'em when we were planting that forest, way back in the twenties,' he said. 'Good sturdy huts, there's toilets even, with running water collected from a beck, a canteen, bedrooms. You could live there . . . we built 'em strong, we knew they'd be used when the trees were harvested, that'll be any time now, I shouldn't be surprised. They'll be usable still, Mr Rhea, dry and warm.'

He explained how to find a route through the endless rows of pines, so that afternoon I set off in my minivan. Once inside the forest, I followed the old tracks, taking note of my route when I turned left or right, and sometimes marking trees with large bows tied from a length of orange tape I carried. It was so easy to get lost in the featureless world of tall tree trunks and when I reached a stream to which Harry had referred, I parked the van and walked.

In total, it took me nearly an hour and a quarter to find the huts, but eventually I did see them through the trees, a small complex of wooden chalets with log walls and felted roofs. All were in first class condition. But as I approached, I heard noises. I could not identify the sound at first, but it did sound like someone chipping at a piece of wood with a chisel. And as I entered the enclosed area before the huts, I saw a long-haired man sitting on an old tree trunk as he chiselled at a block of ash wood before him. I saw him long before he saw me; and there, on a table in front of him, stood Geoffrey Chaucer.

I stood and watched him for a few minutes; he was totally unaware of my uniformed presence as he concentrated upon the work in hand. I could see he was carving a wooden statue; he was, in fact, copying Geoffrey Chaucer, making a smaller version of Mrs Eastwood's famous poet. After observing him for some three or four minutes, I decided, with some reluctance, that I must break his concentration.

I walked into the area and hailed him.

'Mr Chatterton?'

He looked up from his work with never a sign of anger or fear on his face; through all that hair he smiled and said, 'You've come for Geoffrey?'

'I have,' I said. 'I'm PC Rhea from Aidensfield, I've had a complaint that you stole the statue . . .'

'Borrowed, Constable, borrowed. I'm not a thief. I borrow statues to copy them, that's all. The lady at the house would not consent to my borrowing of this one, so I helped myself. I shall return Geoffrey to his plinth when I have finished with him.'

'So what are you doing with him?' I had to ask the question.

'I am copying him. I am a sculptor, Constable, and I specialize in the British poets. I have never yet found a statue of Chaucer, not until this Sunday, and so I have never produced what I believe is a passable image of him. And then I found this Chaucer – at a house just down the dale.'

'So you took him?'

'I borrowed him. I asked the lady, who refused – not surprising, judging by my appearance, but appearance isn't everything. I saw the advert for the open day when I was in the post office last week and, well, her having all those poets in her garden, and me specializing in carving poets . . .'

I looked at some of his work which stood on ledges in what used to be the former canteen and felt sure Mrs Eastwood had bought some. They did look distinctly familiar.

'Where do you sell them?' I asked him.

'Wherever I can, craft shops in York, market stalls in Ashfordly, shops in Malton and Scarborough, London even, or the Lake District. Wordsworth and Coleridge sell very well over there . . .'

'But you must not help yourself to other people's goods,' I said. 'That's larceny.'

'I'm sure she'd have given me permission if I'd been allowed to explain myself,' he said. 'She has a lot of my statues in her garden, that big one of Milton is one of mine, I had to copy that. There aren't many Miltons about, you know . . . I always return them when I've finished.'

Had I proceeded by the rule book, I should have arrested him, seized the statue of Chaucer as evidence, and taken him to Ashfordly Police Station to be charged with larceny. That was then the word for theft.

But equally, I knew the law. For the crime of larceny to be committed there had to be an intention by the thief at the time of removing the property to permanently deprive the owner of the property. That criminal intention was lacking in this case. Unauthorized borrowing was not a criminal offence, except in the case of motor vehicles for which special laws had been made. Any court of law would throw out this case, I felt sure. But I could not let the matter rest – after all, I had received a complaint of a crime and I had found the person responsible for removing the statue.

'Are you going to arrest me?' he said, his smile flashing in the dim light of the forest.

'No, but I am going to ask you to accompany me to Mrs Eastwood's house,' I said. 'I want you to bring Geoffrey Chaucer with you, and some other smaller examples of your work, just to prove that you are what you say you are. You and Mrs Eastwood have a lot in common. And when she meets you, I think she will withdraw her complaint about the stolen statue.'

'You're a gentleman,' he said. 'Well, no time like the present. Come on, I'll put a few small poets in my haversack . . .'

I helped him to pack a selection of his work, and then we journeyed to see Mrs Eastwood with me helping him to carry the burden. As I'd expected, she was astonished, partly because she had indeed been buying his work without realizing he lived and worked nearby.

She was clearly delighted that she now had Geoffrey Chaucer back home. I then explained the law on theft. When I finished, she said, 'Mr Rhea, I could not possibly prosecute this man, not now. Besides, as you have explained, there was no crime, was there? But just think, if I hadn't reported it, I would never have met Mr Chatterton . . .'

Thus I would be able to write off the incident as 'No Crime'. As she showed the scruffy sculptor around her amazing collection I realized that here were two kindred spirits. She made us a cup of tea and produced some home-made cakes, and as we talked it was clear that Mrs Eastwood was happy to permit Chatterton to make use of her own superb collection of poets. And so he would be able to widen the scope of his work as he borrowed some of her rarest examples.

'Tell me,' she said as they grew more absorbed in their

conversation. 'Are you by any chance related to Thomas Chatterton?'

'Yes,' he said. 'I'm from that family, although he died in 1770, aged only seventeen. Even in that short time, he had earned a fine reputation as a poet. That's how my interest in sculpting poets arose.'

'And one of my ancestors was Thomas Love Peacock,' she smiled. 'He died in 1866, and that's how my interest in poets arose . . .'

The time had come for me to leave and I rose to my feet. 'I will run you back to the forest,' I offered to Chatterton.

'No, allow me, Mr Rhea,' begged Mrs Eastwood. 'I do so want to see Mr Chatterton's other work and he can, of course, keep Geoffrey until he has completed his work.'

And so the saga of Poets' Corner was over. I rang Sergeant Blaketon to inform him of the outcome and he said, 'I suppose it's poetic justice, Rhea. Did you know that Geoffrey Chaucer was the first poet to be buried in Poets' Corner at Westminster Abbey?'

'No, Sergeant,' I said. 'But all poets steal from Homer, so they say.'

'So long as they don't steal from Mrs Eastwood, I couldn't care less,' he grunted.

Another problem of dishonesty arose when the Aidensfield coal merchant, a man with the very apt name of Tony Hopper, came to report that small amounts were being stolen from his depot. He ran his business from the goods yard of the railway station and at that time the stocks of coal and coke were not locked away. Anyone could help themselves and, as a new arrival in

Aidensfield, I found this general open trust somewhat unusual. Upon my very first visit to meet Tony, I expressed my doubts about this quaint system, but he assured me that there was no need to lock away the coal or coke – no one ever stole from his stocks. The people of Aidensfield could be trusted, he said. And, as things turned out, that was true.

In thinking about the availability of the coal and coke, it would have needed a wheelbarrow or a vehicle to carry away a sufficient amount to be useful, although the odd lump could be pocketed or carried off by hand. And if anyone did set about stealing from the depot, even at night-time, then surely the villagers would see them at work with their barrows or sacks and inform Tony. And so the coal and coke bays remained open to everyone, and yet none was stolen.

That was until Tony Hopper began to realize his stocks were dwindling, albeit by small amounts. He began to suspect something was amiss when he found evidence which suggested that someone had swept up some loose pieces in one of the bays, so he began to mark the extent of the spread of each of the six bays of coal. Small pebbles, discreetly positioned, showed him the extent of the coal as he finished work each evening. And then, next morning, he saw that at regular intervals a small amount had vanished – enough to half fill the average coal bag on each occasion, in his estimation. The unthinkable was happening – someone was stealing his coal.

He maintained his own system of checking stocks for a few days before involving the police. And when he called at my police house, I could see he was far from happy.

'If it's somebody who's hard up, they could have it for nowt if they asked,' he said. 'Damn it, Mr Rhea, I'll never see folks short, especially in winter. But to sneak down to my depot at night and steal, well, it's a miserable thing to do.'

There is no doubt that this betrayal of trust was hurtful to him, but after checking that no one had been given any authority to remove the coal I decided to 'crime' it, as we say. That meant that the disappearance of the coal was formally logged as a crime and not written off as mere wastage, which in turn meant I had to keep observations and make enquiries about the losses. It also meant that my colleagues from Ashfordly would keep observations during their patrols of the district. Upon learning of these crimes, Sergeant Blaketon laid scorn upon Hopper's method of storage.

'The man's a fool, Rhea,' he grumbled. 'You don't leave valuable materials lying about so that thieves can help themselves. He's asking for trouble . . . serves him right. I'll bet he's been losing coal for years without realizing . . .'

'No, he hasn't, Sergeant. That's the whole point, it's never been locked away, never been placed behind locked gates or in locked yards; for years it has been stored at the railway station in all six bays of that open-fronted depot.'

'CID will think we're idiots, criming this one,' he muttered. 'How much has gone? Do we know?'

'No, Sergeant, not exactly, there's no way of telling.'

'Well, what I'm asking, Rhea, is whether there is one crime or several. If this has been happening once a week for the past six, sixteen or twenty-six weeks, that's a separate crime on each occasion, and that will play havoc with our statistics. All those unsolved crimes . . .'

'It'll be nice if we catch the villain, though,' I beamed. 'We'll be able to write off a lot of crimes as "detected".'

'That's *if* you catch the villain, Rhea! And that is something I feel is highly unlikely! These sneak thieves are the very worst.'

His attitude made me determined to arrest this sneak thief but Blaketon was right in saying that the arrest of this kind of villain was never easy. The thief was not coming to the depot on the same evening each week, for example, and we had no idea of his hour of arrival. It was fairly certain, however, that he came during the night, probably in the early hours, say around two or three in the morning when no one was around. He must have had a vehicle of some kind to carry away his ill-gotten gains, however, so I decided to keep observations whenever I was engaged upon a night patrol. It was a hit-and-miss method, but as I had many other duties to occupy me, I could not afford to spend every night sitting in a coal yard just in case the thief turned up.

Over the next three months I spent many lonely hours hiding in different sections of the railway complex of buildings, listening for sounds of illicit shovelling and watching for people lurking in the shadows armed with shovels and sacks, but, on those nights, no one came. He did arrive several times when I was not there! I began to wonder if the thief knew when I was concealed in his happy hunting ground, but felt not – no one knew. I hadn't even told Tony Hopper or the railway station staff of my intentions. And then I struck lucky.

It was a chilly night in November with a full moon and there was also a thin covering of snow on the ground. It had fallen since midnight and now lay like a virgin white sheet across the landscape. Its presence combined with the light of the moon added a glow to the area, highlighting the heaps of coal, the buildings and the roads in and out of the station. And, in the silence of that night I heard noises near the coal depot. I did not move; I was sitting in the waiting room with the door open (it was never locked at Aidensfield station in those days) and listened as the sounds continued. From this point, every tiny noise in the station could be heard and I guessed no one could steal coal without making some noise.

I also knew that if I was to prove a case of larceny, I would have to catch the thief with the coal in his or her possession – catching him or her in the act of moving towards the supplies was not sufficient. So I waited, ears straining to catch every hint of noise and to identify the sounds. And then, clearly, in spite of the distance between my hiding place and the bays, I could hear the sounds of someone shovelling coal. It was a most distinctive noise and it echoed in the confines of the bay under attack.

On silent sponge-rubber soles and armed with a torch I padded along the platform and down the short track which led towards the coal bays.

The trip took about thirty seconds with my dark uniform effectively hiding my movements within the shadows of the surrounding buildings and trees in spite of the brightness of the night. I left a trail of footprints in the snow and as I approached the bays I could see the distinctive wheelmarks of a pedal cycle in the thin snow on the road surface. The marks headed straight for the depot and vanished somewhere within. Most important of course, was the fact that there was only one track – it meant chummy had arrived but that he had not yet departed; indeed, I could still hear the scraping sounds from within. He was at work. I knew from the noise that he was filling a bag with coal; I knew I had caught the thief.

Guided by the wheel marks in the snow, I crept around the

edge of a protruding wall, my boots making not a sound, and now the noise was louder. In the gloom of the bay in which he was working, I could see the occasional flash of the blade of the shovel as I caught glimpses of his white face and a half full sack standing in a pool of dim light cast by the front lamp of his cycle. He was using its light by which to work.

I waited for a moment, taking in the scene; the cycle stood against the wall of the bay, its lamp fixed low on one of the front forks, the front wheel angled so that the light shone upon his area of operation. I could see the shadowy figure hard at work, his breath forming clouds of vapour on the cool night air. I had no idea who it was, however, except that it looked like a smallish male person.

Having seen all that I wanted, I suddenly switched on my torch to brightly illuminate the man and shouted, 'Police, don't move . . . stay right where you are . . . drop that shovel . . .'

I had to make him drop the shovel; it could have been used as a weapon against me, but with a sharp intake of breath, a sign of shock and surprise, he obeyed. The shovel crashed to the concrete floor of the bay and I was surprised to see the man raise his hands in the air. I approached him with caution, kicked the shovel aside and told him to place his hands behind his back. He obeyed. Quickly, I snapped on my handcuffs; even so, there was always a risk that a person arrested in these circumstances would attempt to make a dash for freedom, but this man did not.

Meekly and with apparent signs of resignation, he submitted to the arrest and said, 'Sorry for doing this, Mr Rhea . . .' Now I recognized him; he was a small, middle-aged man called Dennis Brooks who lived in the council houses with his widowed, invalid mother. I escorted him to my van, sat him in the passenger seat and then drove around to collect the bag of stolen coal and his bike. I squeezed both into the rear of the little van and drove to Ashfordly police station.

Sergeant Bairstow was on night duty and we submitted the meek little man to his fate. He was charged with stealing the coal and we kept his cycle and the half-filled bag as evidence; he was bailed to appear at Ashfordly Magistrates' Court on a date to be notified.

I then drove him back to Aidensfield. During the journey he did nothing but apologize; his actions were certainly out of character for he was a man who never went out drinking, who rarely took part in village events and who seemed to spend most of his time caring for his invalid mother. He'd lost his job as a delivery man with the Co-op and told me he'd been desperate. His mother needed warmth during the winter months and the coal fire was her only means of heating the house; they'd literally spent all their meagre savings on keeping her warm. In desperation he'd resorted to stealing coal to keep her as healthy as possible. Her pension managed to keep them in food but little else. I advised him to tell that story to the court; I felt sure that, in the circumstances, the magistrates would be lenient when imposing sentence upon him. I dropped him at his home and said I would be in touch with him about the date of his court appearance.

Having not got to bed until 4 a.m. I walked to the coal depot the following lunchtime to inform Tony Hopper of the night's developments. He was delighted, but when I identified the culprit, his expression turned to one of sorrow.

'Not poor old Dennis!' he said.

'Why, you've had dealings with him?'

'Aye, he got behind with his payments, I let him have several loads on tick, Mr Rhea, saying he could pay when he got some money in. Well, he never paid, so I stopped delivering his weekly order.'

'He needs the coal for his mother, she needs constant warmth but now he's out of work,' I told Tony. 'He's lost his job with the Co-op.'

'Has he? Poor little devil, he never said! If he'd told me that, I'd have given him the bloody coal! Why didn't he ask instead of just helping himself . . . folks are daft, Mr Rhea, putting themselves at risk for the sake of asking. Too proud to ask for charity, but daft enough to risk being arrested.'

'I've told him to explain all this when he goes to court, Tony,' I said. 'I know they'll treat him with compassion.'

'If I'd known he was out of work, I'd have offered him a job,' he said. 'I need a spare man at the depot, to do a bit of bagging up and delivering. None of the young lads wants that sort of heavy work, so I'll see what he says. If he's willing, I'll set him on.'

'Are you sure?'

'Aye, 'course I am. And I'll tell the court what I've done, that'll mebbe get him off with a caution or summat similar, conditional discharge mebbe.'

And that very same day, Tony Hopper went to visit Dennis Brooks to offer him a job. Dennis accepted with tears in his eyes and within a week I saw him bagging coal at the depot and occasionally driving the delivery wagon around the villages. When Dennis appeared at Ashfordly Magistrates' Court, Tony came along to speak in his defence and proved an eloquent and persuasive witness.

The outcome was that Dennis was given a conditional discharge for stealing coal, the condition being that he did not commit any further offences of a like nature within the next two years.

'I won't,' he promised the court. 'I'll be able to keep mother cosy and warm in winter now because I get free coal. That's one of the perks of my new job. I am allowed as much free coal as I need.'

5 Give a Dog a Bad Name

A good dog, like a good candidate, cannot be of a bad colour.

Peter Beckford (1740–1811)

One of the things that intrigues me is the manner in which a craze will suddenly arise, become popular, and then fade into obscurity. There are times when one wonders what prompted the craze to begin in the first place and why so many normally sane people so slavishly followed it.

My favourite, as I have mentioned on previous occasions, is the Alexandra Limp. During the 1860s, Queen Alexandra, who was then the Princess of Wales, had a minor accident as a result of which she developed a very slight limp. For some weird reason, it then became fashionable for many of the ladies of her time to walk with similar slight limps. This peculiar whim became known as the Alexandra Limp. But why on earth would anyone want to copy someone else's limp? I'm sure Her Royal Highness thought those people were all rather strange.

Similar things happen in the fashion world, such as hair styles, types of shoes, female facial adornments, short skirts, flared trousers or variations in collars and ties, while in other spheres crazes like hula hoops, yo-yos and executive toys seem to come and go with remarkable speed. The world of fashion depends upon people who follow such changes.

None the less, I continue to find it odd that people will surrender to these whims, only to abandon them within a short time. It seems such a waste of money and effort. A lot of men, of course, studiously ignore fashions, having learned that the suit they bought as a lad will be acceptable for many years to come. After all, it really doesn't matter what one wears, so long as one is comfortable.

As I am writing these notes (in 1993), the mobile telephone is the latest fashionable craze but whether it is a rich person's plaything or genuinely useful has not yet been determined. It might merely be part of another fashion.

I cannot understand why some people feel they must emulate others – I can think of all the Elvis Presleys who continue to haunt the world, all the Marilyn Monroes and all those who consider themselves a double of someone famous. Why not be themselves instead of coping another person? I think there is something faintly sad about those who feel compelled to copy other people or who doggedly follow trends which are set by others.

Such a phenomenon burst upon the scene in Aidensfield when Mrs Mildred Prenty of Frankland House bought herself a pair of Afghan hounds. Hers were a beautiful pair of animals, both bitches. They had rich, fawn, silky coats which were worn long around the ears, limbs, feet and hindquarters. These beautiful dogs loped along the village street in a most glamorous and elegant manner.

Their long, slender faces, curly tails and cheerful, gentle nature made them exceedingly popular with all who came into contact with them. There is no doubt they were very nice dogs; extremely well cared for, obedient, lovable and beautiful, they were a credit to Mrs Prenty.

But because Mrs Prenty was one of the most highly respected of social leaders in the neighbourhood, other ladies from Aidensfield and the surrounding villages decided to acquire Afghan hounds. In a very short time, the moors and dales seemed to be full of Afghan hounds in a variety of shades and colours, ranging from cream to fawn to red, brown and even black. For the social climbers of Aidensfield it became very trendy to own a pair of Afghans, and the dogs, with their owners at the end of expensive leashes, would promenade around the village for all to admire.

Some ladies, however, did not wish to be regarded as copiers of fashion; they saw themselves as leaders, and for this reason: they had to do something different. They felt they should not be owners of Afghan hounds. They could not think of anything drastically different which had the same social impact and connotations, so they all decided that ownership of some other kind of distinctive breed of dog was quite acceptable. As a consequence, some bought borzois, others settled for red setters while labradors, golden retrievers and collies were also strongly favoured.

There is little doubt, however, that the Afghan hound owners, being the originals, considered themselves the most superior. Their dogs seemed to think so too – certainly Mrs Prenty's dogs had an air of superiority and so did she. The outcome of all this social manoeuvring was that the Aidensfield and District Afghan Hound Owners' Association was formed, the idea being to organize club meetings, sometimes with talks from experts on matters like grooming and breeding with the climax of the year being the annual Aidensfield and District Afghan Hound Show. The Prenty Challenge Cup would be awarded to the best dog of the year; in prestige, it would be something akin to a miniature Crufts.

The non-Afghan-owning ladies, however, not to be outdone, decided to form their own societies, associations and clubs, each with their own shows and thus there were formed the Aidensfield and District Borzoi Association and Show, and similar associations and shows for labradors, golden retrievers, spaniels and collies, the last named scoring Brownie points by having an obedience section. There was even an association and show for Yorkshire terriers and another for Rhodesian ridgebacks.

One interesting factor about the Aidensfield and District Afghan Hound Owners' Association, however, was that their dogs were all females. Every one was a bitch, a fact which was said to echo the general feeling about some of their owners.

No one outside the Association was quite sure why this all-female trend had developed and various theories were propounded. Although nothing on the matter was ever publicly stated by the owners of the lady dogs, it was generally felt that their owners' delicate upbringing in a ladylike society might not have enabled them to cope with boisterous and randy male dogs. As things were, these devoted ladies could mollycoddle their female dogs as if they were daughters; most of the other villagers reckoned the bitches were more amenable to control than any daughters might have been.

Another factor was, of course, that if all the dogs belonging to the Afghan Association were female, then it would be highly unlikely that any of them would accidentally become pregnant by dogs owned by fellow club members. The owners could freely show off their bitches without rude attention from sex-mad dogs. Their virtue was thus safeguarded, their figures would never be distorted and the ugly question of suckling pups would not arise. Harmony and discretion would reign.

Being the village constable, I heard about these new dog clubs and was quite surprised that the Afghan Association was restricted to only female owners and to female dogs, but the Aidensfield and District Afghan Hound Owners' Association was adamant. No randy male dogs would be allowed at the association meetings or at the annual show, and thus the risk of unwanted canine pregnancies would be avoided. It was the sort of logic one might expect from feminists, being their idea of equality and common sense.

In some ways, their caution was understandable because lots of other lady dogs in Aidensfield had had unfortunate experiences with a highly sexed and very determined masculine dog called Alfred. Alfred, the Lothario of the local canine world, lived with Claude Jeremiah Greengrass on the outskirts of the village and had an awesome ability to woo in spite of the most determined attempts to stop him. Whenever a bitch was in season anywhere in the area, Alfred would leave the comfort of the Greengrass establishment to fulfil his heart's desire as many times as he could muster before he was caught. He would travel miles to complete his lustful urges, being known to leap five-bar gates, cross snow-bound moors and wade through treacherous rivers to bring a little love and romance to his lack-lustre existence. As a result of Alfred's promiscuous roaming, lots of little Alfreds had been whelped in Aidensfield, sometimes to the considerable surprise of their owners, who'd been expecting something looking more like a cocker spaniel, a hare hound or a pedigree Alsatian.

Alfred's achievements had resulted from his ability to capitalize upon the skills he had acquired in poaching for his worthy master; he was able to circumnavigate most attempts to frustrate his urges. After achieving the purpose for which he had risked life and limb, he would then leave the scene of his triumph with a happy smile upon his hairy grey face.

Lots of strange-looking pups had resulted from these activities and many a show-dog had had her reputation of purity ruined by the ardent Alfred. If there was a female dog on heat anywhere within Aidensfield and district, the lustful lurcher would seek her out and release his pent-up passion in a most vigorous, and sometimes spectacular, manner.

When the Aidensfield and district Afghan Hound Owners' Association decided to hold its first annual show, therefore, the organizers were mindful of Alfred's reputation and decided that the event demanded top-quality security measures. No one was quite sure whether or not the village hall defences were capable of thwarting Alfred in his most determined mood.

I was quite surprised, therefore, when they asked me for my recommendations. I was summoned to a meeting between Mrs Mildred Prenty, Chairman of the Association, and two ladies called Leonora Haddock and Ermintrude Appleyard. They had been elected to form a sub-committee with special responsibilities for the good conduct of the show. Over tea and cucumber sandwiches, while wedged between two silky-coated lady Afghan hounds, I listened to their worries.

Eventually, I said, 'Ladies, I cannot see any problem. Alfred will only pursue lady dogs when they are in season, and the answer would seem to be that all bitches on heat are therefore disallowed. They must be forbidden to enter the hall while the show is in progress. That would eliminate all your problems.'

'But Mr Rhea, you do not understand,' simpered Miss Haddock. 'All the dogs on show will be bitches, there will be no male dogs in the show and so the rule about bitches in season should not be necessary.'

'From my own rather limited experience,' I countered. 'I am led to believe that it is one of the courtesies, if not a specific rule in some cases, that bitches in season are not entered for any dog shows. The responsibility rests first with the owners, surely, and then with the adjudicators.'

'In mixed shows, that is understandable,' beamed Mrs Prenty. 'But I see no problem with an all-female entry. This is why we are seeking your advice. We need to keep all male dogs out of the hall during the afternoon of the show.'

'Clearly, a notice to that effect would be enough,' I tried to play down their concern. 'Most dog owners would oblige if they knew the reason – but can't I persuade you to disallow all bitches in season?'

'No, that is not among the rules of our Association,' said Mrs Prenty. 'That is why we are an all-female association; we want equality with those owners who show male dogs. We cannot and will not accept that females are different.'

'Then you need a good authoritative person on the door of the hall,' I suggested. 'And you are fortunate in that Aidensfield village hall does have a foyer; by keeping the inner door closed while coping with arrivals, you could regulate the entry of visitors – and dogs.'

'I think we could do with two door persons,' beamed Mrs Prenty. 'One to staff the outer door and one to control the inner one, with strict instructions to contain every incomer in the foyer until satisfied he or she is not smuggling in a male dog.'

'Absolutely right!' I said.

'Then will you be doorman?' smiled Mrs Prenty.

'It depends whether or not I'm on duty,' I said. I had no wish to become doorman to this gathering but when she gave me the date, I checked my diary and found I would indeed be on duty from 2 p.m. to 10 p.m. that Saturday afternoon.

'Sorry,' I said. 'I can't oblige, but I shall be on duty that afternoon and will make sure I visit the hall as regularly as I can.'

As I left them to their deliberations, I wasn't sure about the sense of allowing bitches in season to partake in a dog show, even one restricted to bitches, but it was their problem, not mine. As the weeks ticked by, I could see that the proud owners were giving their bitches the very best of beauty treatment. The most outstanding was undoubtedly a beautiful and silky bitch called Jacquanetta. She was owned by Leonora Haddock and was clearly the favourite to take the Afghan of the Show award.

On the day of the show, a Saturday in late July, I walked across to the village hall to find that the security arrangements were in operation.

Large signs outside the hall, equally large ones on the internal doors and a forbidding lady in tweeds, called Olga Pitkin, standing at the main entrance, were suitable deterrents to any masculine dogs. I did see several dogs hanging around outside the hall, however; there'd be a dozen or more and among them was a Yorkshire terrier, a Jack Russell terrier, a

Scottie, two whippets and a Pyrenean mountain dog. All were scenting the air and getting restless. The lady on the door kept shooing them away, sometimes resorting to a shepherd's crook to propel them from the entrance.

I went over to her. 'You've not got a bitch in season in there, have you?'

'Well, actually, yes, Mr Rhea. Three or four, in fact . . . you see, Mrs Haddock's Jacquanetta is such a lovely dog and we know she has come in season, only yesterday in fact, and we dare not ban her, being Mrs Haddock's bitch. And if she was allowed in, then we could not ban the others who were in season . . .'

'So you've got several bitches on heat in there? There's no wonder half the dog population is gathering outside! You'll have to keep these doors firmly closed,' I said. 'If any of those lustful dogs get half a chance, they'll be in there.'

'I know, that's why I am here,' she beamed. 'None shall pass, Mr Rhea, I know how to deal with randy males!'

There was no answer to that remark, and so I left her to her guard duties.

I undertook a patrol around the village, advising on car parking, checking that car owners locked their doors against thieves and generally making sure things were in order. It was a nice gentle way of spending a couple of hours on a Saturday afternoon. At least, that was my view until I saw the familiar unkempt shape of Alfred the lurcher loping along behind a hedgerow. His master was not with him; I could see no sign of Claude Jeremiah and wondered why Alfred was skulking along the hedge in that furtive manner. But than, of course, everything he did was furtive; whatever Alfred did was usually devious, troublesome or illegal. Judging by the urgency of his manner, I felt sure he was heading for the village hall to attempt to partake in a spot of doggy courting, but in this instance he had a lot of competition. There were some very fit and aggressive dogs waiting on the green. Alfred would be unaware that this pack of lovesick hounds had already gathered; furthermore, he would never get past Miss Pitkin, her shepherd's crook and her system of closed doors. I was confident that the security network would defeat Alfred.

But I was wrong.

Unbeknown to anyone, Alfred had not attempted to enter the village hall via the obvious route. He had probably observed the crowd of panting dogs outside and had surely seen Olga Pitkin and her stick as she defended the front door. Being a cunning dog, he must have realized that all attempts to enter via the main door would fail.

With considerable intelligence, therefore, he sneaked around to the back of the hall. In a small room at the back the tea ladies were busy; the electric boilers were heating the water, the ladies had prepared all the cups and saucers, they had put bread and cakes on plates and were ready to distribute the teas. At a given signal, the MC would announce that teas could be purchased at the hatch, these ladies would then transfer their carefully prepared products to the point of sale. It was very hot work in the kitchen, what with the crowd of hard-pressed ladies and the steam that rose from the boilers. One of the ladies had opened a sash window, raising the bottom portion some three inches and lowering the top portion about a foot to produce a circulation of cool air.

Had anyone kept an eye on that window, they would have

seen the distinctive grey snout of a lurcher as it sniffed the air through the open portion at the bottom. As the ladies set about selling their wares Alfred pushed his head through the gap, easing the window higher as he struggled to gain entry; eventually, he succeeded in pushing the window high enough to admit the whole of his body. He crawled through like a snake, writhing until he was able to drop the eighteen inches or so on to the floor of the tea room. From there it was but the work of a moment to sneak into the main body of the hall, where all the lady dogs were displaying their charms.

From eye witness accounts which later circulated the village, it seems that Alfred succeeded in keeping his presence concealed from everyone during his critical journey across the floor of the hall. He did this chiefly by sneaking under display tables and chairs until he arrived at the stand upon which Jacquanetta was displayed. Acting with the speed of a poacher's trained companion, he launched himself at Jacquanetta with all the skill necessary to achieve his purpose. Before any human being realized what was happening Alfred was locked in close embrace with his sweetheart. The moment he was sighted, however, there was pandemonium. Women screamed, chairs were knocked over, cups and saucers rattled to the floor, stands were overturned and sticks were discovered as a horde of angry women began to chase Alfred. He disentangled himself from Jacquanetta in a manner which brought tears to his eyes, and once again using his poaching skills managed to conceal his movements beneath chairs, tables, stalls, female legs and long dresses. Miss Pitkin, armed with her crook, sallied forth into battle as guardian of the show, and the chase began in earnest.

But when Miss Pitkin left her vigil on the doorway, all those other dogs which had waited so patiently outside saw their opportunity and rushed into the mêlée. There was a lot of barking and snarling, a lot of dog-fighting and a lot of love-making as Aidensfield village hall turned into a canine battlefield.

I heard the commotion and went to investigate, but as I entered I realized the entire show was an utter shambles and several women had been reduced to tears. It looked as if a whirlwind had gusted through the premises, destroying all before it and reducing highly bred dogs to quivering lumps of hairy flesh. And as I strode among the turmoil of dogs, people and village hall furnishings, I saw the distinctive figure of Alfred sneaking at a fast pace towards the tea room. I followed, thinking he was using the opportunity to steal some food.

But I was in time to see him disappear through the open window, albeit with a ham sandwich in his jaws, and I realized how he had breached the security systems of the Aidensfield and District Afghan Hound Owners' Association to wreck their annual show. That was the first and last dog show to be organized by the Association, but some months afterwards a lot of strange-looking pups appeared on the streets. None could really be called handsome or of show quality.

Not surprisingly, there were several Alfred look-alikes among them. Alfred had had his day.

The Afghan/Alfred incident, as it became known, did concentrate the minds of those who wished to show their dogs. The ladies who had insisted on bringing their in-season bitches to the show were constantly reminded of their folly; their social pride had backfired upon them and no one was sorry.

But others began to argue that if in-season bitches were not allowed at the shows, there was no point in having an all-female entry. Male dogs could and should be allowed to compete. This then led to the other associations asking about the logic of having several such clubs, all paying separate fees for the hire of the hall, separate fees for speakers, separate bills for printing posters or the expense of organizing separate association events. If one of the clubs hired an expert to talk about dog hygiene, then the topic would surely be of interest to all the clubs. There were very few topics which were of interest only to owners of specific breeds. The outcome of several informal discussions led everyone to believe that it made financial sense to incorporate all the associations and to have one show for all members' dogs, irrespective of breed or sex. Numbers would be greater, costs would be shared and more opportunities would be created.

This led to a meeting of the committees of all the doggy associations in Aidensfield and the outcome was a decision to scrap all the individual clubs and to form one society as a replacement. While it was appreciated that more of the members would be dog owners whose desire was to breed and show their specimens to the world, it was also pointed out that many village people did own dogs which were not, and never would be, show material. There was a large number of mongrels in Aidensfield, most of whom were loved by their owners and it was felt they should also be allowed to join the society. They might enjoy and benefit from talks by experts; they'd learn from demonstrations about grooming, health and general welfare. Admitting 'ordinary' dog owners did present problems so far as the name of the new organization was concerned but after a great deal of argument it was declared that it should be known as 'The Aidensfield and District Dog Lovers' Society'.

It was felt that this name highlighted the love that existed between man and his so-called best friend and it included anyone who felt that the club would be of benefit to them and their pets. The outcome was a huge surge in membership – lots of country people kept dogs of one kind or another but few had access to expert advice about the training or care of their pets and so the new club became very popular.

One of the most ardent members was Claude Jeremiah Greengrass who felt that the lessons in canine control and behaviour, hygiene, welfare and treatment for illnesses would be of great benefit to his Alfred. As time went on, it became clear that Alfred was a highly intelligent animal, often knowing how to sneak away from the class to steal a piece of sandwich or how never to lie down or sit when instructed. Claude could make him obey, but few others possessed the knack. This was a device taught to their dogs by poachers so that no one could catch them when they were 'working' – indeed, some old poachers taught their dogs to come to heel by the command 'go away', and to leave the area by saying 'here, boy, here'.

Thus if anyone saw a poacher's dog at work and ordered it to 'come here boy', it would immediately run away. The order to 'go away' or 'go home', would result in the dog coming to the heel of its master. It was part of a cunning system to ensure that no poacher's dog was every caught by a gamekeeper, police officer or landowner. By the time of my spell of duty at Aidensfield, this ruse had been discovered and so most poachers had ceased to make use of it. None the less, poachers' dogs were still notoriously difficult to catch.

There was a great deal of interest in the dog training aspect and I was asked if the police-dog handlers would come to show

how their Alsatians were trained. They readily agreed; their skills were appreciated and it was this kind of expert advice that made the new dog lovers' club both popular and successful.

It was inevitable that the club decided to stage its own dog show. This time it would be open to all dogs whether male or female, and whether of pedigree birth or not. There were classes for various breeds, classes for pups, classes for toy dogs, working dogs, sheep dogs and a whole host of others, with the inevitable 'best dog of the show' contest. The organizers, having learned from the Afghan/Alfred fiasco, did make a good job of the arrangements and, most certainly, no bitches would be admitted if they were in season. A state of calm should therefore prevail.

One of the classes was for the 'Best Working Dog' and as I examined the list of entries, I was surprised to see that Claude Jeremiah Greengrass had entered Alfred. There were no classes for lurchers, some purists refusing to recognize them as being a pure breed, and so this class seemed to provide an opportunity for Claude to show off his best friend.

The dogs had to be presented to the judges by no later than noon that Saturday; the dogs would be walked before the judges, examined and adjudicated upon before 2.30 p.m., after which time the public would be admitted. Members of the public would be able to tour the dogs on exhibition and witness further categories, such as the obedience section and the final walking of those dogs that had been placed on the short list for the best of breed, best in category and best in the show.

I decided to pay a visit to the show, purely out of interest. As I walked towards the main door just after the public had been admitted I was surprised to see Claude Jeremiah Greengrass galloping out with a look of absolute distress and misery on his face.

'Claude!' I knew something awful had happened. 'Claude, what's wrong?'

'Wrong? Alfred's been stolen, Mr Rhea. That's what's wrong. Gone, he has. Spirited away. You can't trust anybody these days!'

'You're mistaken,' I said. 'If you left him there to be judged, he'll be with one of the officials, surely?'

'He's not, I've checked. Nobody's seen him, he's been spirited away, that's always a risk with valuable animals. Alfred is a rare dog, you know, Mr Rhea, the only one of his kind in these parts . . .'

I had to check his complaint, and when I entered the hall it was busy with members of the public and proud dog owners. Some exhibitors had rosettes pinned to their cubicles, and others were awaiting the final judging sessions, but when Claude took me to a section marked 'Miscellaneous Working Dogs' there was no sign of Alfred. There was a hook at the back of his stall, and I knew he would have been attached to that by either a chain or a lead.

'He was there, Mr Rhea, he was chained to that hook, sitting as good as gold when I left him, not making a fuss.'

'Was he a winner, did he get on the short list?' I asked.

'No, there's no other lurcher in the show, Mr Rhea, so he's a winner without coming here . . . no, he's been nicked. I asked that chap over there,' and he pointed to one of the stewards, 'but he said he has no idea where Alfred's gone.'

I approached the steward, who couldn't help; he'd come on

duty at two o'clock, and said that Alfred had been absent at that time. I decided I had to make enquiries from the show secretary, for I had no wish to log this as a crime if there was some other explanation. Knowing Alfred, he'd probably sneaked off upon some doubtful enterprise, but it did mean someone must have released him from the securing hook in his stall.

The show secretary, Major Kennedy, was very helpful, checking all his judges' returns until he said, 'Well, Mr Rhea, Alfred was in his allotted position at five minutes to one. That's when Mr Evans, the working dogs judge, assessed him.'

'Did he win?' beamed Claude.

'No, sorry, Mr Greengrass. The record just says – "examined, no award made".'

'Aye, well, I expect yon judge'll be coming back to have another look, mebbe he went off to bring a second opinion feller, Alfred's quality was mebbe that good that no one judge could believe his eyes. So where is he?'

'Well, Mr Evans has gone for his lunch, and I had mine at one o'clock, but must admit I never saw anyone remove your dog.'

It was far from easy making enquiries with Claude Jeremiah always trailing behind me, but by a process of elimination of officials it seemed that no one had seen Alfred leave the hall, either alone or with another person. I did learn, however, that the last person to have seen Alfred in his stall was Philip Crawford, a veterinary surgeon who lived in Aidensfield. He had a practice at Strensford, but often volunteered to help with Aidensfield events – on this occasion he was the show vet.

There was nothing in the secretary's files to show what the

outcome of Crawford's inspection had been but I did detect a certain caution in Major Kennedy's demeanour. I felt sure he was withholding some information, but I failed in my efforts to gain any more from him. The only thing I did learn was that Mr Crawford had gone home for lunch. He was expected to return within half and hour or so. I said I would wait.

'Why would a vet want to see my Alfred?' asked Claude.

'He examines all the dogs in the show,' said Major Kennedy. 'We hire him to ensure that all dogs are fit to be here, his job is to check for illness, injuries, diseases and so forth, anything that might render a dog unsuitable for show purposes.'

Kennedy looked at me with steady eyes, almost as if willing me to remove the troublesome Claude, but Claude hadn't finished.

'Well, there was nowt wrong with my Alfred. Anyroad, I can't hang about here doing nothing,' he grumbled, and I could see the relief in Kennedy's eyes. 'My Alfred's gone and he could be anywhere out here, lying hurt . . .'

'I'm sure he has come to no harm,' said Kennedy reassuringly.

'What about your house?' I suggested. 'Has he returned there? If he slipped his lead, he might have gone home. I know he often goes out alone and always returns to base by himself. He knows his way back to your house, doesn't he?'

'Shall I go and have a look?'

'I think that's a good idea,' I suggested, with the distinct feeling that Kennedy wanted to be rid of Claude.

I was delighted when he said he'd drive his old pick-up to the smallholding to check for signs of Alfred. I said I would remain here to continue my enquiries. With Claude out of the way, Major Kennedy relaxed.

I asked him, 'Is there something I should know, Major Kennedy?'

'Just that Claude's dog hasn't been stolen,' he whispered almost conspiratorially. 'Please keep this incident in low profile, Mr Rhea, we do not want a fuss, especially among the other exhibitors. May I suggest you visit Mr Crawford while Claude is absent? And depending upon what he tells you, may I then ask for the utmost discretion?'

'Yes, of course.' I was puzzled by this attitude and wondered what grave secrets lay with Alfred the lurcher. I decided that if the show secretary did not wish to tell me, then the answer must lie with Philip Crawford. Crawford lived in a large detached house on the outskirts of Aidensfield but within a ten-minute walk, and so I left the hall to visit him. He was just finishing his lunch as I knocked on his door and he invited me to have a coffee with him. I accepted.

'I'm here about the lurcher that was removed from the show,' I began. 'Claude Jeremiah Greengrass's dog.'

'The infamous Alfred,' smiled the vet. 'Yes, he's here in a kennel in my back yard. He's locked in, Mr Rhea.'

'A prisoner? Can I ask why?'

'He's covered with fleas, Mr Rhea, he's a walking flea pit. He should never have been allowed into that hall among the other dogs. So I removed him quietly, led him out of the back door and across the fields to my house. A small sub-committee, convened within a couple of minutes, decided we should not inform the other exhibitors, that the matter should remain secret. If any of them had known about this flea carrier, most of them would have withdrawn their dogs in the fear they'd become infected with the Greengrass flea strain. Some of those owners have spent hours grooming their dogs and some have spend a fortune on shampoos and beauty treatment. It would be awful if they became alarmed about Alfred's fleas. So it was a case of discretion being a better solution than valour. I smuggled him out of the show before anyone knew what had happened. I'm sorry if I caused you extra work, but he's in one of my kennels now, smothered in flea powder.'

'So he stays here until the show is over?'

'Yes, under house arrest, as you might say. I'll release him when the show's over.'

'OK, I agree. I'll get back to the hall and tell Claude we haven't located him yet. It might be best to spread the tale that he appears to have run away – perhaps his discarded lead might lend strength to that tale?'

Crawford smiled, gave me the old leather lead and I returned to the show. And so, to ensure that the show continued without disruption or alarm, I said I had found the lead lying in the long grass near the hall's south-facing wall. When Claude returned, I showed it to him.

'He's escaped, Claude,' I said. 'He's run off. The vet saw him when he examined him, he has to examine all the competitors and he was in the hall at that time.'

'He wasn't at home when I got there. I'll skin him alive if he's been up to summat!' snarled Claude.

And so the Aidensfield and District Dog Show concluded without any alarm; prizes were won, honours were achieved and the general opinion was that it had been a well-conducted and successful event. But as the dogs left with their proud owners, I did notice that several were scratching themselves rather vigorously. I said nothing.

Claude's Alfred would end the day without any fleas, thanks
to a caring vet and a liberal coating of powder, but the legacy of
his show appearance was that several other dogs had been
infected. I knew of no criminal offence with which to threaten
Claude, but I would be careful how I patted Alfred in the future.
Later that night I rang Claude.

'Has your Alfred turned up, Claude?' I asked.

'Aye, he's back, Mr Rhea,' said Claude. 'I don't know where
the hell he's been, but he's covered in powder and smells like a
hospital sick bay.'

6 On With the Dance

Love's but a dance.
Henry Austin Dobson (1840–1921)

One of the more pleasant aspects of working as a rural constable was that there were few real trouble spots on one's patch. Problem places like night-clubs, football grounds and city centre pubs were unknown in villages like Aidensfield, Crampton and Elsinby; fights, mayhem and senseless violence were virtually non-existent. I must admit I was delighted with my work in such a peaceful haven, but we rural bobbies did have compassion for our town-working colleagues. They had to contend nightly with fights and disturbances in the vicinity of such places while we enjoyed a calm and contented way of life.

Even so, trouble could arise in rural areas. The two places most likely to attract it were the village pub and the village hall when dances were in progress. Fortunately, the landlords on my patch all kept their pubs in good order, often quelling trouble before it started, and it was very rare for the police to be called to a disturbance at any rural inn.

When dances were held at the village hall, however, they did seem to attract an unruly element. At one stage, weekly dances were held in Aidensfield village hall, but the ensuing trouble and vandalism quickly brought these dances to an end.

The weekly dances had ended just before my arrival; I recall my predecessor telling of one awful night when all the huge windows of the hall were put out by vandals during a bout of drunken stupidity. But that sort of violence was rare. The usual kind of bother consisted of punch-ups between rival gangs of youths. A gang would arrive from Thirsk with the sole intention of setting about another gang from Malton, with Aidensfield as their battle ground. There was no reason for these fights, other than the fact that the Thirsk lot disliked the Malton lot. And vice versa, of course. So the happiness of the dances was ruined, a sad thing for those who came for a good fun-filled time free from such idiocy.

In comparison with city problems, though, our type of trouble was fairly petty stuff; none the less, the villagers were not prepared to tolerate it. They did not want to suffer fights in the street, vandalism to property in the hall or in the village, discarded beer bottles on the green, cast-off ladies' underwear behind the hedgerows or chip papers dumped in smart gardens. The noises resulting from loud music, revving cars and shouting youngsters were all added nuisances which the people of Aidensfield felt they could do without.

So, after representations from the community, the village hall committee decided it would not allow the premises to be used for weekly dances. Even if the fees did help to pay the bills, it was a chore they could do without.

It was stated though, that the hall could be rented for the annual Hunt Ball and consideration would be given to renting it for specified other dances if the organizers could guarantee good behaviour. In the case of the Hunt Ball, the high price of the tickets kept away the rabble and I never suffered any problems during those events. Similarly, other high-quality organizations rented the hall for their dances, charged high entrance fees or made them all-ticket affairs, and so eliminated bother.

After a period of tranquillity, therefore, the committee saw no reason to deny use of the hall for the annual dance of the Ashfordly, Elsinby and Aidensfield Indoor Plant Society. People who spent their spare time growing plants in greenhouses, conservatories and on kitchen window-sills were hardly the sort to cause public disorder or grievous bodily harm to one another. The committee gave its approval and the dance was arranged for the last Saturday in August. It would run from 8 p.m. to midnight, all dances then having to end before Sunday. There would be a buffet supper and George Ward gained approval from the magistrates to have a bar in the premises until 10.30 p.m. It was an all-ticket dance and knowing the type of person who would be present I did not foresee any problems. Most of them were genteel people of late middle age whose biggest excitement in life was seeing a *Cymbidium devonianum* burst into flower or nursing an ailing *Kalanchoe beharensis* back to life.

When Inspector Pollock met me on the Wednesday afternoon prior to the dance, he said, 'I see from the duty sheets that you have a dance in the village hall on Saturday? Is this likely to cause a threat to the community? Public disorder? Illicit sales of drugs? Mayhem in the street? Knifings? Drunkenness?'

'No, sir,' I said with confidence. 'I expect it to be trouble-free,' and I explained the nature of the event, stressing the peaceful qualities of the organizers and the anticipated revellers.

'I can authorize the dog section to be present,' he said. 'Two dogs, two handlers, one van. They're a very good deterrent. And the Task Force. . .'

'I can cope on my own, sir,' I assured him. 'I've always managed to deal with problems at local dances, and this is no exception. In fact, so far as policing is concerned, this dance will be the easiest I've had to deal with in years. They're plant enthusiasts, sir. Lovely people, I cannot see them causing trouble anywhere, and certainly not in the streets.'

'Well, all I'm saying is that support is available if you need it, PC Rhea. And I shall be on patrol myself, so I might pay you an official visit.'

'I shall be here, sir,' I said.

On the evening of the great event, therefore, I paid an early visit to the hall and found the massive figure of Jim Blake acting as doorman. Jim was a retired railway worker and was the ideal shape and size to act as bouncer. Single-handed and by his physical appearance alone, he'd keep any crowd of yobbos under control. As we chatted, the dancers were beginning to arrive and I was pleased to see several young people among them. They were probably members of the families of the plant enthusiasts, and they all seemed decent and well-behaved. Inside I could hear the music from a six-piece orchestra as they played old-fashioned dances like the Eva three-step, modern waltz, foxtrot, St Bernard's waltz and other old favourites. This would never attract the ruffians who resorted to such dances simply to cause trouble; I was enjoying the music and my feet were tapping to the gentle rhythms.

By nine o'clock that evening, the hall was full and the music was filling the night air outside. Inside there was the happy sound of chatter as the dancers whirled and frolicked to the music. Even the youngsters were joining in, I noted, and when I popped inside to show my uniform at George's bar, there was a good-natured aura within the hall.

'A nice crowd,' I commented to Jim on the door.

'I wish all dances were as peaceful as this,' he smiled. 'I could have got old Mrs Brownlee to act as bouncer for this and I could have gone to the pub!'

'Are there any more to come?' I asked him.

'A few,' he said. 'Some will have gone to the pub before coming here; they always do that, even though there's a bar here. I close the doors at half-past ten; if you want to get in, knock three times and I'll respond. But I'll allow no more entries after then, even if they have tickets.'

'That'll help to keep trouble at bay!' I said, knowing that a late influx of drinkers was always likely to cause problems even if they were not allowed in.

'Not that we need have worried about this lot!' he beamed.

And so the evening passed in peace and happiness; some youngsters did arrive fairly late, having spent the early part of the evening in the pub, but they were not drunk and Jim permitted them to enter. Then, as he'd told me, he closed the doors at 10.30 and I knew he would not tolerate any further admissions. I decided to potter around the village checking the pub in George's absence, deterring would-be car thieves and generally keeping order.

While I was patrolling in the hot August air, I saw Inspector Pollock's car arrive. He parked immediately before the main door and I went to meet him, slinging up a fine salute.

'All correct, sir,' I chanted as he emerged from his car.

'Good, very good, PC Rhea,' he looked around and saw none of the usual signs of dance-hall bother – no crowds of youths hanging about or lurking in the dark, no giggling girls hiding in corners.

'Would you like to go in, sir?' I asked. 'There is a bar, it's being run quietly and with no trouble.'

'Yes, show me your dance hall, PC Rhea, and all these flower power people.'

As we entered, a pair of youngsters rushed out, brushed past us and shouted 'good night' to Jim Blake. One was a pretty young woman with long blonde hair and dangling ear-rings and the other was a tall young man with dark hair; he wore jeans and a multi-coloured shirt with long sleeves. As the youngsters galloped away, Jim smiled. 'They didn't stay long, they were last in and first out! She must have given him a promise. I wish I was young like that,' he said.

Inside all was peace and calm too; we paraded around the edge of the floor, got kissed by some happy young women, were offered cups of coffee but refused because Pollock would not accept gifts, and checked the bar. It was all quiet and lovely.

'A nice evening, PC Rhea, I'm impressed,' he said. 'I wish I could record the same success at other dance halls. Ashfordly and Strensford could learn from this!'

So the evening continued without incident. At half-past ten, George had to close his bar and at midnight the dance ended, the music stopped and people began to drift homewards. I remained until the band had left, the organizers had counted their takings and Jim had closed the doors.

He had checked the premises – the hall was empty with no one lurking in the toilets, back rooms or bar area. He locked the door and said, 'Well, that's the most peaceful dance I've ever been to, Mr Rhea. What a tonic. Good night.'

And I went home too. It was a quarter-past one as I crept upstairs hoping I would not arouse Mary and the children and by half past one I was fast asleep.

At three o'clock, I was roused by the telephone. It was shrilling in my ear. Thick with sleep I lifted the bedside extension and said, 'Aidensfield Police.'

'Mr Rhea? Look, I'm sorry to bother you, but it's our Glenys, she hasn't come home.'

'Glenys?' I must have sounded dopey but it was difficult to switch my brain into gear having been in such a deep and short sleep.

'It's Ruth Basnett . . .'

'Ah, from Elsinby Road,' I knew her husband, Leslie. He was manager of the local Co-op and famed for his collection of rare orchids. He was an authority on the flower and grew them in huge hothouses behind his home.

'Yes, it's our Glenys, she went to the dance and it's unlike her to stay out like this, we're so worried.'

'What time is it?' I muttered.

'Three o'clock,' she said. 'Look, I am sorry, I don't like troubling you, but we're frantic . . .'

'I'll come right away,' I promised her.

I muttered something to Mary about being called out but she just grunted in her sleep, and twenty minutes later I was sitting at the Basnetts' kitchen table with a cup of coffee. I was fully awake by now and clad in my uniform.

'So,' I said, 'Glenys said she was going to the dance; she had a ticket and she arrived late.'

'Yes,' said Leslie. 'We said she could come with us, I'm on the committee and had to be there early, but Glenys said she would be meeting some friends who'd be coming to the dance. She said they'd arranged to meet in the pub and come on to the dance later, when everyone had turned up.'

'And did she come later?'

Ruth Basnett, with tears in her eyes, said, 'Yes, I saw her but only briefly. We were at the back of the hall, we were so busy, Leslie and me, with suppers and things; we should have finished serving at half past nine but were kept going until nearly half past ten. We intended leaving the hall by about ten o'clock, once our work was over, we're not dancers, Leslie and I, but we had to keep working for another hour or so, due to the demand. That's when we saw Glenys, just before half-past ten. But we never spoke to her. I saw her across the room, I was at the doorway of the tearoom and I could see across the hall towards the main door, she was near the entrance to the ladies' toilets, standing there. I wondered if she was looking for us, seeing we hadn't gone home by then.'

'Was she alone at that point?' I asked.

'Yes, there was no one with her.'

'And these friends, who were they? Did they come to the dance?'

'She said they were girls she works with, she's at the clothing factory in Strensford. She goes in every day by train. She told us a gang of them said they'd come to the dance with her as a bit of fun; they borrowed one of their dads' cars, she said. Four girls there were. We had tickets waiting at the door, not paid for I might add!'

'And she told you they were all coming to the dance?'

'Yes, that's what she said.'

This puzzled me because I'd not seen a small crowd of young girls at the dance or in the village that evening. During my rounds I had called at George's pub and could not remember seeing the four young women. If they had been there I was sure I would have noticed. The giggles and chatter of a group of excited young women would not have escaped anyone's notice. I must admit I doubted this part of the tale and wondered if Glenys had been meeting a secret admirer.

'Was there a boyfriend among the pals she was meeting?'

'No, she never mentioned one. She hasn't a steady boyfriend, I don't think, not to go out with alone. They go out in groups these days.'

'And what was she wearing? Can you give me a detailed description?'

In my notebook, I began to write down that Glenys was eighteen years old, about five feet five inches tall and of fairly slim build with long fair hair worn loose. She had a fresh complexion and narrow features and was wearing a pair of large, dangling ear-rings in the form of sea shells. She was dressed in a white blouse, a dark blue short skirt and black stockings with black low-heeled shoes. She had a navy blue handbag but, due to the warm evening, had not taken a coat. As the Basnetts gave me these details, I realized they were describing the girl who'd rushed past me and Jim Blake.

She was the girl who had arrived last at the dance and the one who had left first. Both Jim Blake and I had seen her. But she had been accompanied by a young man, *not* by a group of girls from work. So she *was* keeping secrets from mum and dad!

And if she was with him, I doubted if she would be in any mortal danger. Lustful risks might feature in tonight's adventure, but I did not think she was at risk of death or injury. I wondered if I should mention my own sighting of her and the boy. But for some reason which I shall never know I did not. I did not wish to betray this young woman's personal secrets if she felt it unwise to reveal them.

'I'll circulate this to our patrols,' I assured the distraught parents. 'We won't make too much of a fuss, though, because she is over eighteen and not classed as a juvenile for our purposes. There is nothing to suggest her life is at risk.'

'If she'd gone off with friends, I'm sure she would have told us . . . we were at the dance almost till the end, she knew where we were.'

She might have gone for a ride in her friends' car,' I suggested. 'It might have broken down . . . I'm afraid this sort of thing is all part and parcel of having teenagers in the house!'

'It's so unlike her though, Mr Rhea, we don't object to her having boyfriends, or going out, we're broadminded in such things, but she had never been as late as this . . .'

In cases of this kind, where adults disappear without reason, we rarely take actions simply because they are entitled to go where they want and with whom they want. At that time, the mid nineteen-sixties, a person was not classed as an adult until reaching twenty-one years of age. Glenys was over seventeen and not therefore classified as a child or young person, so she fell between two areas of concern – she wasn't really a missing adult, nor was she a missing child or young person. In spite of the general rules about adults who leave home, so far as young women are concerned there is always an element of risk if they disappear without reason, so I decided I would circulate details of Glenys Basnett.

It was just possible that some of our patrols might have come across an accident or a broken-down vehicle in which she was involved. Before I left the Basnetts' house, though, I asked if her parents knew the names of any of her friends from the clothing factory.

They did not, nor could they describe the car the girls were supposed to have used to drive to Aidensfield. I next rang the hospital and the control room at Strensford police station, but there had been no reports of accidents. Glenys had vanished in mysterious circumstances, so it seemed, and I knew she had been accompanied by a young man, so I assured them I would do all in my power to trace their missing daughter.

I left them huddled over the kitchen table and first did a search of the village, checking parked cars, quiet corners and all the places I knew were used by courting couples, but there was no sign of Glenys. As I made my search I tried to recall more about the youth who'd rushed out of the dance hall with her. It had been in the dark, albeit with the lights of the hall to help a little, and although I felt I'd seen him in the village from time to time, I could not name him.

Back in my office I rang Strensford police station and asked the duty constable to issue a description of the missing girl; I knew this would be circulated among the night patrols of the locality but there was little else I could do. I spent half-an-hour or so completing my notebook and crept upstairs for a few hours' sleep. It was then 4.30 a.m.

The children woke me at 7.30 next morning and as I struggled out of bed my first thought was to ring the Basnetts; but first I rang Strensford police station to see if Glenys had turned up. She hadn't. Next, I rang the Basnetts.

Sounding physically exhausted, Leslie said that Glenys had not come home nor had there been any message. He had searched the village himself and had toured the area in his own car, but had found no trace of her. He said he was at his wits' end and I responded by saying we, the police, would continue our search today.

Then, just before nine o'clock, I received a telephone call from a man called Burton. I knew from the pips and the sound of money dropping into the box that he was ringing from a kiosk.

'Is that t'police?' the strong Yorkshire voice said.

'Yes, Aidenfield Police, PC Rhea speaking,' I responded.

'There somebody fast in one of them garages down near t'old folks' bungalows,' he said.

'Trapped you mean,' I asked.

'Aye, locked in. I can hear 'em shouting but can't open t'door, it's locked.'

'Whose is the garage?' I put to him.

'Nobody's, it's a council garage, goes with t'old folks' bungalows, but nobody's got it let. It's been empty for months. Number 5 it is.'

'So where will the key be?'

'Council offices at Strensford I should think,' he said. 'Now, I've got to be off, thought I'd better let you know, they're shouting and bellowing from inside, a man and a woman by t'sound of things.'

And the phone went dead, the money having run out. Without wasting any time, I drove down to the little council estate of old folks' bungalows and stopped outside garage No. 5. Sure enough, the sound of my approach set off a barrage of shouting from inside, so I tapped on the door and said, 'It's PC Rhea. Who's that?'

A man's voice said, 'Neil Hanby, Mr Rhea, and Glenys Basnett. Can you get us out?'

'Have you a key in there?' I asked.

'No.'

'I'll have to contact the council offices,' I called back. 'It might take a while . . .'

'So long as somebody knows we're here,' he said. 'Can you let our parents know? Mine are at Elsinby, Fleetham House.'

'You're not hurt, are you? I asked. 'Do you need a doctor, ambulance?'

'No, just a toilet!' simpered a girl's voice. 'I'm frozen . . .'

'OK, leave it with me,' I assured them. 'We'll soon have you out.'

From my office I rang the council offices at Strensford and after spending twenty minutes finding the right person to answer my question, did learn that a key to No 5 garage was kept there. Next I rang the Basnetts with the good news and then the Hanbys at Elsinby; the Hanbys weren't too worried about their son as he often stayed away from home at night.

I then had to drive into town to collect the key, a return journey of about forty minutes. When I returned to the garage I found the Basnetts waiting outside, holding a conversation with their daughter through the metal door. It was an up-and-over door with a handle in the centre. The centre of the handle accepted the key, rather like the door handle of a motor car, and it was the work of a moment to free the lock and raise the door. Inside, the young couple were momentarily dazzled by the light, because this garage, midway along a block of ten and built of breeze blocks, had no windows.

Then Leslie Basnett realized who the youth was.

'You!' he snarled in a most uncharacteristic way. 'It's you . . . you bastard . . .'

And he launched himself at the young fellow. Ruth Basnett screamed, Glenys cried that she wanted the toilet and I found myself trying to separate the warring duo. In the ensuing mêlée they fell to the ground with the two women and me doing our best to separate them, but Leslie Basnett's arms and fists were flailing like windmill sails while Neil tried to defend himself against the onslaught.

Between us we managed to separate the pair, with me holding the two contestants at arm's length, shouting at both to cease their warring. At last they did calm down and I relaxed my grip on their collars.

'Les,' I said quietly. 'Glenys is not harmed, she's just a bit tired and needs a wash and a good sleep . . .'

'It's not that!' snarled Basnett. 'That bastard ruined my orchids . . . last year . . . he knows, he daren't show his face near me and yet he dares to court my daughter . . .'

'Dad, it was an accident, Neil didn't mean to . . .'

'Shut up, all of you!' Ruth entered the fray. 'You're all behaving stupidly. Now just stop it, all of you. Leslie, Glenys needs to get home . . . I'm going home with her. PC Rhea, you are welcome to come and have a coffee with us while this escapade is explained, and you, Neil . . .'

The young man, his hair awry, his face looking pale and anxious, looked at the formidable lady.

'Yes, Mrs Basnett?'

'I think you'd better join us. Leslie, let old bygones be bygones, you've got some far better orchids now, prize-winners of a quality that's far better than last year . . . so come along, let's all go home and forget about this.'

And so we all went back to the Basnetts' house.

After Glenys had been to the loo we all settled around the kitchen table with Leslie still glaring at Neil; there was deep animosity in that glance.

'So,' I said. 'I need some explanations. Glenys, you first.'

'I wanted to go to the dance with Neil, but I knew dad would never let me go with him, not after that business with the orchids . . .'

'You're dead right!' snapped Leslie.

'Be quiet!' his wife demanded. 'Let Glenys say her piece!'

'Well, we went to the pub for a drink, intending to go to the dance when mum and dad had gone home. We thought they were going to leave early, but when we got inside they were still there so we decided to go back outside, to be alone.'

'I didn't want to face Mr Basnett, not after the carry-on with the orchids,' said Neil, blushing. 'So we went outside and just walked around, then we saw the empty garage. It was spotting with rain, so we went inside. The door was open, there was nothing inside and we thought it would be a nice shelter for a few minutes, and then I pulled the door down . . . I didn't intend closing it but it suddenly crashed shut. And you can't open those doors from the inside, so we were locked in . . . we shouted and shouted, but no one heard us, so we had to stay there all night till that man heard us this morning. He couldn't open it, it had locked itself, like a Yale. It was awful, believe me, dark, nowhere to sit, cold . . .'

'All right,' I said. 'Accidents will happen. I can record you as found safe and sound. But Mr Basnett, assaulting a young man like you did means you could be prosecuted for assault or breach of the peace. That's if Neil wishes to press charges.'

'No,' said the youngster. 'I can understand how Mr Basnett felt about those orchids. It was my fault, I deserved it. I just wish I could make amends somehow.'

'Look, I have no idea what happened about the orchids,' I grumbled. 'So can somebody enlighten me?'

I noticed the beginnings of a smile on Basnett's face. 'I suppose I did over-react,' he admitted. 'But you know I'm a fanatic, a really keen orchid grower?'

'I know you are highly regarded hereabouts as an expert on orchids,' I said.

'Well, the glass got broken in one of the frames of my large hothouse, that one behind the house. I called in a local glazier to refit some glass . . .'

'Me,' said Neil. 'My dad's a plumber, we do glazing as well.'

'So this young man came to fix the glass,' sighed Basnett. 'I had to go to work, so I explained exactly what had to be done to maintain both humidity and temperature, but when I got home, he'd left all the doors open. It was a cold, frosty day and I lost hundreds of valuable plants . . .'

'No, you didn't!' snapped Ruth. 'Most of them recovered,

you lost a few, those nearest the door; some failed to flower afterwards, but it wasn't a catastrophe, not by any means.'

'But my orchids did suffer . . .'

'He rang my dad up and threatened to do all sort of unmentionable things to me if I showed my face in his hothouses again,' grimaced Neil. 'So you can imagine my reaction when I turned up at the dance with Glenys and saw Mr Basnett was there . . . I just turned tail and got out as fast as I could . . .'

'And I thought flower growers were a peaceful lot!' I said. 'So, Neil, shall we prosecute Mr Basnett for assaulting you? I need your consent before I can proceed . . .'

'No, 'course not,' smiled the youth. 'I was careless. I'm sorry, Mr Basnett. I deserved it, not for keeping Glenys out late but for being careless with your hothouse doors. I never said sorry before, but I do now. I was too scared to ring you or call before . . .'

'How about shaking hands?' I said to them both. After a moment of hesitation, they did. Mrs Barnett hugged her daughter and I could see there was going to be a few moments of emotion, so I decided to leave. From my office I rang Strensford police station to report the safe return of Glenys Basnett and asked for her name to be crossed off the list of missing persons.

Any father will worry when his daughter first attends a dance, whether it is a school dance or one in town where young people congregate. As a policeman and father of three daughters, I could easily understand this concern.

Certainly, a lot of the trouble outside dance halls was due to youths fighting for the favours of a girl but I was still fairly surprised to receive a visit from Robin Mallaby, a newsagent from Ashfordly. He found me in my minivan, patrolling Aidensfield one Friday afternoon, and he hailed me.

'Mr Rhea,' he called after he flagged me down. 'Can you spare a moment?'

'Yes, of course.'

'I'm glad I caught you. You know there's a Young Farmers' dance in your village hall tomorrow?' he said. 'You'll be on duty?'

'Yes, Robin, I'll be there. Why? Are you anticipating a problem?'

'Well, no, not really. But you know my daughter? Charlotte? She works in the shop sometimes, delivers evening papers around Ashfordly.'

'I've seen her, yes,' I agreed. 'A good-looking girl.'

'Yes, well, that's the problem,' he muttered. 'Look, I'm not quite sure how to say this, or I might be over-reacting, but can you keep an eye on her at that dance?'

'An eye on her? Is she in trouble?'

'No, but, well, it's her first dance, Mr Rhea. She's only sixteen, we don't want to stop her enjoying herself, and we can't really go, can we? Not to a dance for youngsters, so if you're on duty, I wondered if you'd just keep an eye on her.'

'Well, I can make sure she comes to no harm, but you can't expect me to forbid her going out with a boy, Robin, that's hardly my job!'

'No, but, well, just pretend you're keeping a fatherly eye on her, make sure she's safe, that none of those ruffians get their hands on her.'

'Well, I'll do what I can if it'll make you happier, Robin.'

'Thanks, that's put my mind at rest . . . I do worry about her, you know . . .'

'You're remembering what you did to girls when you were sixteen! That's your problem!' I laughed.

'I know, that's what makes it so bloody hard to let her go, but I know I can't stop her and I wouldn't want to stop her, but it doesn't stop me fretting about her. Damn it, she's just a child.'

'I'll be there, Robin, you sit at home and relax.'

'Aye, well, there won't be much relaxing, not till she's back home and in bed.'

'How's she getting to Aidensfield?' I asked.

'Her cousin's got a car, he's called Maurice, lad of eighteen. He's in the Young Farmers' club and he's taking his own girlfriend, her brother and our Charlotte.'

'I know the lad. OK, Robin, for you I'll keep an eye on her, at a discreet distance, of course!'

And so I found myself agreeing to watch over and protect the sixteen-year-old daughter of a local newsagent. I knew I could never give her my entire protection that evening for I had other duties to perform, but I would keep an eye on the girl, just as I would keep an eye on other vulnerable youngsters that evening. I knew Charlotte by sight and noticed her arrival; she was accompanied by her cousin and his companions. They did not go down to the pub as many others had done, but went straight into the village hall where music was playing. There was a bar in the hall, I knew; it was run by George Ward from the Aidensfield Arms so I knew there would be no bother. At such dances there was often the risk of under-age drinkers being served, thus causing problems later, so I would pop in from time to time to allow the sight of my uniform to act as a warning.

But, like the Ashfordly, Elsinby and Aidensfield Indoor Plant Society's annual dance, this function was completed with the minimum of fuss. I saw Charlotte's burly cousin, Maurice, dancing with his girlfriend, Jill, and her brother Clive had also found a partner whom I did not know. I got the impression he'd come to meet her here because Charlotte did not get many dances. One or two lads twirled her around the floor, but afterwards she sat with Maurice and his party.

Outside the hall, I had to warn one or two merry youngsters about their foul language. I warned some about using the outside of the hall as a public toilet and had to remind others that driving when under the influence of drink could land them in the cells with a court appearance to follow. It was all routine stuff and could not really be classed as a major headache. And then, at quarter to midnight, the dance ended and the cheerful dancers began to leave the premises. I watched them from the comfort of my minivan.

I had parked it in a strategic position, with its lights glowing, so that I could observe a wide area; if there was going to be any real trouble it would occur as the merrymakers were leaving the dance. From the security of my van I could see most of them and, in the event of a real problem, my radio was immediately available.

As the crowds filtered away without any cause for concern, I noticed Charlotte Mallaby. I could see her in the dim glow from a distant street lamp; she was alone and she was standing near Maurice's car, clearly awaiting his return. But the car was locked and she could not get in; I saw her standing somewhat forlornly as the happy crowd evaporated, some arm-in-arm with their new-found friends, others kissing one another and some departing in happy groups.

I decided to wander across and talk to her; in reality, I wanted to make sure she came to no harm. She did look vulnerable and lonely and I found myself recalling her father's concern.

I left my van without bothering to put on my uniform cap – we did not wear caps when in those minivans because the roofs were too low – to wear one's cap in such a tiny vehicle would mean we'd be sitting like hunchbacks! I wandered across to her in the gloom and as I drew near she turned and saw me. I saw a fleeting smile cross her face. She had someone to talk to, even if it was just a policeman. She knew me by sight, for I was a fairly regular visitor to her father's shop, so I asked how she had enjoyed the dance. She began to say she hadn't really enjoyed it.

She'd had no one to dance with and her friends all had other friends to talk to. She'd felt a bit lonely, she said, and then, as I chatted to her, leaning on the car roof with my elbow, I heard a footfall behind me – someone had crept around the rear of the car and was now approaching. My hair stood on end, a warning of some impending crisis and I whirled around in time to see a massive fist heading for my face. Instinctively I ducked; moving quickly in the manner taught me by our unarmed combat instructor, I seized the outstretched arm, twisted it and succeeded in bringing it high and powerfully up the back of the oncoming assailant. In seconds, I had him on his knees, crying in pain.

'Maurice!' cried Charlotte. 'What on earth do you think you're doing? This is PC Rhea!'

'The policeman?' the big man whispered. 'Oh, God, I'm sorry, Mr Rhea . . . I thought it was . . .'

I hauled him to his feet and released him; he rubbed his arm as I said, 'You thought it was who?'

'I thought it was somebody annoying Charlotte,' he said meekly.

'Well, even if it was, you don't rush in with all guns blazing before finding out for certain!' I said. 'With a pile-driving fist like yours, you could have felled me – or whoever else it was aimed at.'

Charlotte said, 'Maurice, why? Why won't you let me talk to people? You refused to let me dance with whom I wanted and now this . . .'

'Your dad asked me to keep an eye on you,' he told her. 'I was responsible for you! I thought it was somebody pestering you . . . I just went over to chat to Alan Cooper about a cattle deal and came back to see you with a man . . . I had no idea it was you, Mr Rhea, without your cap . . . in the dark . . . look, I'm sorry . . .'

'Why does dad worry about me so much?' Charlotte cried. 'He's ruined my night out, he's told everybody to keep an eye on me. Everybody! Even the bloody bandsmen were keeping an eye on me! Now, leave me alone, Maurice, take me home. I'm never coming to a dance with you again!'

I daren't tell the poor girl that I had also been keeping an eye on her and that my reason for speaking to her was not one of mere friendship. It was because her father had asked me to watch her.

Maybe all the men at the dance had been watching one another, with requests to report back to her father? No wonder the poor girl had been so alone at her first dance.

'Mr Rhea, I want to apologize,' said Maurice.

'Accepted,' I said. 'Forget it, I'll take no action – this time! But if you go around punching people who chat to your cousin, you're going to finish up in court, or on your back in some gutter with your nose out of joint.'

'Thanks, I'll be careful.'

'And make sure Charlotte enjoys her dance next time, leave her alone,' I said. 'She's grown up now, she can dance with who she wants to, in spite of what her dad says!'

'Thanks, Mr Rhea,' said Charlotte, getting into the car as Maurice unlocked the doors.

'Don't let this put you off going to dances,' I said to her. 'It's just that everyone loves you so much. They don't want to see you come to any harm.'

'I'll try to remember that,' she said sinking into the rear seat.

And she did go to more dances. Six weeks later I was on duty at the Ashfordly Football Supporters' Club dance and saw Charlotte was there. And she was having a marvellous time. But as I patrolled my lonely beat outside the dance hall I did see her father lurking in the shadows near the Town Hall. Clearly the fellow had some kind of complex about his daughter so I went across to reassure him.

'She'll be safe, Robin, leave her alone, she'll not come to any harm.'

'Somebody attacked my sister at a dance like this, Mr Rhea, years ago when she was sixteen. I can't get it out of my mind. I don't want the same thing to happen to Charlotte.'

'You've not told Charlotte about that, have you?'

'No,' he said.

'Then don't,' I asked him. 'Let her grow up and be happy,'

'It's tough,' he said. 'So bloody tough.'

'I know,' I patted him on the shoulder. 'But youngsters are tough as well. She'll respect you for your love, but don't smother her.'

'Aye, you're right,' and he turned to walk away towards his shop with the house above the premises. As the dance drew to an end I saw Charlotte walking along the street with a tall and handsome young man.

She did not see me watching from the shadows.

7 If You Go Down to the Woods Today

Up he starts, discover'd and surpris'd.
John Milton (1608–1674)

When I was a small child I believed that if I went down to the woods I would be in for a big surprise. It was all connected with a popular song about some teddy bears having a picnic in the woods. Perhaps because of that yearning for a big surprise, I spent a lot of time in the woods looking for teddy bears having picnics. I never found any.

There were, however, several fascinating woods around my childhood village even if I failed to experience that big surprise. They contained lots of small surprises and pleasures such as enabling me to discover otter cubs at play, to find caves, lakes and cliffs, to explore an old ruined millhouse, to watch salmon and trout swimming against the strong current of the river, to climb trees and peer into wood pigeons' nests, to listen to woodpeckers, to scramble up cliffs and poke my hands into the nests of jackdaws and to touch the eggs as the female sat on them, to walk nine times around the wishing stone and then wonder why none of my wishes came true. In those magical days, I carried a pocket book of British birds and learned to identify those I saw; in spite of my nesting exploits I never took or destroyed any birds' eggs.

Another secret I kept was the location of the holt of the otters whose cubs I watched. I knew that otters were hunted along that salmon river because they did kill these splendid fish, but even as a child, I felt I wanted to protect all forms of wildlife. I was fortunate to grow up in such a wonderful place and I suppose some would say my childhood was idyllic. For me, though, it was normal. I thought all children had such a splendid and wide-ranging playground because, in addition to those woods and rivers, I had the open moors on my doorstep with expansive views, rugged terrain and untold freedom to explore. I spent hours in those woods and upon those moors.

It was those superb woods which contained my own secret place and yet, throughout my childhood, I never did experience that magical *big* surprise. Maybe all my experiences were big surprises? How was I to know? As I matured into my teens and then my twenties, however, I must admit that those expectations began to evaporate. By the time I went walking in the woods as an adult, I had forgotten about big surprises.

But as a young policeman with new stretches of woodland on my beat at Aidensfield I did in fact experience a curious surprise – so, after the passage of all those years, that long-held childhood wish did come true.

It happened one day as I was patrolling through Low Hollins Wood which bordered the river between Aidensfield and Thackerston. It was a wonderful place, rich with a variety of deciduous trees and riddled with interesting footpaths.

I had never walked the length of this wood, either on duty or off, and on this breezy July day I found myself with a couple of hours to spare. I was on duty and decided to acquaint myself with the geography of the woodland and its maze of paths just in case I ever had to search it for any reason. I considered that a detailed knowledge of its terrain should be gained as part of my local knowledge; it was in my professional interest to know every inch of my beat, I told myself.

Off I went, therefore, in full uniform, to explore the main footpath. The wood was noisy with birdsong and the movement of animals in the undergrowth; I could hear the sound of tiny creatures like shrews and wood mice, I caught sight of a fox lurking behind some rhododendrons and knew that badgers had a safe haven nearby. I watched a green woodpecker hammering on a dead tree in search of grubs and spotted two jays, the most shy of birds, flitting among a small group of conifers. Wood warblers and willow warblers, blackbirds, spotted flycatchers, tree-creepers, wood pigeons, pheasants, a kestrel – those and more were in that wood, some sounding their alarm calls at my intrusion into their territory and others almost ignoring my presence. It was rather like a re-run of some of my childhood joys.

But then I saw a very strange but handsome bird. I caught a mere glimpse of it but in that fleeting moment gained the impression that it was about the size of a pheasant with a long, feathery tail and dark bottle-green plumage. It flew across the path ahead of me and its flight appeared to be clumsy, rather like that of a pheasant. Pheasants are not the most agile of birds when in the air and this bird appeared to be similarly cumbersome. None the less, it did clear the shrubs ahead of me before it vanished into the undergrowth.

I was baffled. It was not like any British bird that I knew. I realized that exotic birds did escape from captivity from time to time, and some people in the district did breed ornamental pheasants. I wondered if this was one that had escaped. I could have been wrong, of course, for I had gained but a very fleeting glimpse of the bird, so I was unsure what it was. But the sighting did arouse my interest and I concentrated upon trying to see it again.

I decided I would follow the direction the curious bird had taken, so I diverted from the main footpath and followed a far less well defined one. I must have walked for about a quarter of a mile when another strange-looking bird bolted from the undergrowth, half flew and half scrambled through a patch of briars and then disappeared with a cackling noise. It was more of a russet colour and did not look like the first one, although there were similarities, the chief one being the clumsy attempt at flight. Now I was very interested in these odd birds. I racked my brains in an effort to identify them, but failed to produce a name. I wished I'd had my bird book!

Without going into too much detail about the experiences which followed, it is fair to say that during the next hour I came across about a dozen strange birds, none of which was like any other except that all had the same clumsy method of flying. Their colours were varied – I saw one which was pure white and very heavy, another with greys and yellows dominating, a grey one and a tiny, cheeky looking thing with green plumage below and reddish-brown above. From time to time I noticed one which seemed similar to earlier sightings and could not decide whether I had seen the same bird twice, or whether this was another. As I had sighted the creatures some distance from my first experience, I guessed that, for each colourful bird, there were several examples in this wood.

As I found more of these odd birds during that ramble through the deep quiet part of this wood, I thought they looked like cockerels or even fighting cocks. To my knowledge, however, the awful and highly illegal sport of cockfighting was not practised in this area, although rumours of its existence in some parts of rural Yorkshire did persist. But no breeder of fighting cocks would risk rearing his valuable birds in the wild like this.

If these were all cock birds, though, where were the hens? How were they breeding? I felt sure there were no hens around and was equally unsure whether these were some exotic breed or several exotic breeds which had reverted to the wild.

Another factor to consider was whether new species of wild birds had come to this country since my knowledgeable childhood days. I knew that this did happen – birds moved around the world in quite an astonishing way and exotic or rare species did sometimes find their way to Britain.

Whatever they were, these birds were very shy and they were not domesticated; they concealed themselves from view and flew away at the slightest hint of danger, just like any other wild bird, so I never achieved a really good view of any one of them. All my sightings were brief, too brief to really secure a proper description, but as I explored that part of Low Hollins Wood I began to realize there was a colony of these strange birds, with many different types living here. I had not counted the numbers of different varieties I'd seen, but guessed it was about a dozen, in some cases with two or more examples of the same bird.

Baffled, I decided it was time to return to the village. I had not reached the far end of the footpath but my short period of exploration had come to an end because time had run out. As I

walked back my mind was ranging across the varieties of large
game birds such as pheasant, capercaillie, partridge or even the
tiny quail, but none fitted the description of my sightings. I was
convinced they looked very much like farmyard cockerels but
their colours were far more exquisite and, of course, they were
wild birds.

As I entered Aidensfield luck was on my side because,
emerging from the post office, was the familiar figure of Albert
Firth, chairman of the Ryedale Hen Watching Society. In his
late seventies, Albert was a mine of information about domestic
poultry and had been chairman of the society for more than fifty
years. The ancient and highly active group of experts held
regular meetings about all aspects of domestic poultry, listening
to lectures about their history, breeding, care, behaviour and
lore. Society members kept observations upon hens in the
domestic situation, keeping detailed records of their behavioural
traits, language, nesting habits and the effect of the moon and
the wind upon egg-laying. In addition, the society discussed
difficult problems such as whether eggs with brown shells are
more nutritious than those with white ones, why hens always
take two steps backwards after scratching for grubs, whether
mood music affects egg-laying, whether the feathers of a
cockerel's tail make good flies for fishermen and a whole range
of similar topics. One of the problems which caused immense
discussion was why hens run across the road when a car is
approaching. No one has yet found a satisfactory answer and it
is the theory of the society that not even hens know why they
cross the road.

'Now then, Mr Rhea,' said the ruddy-faced Albert when he
saw me approaching.

'Now then, Albert,' I returned the traditional greeting. 'Not a bad day for the time of year.'

'It could be better and it could be worse,' he nodded gravely.

'It could indeed,' I agreed with him. 'But we've got to take what we've got, we can't change it. There's always something different happening with our weather.'

'Aye,' he nodded, 'And there's allus a lot of weather about at this time of year.'

'True,' I muttered. 'Well, Albert, I'm really pleased I caught you. I need the benefit of your expertise on hens. I've come across some very strange birds down Low Hollins Wood,' and I explained what I had just seen, adding that they did look very like unusual types of cockerels.

'They're not hoopoes or rollers, are they?' he suggested.

'No,' I said firmly. 'I know what they look like.'

'Ornamental pheasants? Lady Amherst's pheasants? Silver pheasants?'

'Nope,' I shook my head. 'They don't have the long tails of pheasants.'

'Well, that caps hen racing,' he said.

'Could they be fighting cocks gone wild?' I suggested.

'Not in all them colours you mentioned.' he shook his old head. 'And you say there were no hens?'

'They didn't look like hens to me,' I said, adding, 'But I'm no expert, Albert. They might have been hen birds of some species I've never come across.'

'Well, if there's no hens, they'll not be breeding, will they?'

'That's true,' I admitted.

'Nor laying eggs,' he added.

'True,' I agreed.

'Nor nesting.'

'No,' I had to admit.

'That's a rum 'un, if they're not nesting either,' he was thinking seriously now. 'Now, that is a fair capper, Mr Rhea. I'd better get myself down there for a look.'

I gave him directions to the spot where I'd seen most of the birds and he said he would take a walk down there this afternoon. I left him to go about his business and I continued my patrol, now engaging myself on more conventional police work. I had an appointment to interview a witness to a road accident which had occurred in Middlesbrough a week earlier and therefore made my way to the witness's house.

It would be a week later when I next saw Albert and he hailed me with a huge wave of his hand. I halted my van and climbed out.

'Now then, Mr Rhea,' he said.

'Now then, Albert,' I returned.

'Not a bad day for the time of year,' he smiled. 'And I shouldn't be surprised if it rains before night.'

'It'll do a bit of good,' I said. 'We need a bit of rain, things are very dry.'

'Aye, you're right. Well, what I stopped you for was this. I went down Low Hollins Wood and saw them birds.'

'Oh, good. So what's your opinion?' I put to him.

'Cock birds,' he said. 'They're all cock birds, different breeds, all living wild down there.'

'You mean ordinary domestic cockerels?' I was surprised.

'Not ordinary ones, Mr Rhea. Decorative ones. Did you know there's more than seventy species of domestic hen? And as many species of cock birds? All descended from *gallus*

gallus, that's the red jungle fowl that still lives wild in some parts of Asia.'

'No, I never knew that,' I had to admit.

'Well, that's summat you've learned. Now them birds down Low Hollins Wood, they're all species of cock birds, different ones, all living wild.'

'Don't they fight for territory?' I sought expert advice on this.

'I wouldn't be surprised if there was a bit of jockeying for position,' he said. 'Boss bird an' all that. Anyroad, that's what they are. Cock birds living wild. Probably with their own bit of woodland as territory, but all staying in one spot or near enough to one spot.'

'But Albert, this raises more questions. How did they get there? If they're all cockerels, how are they sustaining their numbers?'

'You've got me now, Mr Rhea,' and he shook his head.

'So you don't think it's got anything to do with any of your members?' I suggested.

'Nay, lad, I would think not. Our folks would never turn good cocks into t'wild like yon.'

'So where could they have come from?'

'Now that's a right capper. I couldn't rightly say, but I'll tell you what. Next time our society has a meeting, I'll see if anybody knows owt about them birds. But you'd think we would know, being the only Hen Watching Society hereabouts.'

'Exactly my sentiments, Albert.'

'Aye, well, it's summat for t'society to get their teeth into, it'll stop 'em arguing about whether free range eggs is better than them from battery hens, or whether hens can see t'colours of traffic lights. Now that happened because awd Mrs Rymer from Rigg Top Farm reckoned her hens would never cross t'road when t'red light was showing on some road works up yonder. Makes you think, that sort o' thing, Mr Rhea.'

'It does indeed, Albert. There's something I've always wondered as well. That's whether hens can recognize their own names. When I was a child, we had pet hens, you see, one called Clara Cluck, another was Bunty Chops and another was Biffy. When we took their food out and called their names, they all came running. I often wonder what would have happened if we'd only shouted for Clara Cluck.'

'By gum, Mr Rhea, that's a puzzler, it's summat else we can discuss. Can hens recognize their own names? That'll keep our members going for weeks and I reckon some'll want to run tests with their own stock. Thanks, it's a good subject.'

'Well, thanks for your help, Albert,' I said. 'It would be nice if we knew why those birds were living there, so I'll make my own enquiries too. I'll let you know if I discover anything.'

'Aye, right you are, Mr Rhea. Now while I've got you here there's a matter to settle about them cocks in yon wood. You're not interested in them from an official police point of view, are you? I mean, have they been stolen from somewhere? Are they t'proceeds of crime, is that why you're interested? Keeping 'em under observations in case t'thief comes back for 'em, perhaps?'

'To my knowledge, Albert, they are not the subjects of any crime. We've had no reports of any stolen cockerels, I think we would have known if exotic or rare ones had been stolen. I just happened to come across them the other week and was curious about them, that's all. It's a personal puzzle.'

'Well, it's just that there's a lot of good blood stock going to waste down there and some of our members' hens might enjoy meeting them lads. I did wonder what the position would be if we rounded 'em up and brought 'em into domestic use.'

'I can't see anything wrong with that,' I said. 'They're not a protected species of wild bird, and they don't have an owner, so it appears. So I can't see why you shouldn't try and capture them, although they're a bit cunning, I reckon.'

'Not as cunning as some of our chaps, though,' he grinned. 'In fact, one of our members is just the fellow to round them up for us. He's an expert in that sort of thing.'

'Who's that?' I asked.

'Claude Jeremiah Greengrass,' he said. 'He keeps hens, you know, and is very knowledgeable. It was him who reckoned his hens prefer brown bread to white bread, and he reckons if you feed 'em with brown bread, it makes 'em lay brown eggs while white bread produces white eggs.'

'I've never heard that before,' I told him, adding, 'But a lot of hens never eat bread at all, do they?'

'Nay, you've got a point there, Mr Rhea,' smiled Albert. 'Well, I'd better be getting along. You've given me a lot to think about, a lot for the Ryedale Hen Watching Society to discuss and test. They might even make you a member, Mr Rhea. How about that?'

'I should be very honoured, Albert,' I said. 'But I don't keep any hens now.'

'You don't have to keep hens to qualify, Mr Rhea, you've just got to be interested. We're a Hen Watching society, not Hen Keeping society. You've just got to study and watch 'em and I reckon you'll see a lot of hens when you're on duty.'

'Well, we do see a lot which are injured, Albert. In road

accidents, generally. Did you know that a hen is not classed as an animal for road accident purposes?'

'Nay, I never knew that!'

'Well, it means we have no statistics about hen casualties on the roads, so the society might be able to campaign for hens to be classified as animals, like dogs, goats, cattle, horses, asses, mules, pigs and sheep.'

'Not cats?' he asked.

'Not cats or hens,' I said. 'Nor even ducks, geese, turkeys or peacocks for that matter.'

'By gum, you learn summat every day! You would be a very useful chap to have on our committee, Mr Rhea. Knowing the law like you do. Now, talking about the law, if you see Claude Jeremiah Greengrass chasing hens in yon wood, you won't arrest him for poaching, will you?'

'Not if he gets permission to take them. He'll have to inform the owner of the wood. It's part of Elsinby estate, isn't it?'

'Aye, right, good thinking, Mr Rhea.'

'If he gets permission from the landowner, it means he's not trespassing, Albert, and if he's not trespassing, it means he can't be prosecuted for trespassing in pursuit of game, just in case some bright spark thinks those cockerels are game birds. Maybe a note from the chairman of your society authorizing him to round them up might be a good idea?'

'By gum, that's me, that's another bright idea!' beamed Albert and so he trotted off to organize the great cockerel round-up.

I thought I had better have words about this charade with the gamekeeper for Elsinby estate and found him in the estate office the following morning. A genial man, he was called Doug

Thorpe and invited me to join him for a coffee. As I enjoyed his hospitality, I explained about the curious birds in Low Hollins Wood and he smiled.

'Oh, those, Nick. Sure, I know about them. Actually, they've become a bit of a nuisance now. There's rather too many. Some of them get a bit frisky and they're moving towards the farms and villages, to have a go at the hens. Some farmers have been getting very strange chicks!'

'Where have they come from?' I asked.

'It's a chap from Strensford, I think, he's a breeder of chickens and has dozens of varieties, so he says. Well, when his broods hatch, he always has too many cockerels. As you know, most farmers destroy any surplus cock chickens but well, this chap can't bring himself to do that. So instead of wringing their necks, he releases them in the wild. He never asked us permission to dump them in our wood, but I caught him one day and well, I couldn't see why he shouldn't release one or two. But I never got his name and address, so I don't know who he is or how to get in touch with him. Anyway, he keeps coming back when I'm not around and dumps a few more.'

'So there's generations of cock-birds living in that wood?'

'There is, it's been going on for a few years now, Nick.'

'Well, Doug, I've got news for you,' I told him. 'The Ryedale Hen Watching Society wants to round up a few of those birds for their own domestic purposes.'

'They're welcome to as many as they can catch!' he expressed a sigh of relief.

'There's only one problem,' I added, tongue in cheek.

'What's that?' he frowned.

'Their chief rounder-up of hens will be none other than

Claude Jeremiah Greengrass,' I said.

'Well, so far as rounding up game birds goes, they couldn't have found a chap with more skill, but I'm not sure I can trust him to be at large in our woods! He might get his eye on some of our pheasants instead!'

'I suppose if he was supervised, it would help?' I put to him.

'I could help him,' said Doug. 'Yes, that's it. Tell whoever's making the arrangements to get in touch with me and I'll help Claude to round up a few of those cockerels. I'll be glad to see the back of them, to be honest.'

'If we can find out who the phantom cockerel depositor is,' I suggested, 'we could ask him to get in touch with the Ryedale Hen Watching Society direct, I'm sure they'd take some good specimens off his hands instead of him having to leave them to fend for themselves.'

'If I see him, I'll tell him,' said Doug.

And so Claude Jeremiah Greengrass found himself performing an authorized type of poaching, using his skills with nets and brandy-filled raisins to round up a few wild cockerels. The trick was to persuade the cockerels to eat lots of the brandy-filled raisins, which would make them drunk and fall asleep. It was easy thereafter to collect them, pop them into hessian sacks and deliver them to Albert Firth and his society members.

So far as I know, the phantom dumper of the cockerels was never located, but new birds did continue to arrive in that wood, whereupon the society would capture them with the aid of Claude Jeremiah and the Estate.

For my efforts I was made a honorary member of the Ryedale Hen Watching Society. I was quite pleased by this because membership of such an august society might enable me to discover whether it is possible to house-train a pet hen.

I was to call upon Claude Jeremiah's woodcraftsmanship on another occasion. It was a quiet summer morning when someone knocked on my police office door. When I opened it, I found Claude Jeremiah outside looking as pale as a piece of putty and visibly shivering.

'By gum, Mr Rhea, I've had summat of a shock . . .'

'You look shattered, Claude, what is it?'

'I'll have to come and sit down,' he said, 'My legs are like jelly . . . I nearly died out there, so I did.'

'Has somebody taken a pot shot at you?' I wondered if he'd been on a poaching expedition or engaged upon some other nefarious deed.

'Nay, worse than that. I nearly got blown to bits. Up in Howe Plantation.'

He was literally quivering with fright so I invited him into the office and called through to Mary to make him a hot, strong coffee with lots of sugar. I said I'd have one too, though not quite so sweet.

When he'd calmed down and was drinking the coffee I asked for an account of his experience. It seemed that, for some reason he declined to explain, he had been walking with his lurcher, Alfred, in Howe Plantation early that morning. It had been about half past seven, when he was homeward bound, that his boot had caught a metal object which was almost entirely buried. Thinking he might have stumbled across some concealed treasure, he'd begun to scrape away the earth with a piece of wood when he realized what the object was. It was un unexploded bomb from the Second World War; it was German, four feet long and apparently in a very fragile condition.

At that point, he'd run for his life.

The bomb had not exploded and after he'd had a stiff whisky at home he decided to report his discovery. Clearly the fellow had been shocked, but for the police of the North York moors this was a fairly regular occurrence in the years following the Second World War.

The moors were littered with discarded bombs and shells because when the Germans had flown over them towards Teesside during their raids, they sometimes completed their missions over the target area without dropping all their payload. The surplus bombs were jettisoned on the homeward run. Many of them fell on to the open moors and failed to explode; some lay buried for years, often in a state where they were capable of exploding and causing considerable damage.

Another reason for the large crop of bombs on the moors, in both an exploded and unexploded condition, was that during the Second World War false towns were established on the remoter heights. These consisted of nothing more than large groups of makeshift buildings with lights, set in the middle of the moors. At night-time, from a high-flying plane, they had all the appearances of townships. The incoming Germans dropped their precious bombs on these places – a useless exercise. Even today unexploded bombs (UXBs) are still discovered on the moors, especially in the soft, marshy areas. Claude had found one of them.

For the police the procedure was simple. We had to identify the precise location of the discovery, mark it in some way so that the bomb disposal experts could locate it, and keep the public away.

Howe Plantation, on the moors to the west of Aidensfield, was shown on recent Ordnance Survey maps of the district, and after discussion with Claude about the most suitable route to the bomb I was able to pinpoint the general area. I would, however, require Claude's presence to guide the military experts to its precise position. I rang Sergeant Blaketon to inform him of the discovery and said I would deal with it; my next task was to call the Bomb Disposal Unit of the Royal Engineers at Catterick Camp. They dealt with reports of all foreign or enemy bombs while the Ministry of Defence, Directorate of Weapon Engineering, dealt with reports of British or Allied bombs.

I rang them and made my report; they wanted to speak to Claude to establish as much detail as possible, and finally we agreed to a rendezvous on the southern edge of Howe Plantation. The maps showed a rough track to that point and the Bomb Disposal Unit spokesman said his men would arrive at that location by 11 a.m. I assured him that Claude and I would be there to meet his team.

'You're not expecting me to go back there, Mr Rhea, are you?' He was still nervous.

'No one else can tell us where to find this infernal machine,' I said. 'And I thought you'd done service in the army, I thought you'd undertaken all manner of dangerous missions and daring deeds on behalf of the country.'

'Aye, well, mebbe I did, when I was younger and dafter, but this is dangerous work, Mr Rhea.'

'No it isn't! All we require of you is to show us precisely where the bomb is, you don't have to touch it or go near it. If you don't show us, it could kill somebody.'

And so he agreed.

In my police minivan, Claude and I, accompanied by the faithful Alfred, arrived some twenty minutes before the appointed rendezvous time. I was surprised to see an open-topped military jeep standing at the meeting point. It was occupied by a driver and a major both clad in camouflaged outfits. The major leapt out and came towards me.

'Ah, Constable, you are on routine patrol here?'

'No, not really, not routine . . .'

'Then I wonder if I might ask you to depart, we are engaged upon a secret escape and evasion exercise in this plantation, we start at eleven, we must secure the entire area. It's the SAS, top secret work, you understand, we are guarding all entrances to the forest to prevent unauthorized access.'

'But . . .' I began.

'I have seniority here, Constable, I am a major in Her Majesty's Special Air Services and I am in command. This is a military operation. I must ask you both to leave.'

'You have men in this wood?' I asked.

'Yes, a dozen, they are already concealed and camouflaged, they must not be taken by a team of 'enemy' invaders who are due at eleven o'clock . . . the invaders will comb this wood for my men, and my men must evade them at all costs.'

'And I am here because this friend of mine, Mr Greengrass, has discovered an unexploded German bomb in this plantation.'

'You tell him, Mr Rhea!' chipped in Claude.

'Oh my God!' The major went a ghastly shade of white.

'I have called the Bomb Disposal Unit at Catterick,' I went on. 'They are due to arrive at eleven o'clock to deal with the bomb. We are here to show them where it is.'

'But I have spent months organizing this exercise, it's vital for my unit . . .'

'It seems to me that you will have to cancel or postpone it,' I said. 'I should hate any of your men to tread on Claude's bomb. It might just explode and it would blow a huge hole in these moors if it did. And the Germans might claim it had killed a few British soldiers!'

'I can't call it off,' the major spoke weakly. 'My men are all concealed in this plantation, there's about ten square miles and I have no idea where they are. I cannot contact them because they have no radios. They are all hidden and will remain concealed until eleven o'clock tomorrow morning – unless they are located and captured by the enemy.'

'But surely they'll emerge if we can get a message to them?' I suggested. 'Loudhailers or something.'

'No, whatever you do, they'll think it is a piece of trickery by the enemy, that's what they have been told. They know the enemy will make use of all kinds of devices and devious tactics to persuade them to leave their hiding-places and get caught. They will resist every move which encourages them to show themselves.'

'So when will they come out?' I asked.

'Tomorrow. Those who are not caught will rendezvous here, with me, at eleven tomorrow morning.'

'If the bomb is made secure, there will be no problem,' I said. 'But if it goes off, it could kill everyone within range – and I've no idea what the range of this bomb is. If any of your men are hiding within range of it, they could be killed. Surely you have some official and acceptable means of recalling your men?'

'Well, actually no,' he admitted. 'We haven't. The only way

they can be persuaded to emerge is if they are arrested by the enemy, who will be arriving soon for their briefing.'

'So that means we shall have to find and arrest them all before the bomb can be made safe? But if one of them treads on the bomb or disturbs it during their exercise, it could go off and kill several. It has been partly uncovered already.'

Claude had been listening to us during these useless exchanges and said, 'PC Rhea, if I went into that wood with Alfred, we could find 'em. We're good at tracking, we're a crack team, me and Alfred.'

'You?' I smiled.

'I mean it. I'm the best. Me and Alfred that is. We could search the area within range of that bomb and arrest 'em all.'

'Could you really?' I must have sounded surprised.

'Aye, course I can. Us old soldiers have to stick together, eh, Major? Alfred would point 'em out to me, he'd tell me where they were hiding, he's good at that sort o' thing, flushing out them that thinks they're well hidden.'

'You'd need one of the enemy soldiers with you,' said the major. 'They have a coloured tag on their uniforms, the concealed men know what colour it is.'

'Colour sergeants, are they?' blinked Claude, jokingly.

The major ignored this and said, 'Those colours will authenticate an enemy soldier. They will only submit to soldiers wearing those tags, everyone else will be regarded as a decoy and thus ignored or even captured and held until the conclusion of the exercise. They would be regarded as collaborators.'

Minutes later some army vehicles carrying two dozen soldiers with rifles and in heavy camouflage came to a halt at our point. The 'enemy' had arrived. They were followed by a smaller vehicle bearing a sign saying 'Bomb Disposal Unit' and sporting a blue light. A captain and a sergeant disembarked from the latter while another major descended from the 'enemy' vehicle. The officer in charge of each arrival wondered what the other was doing in this vicinity and there followed some rather intense and heated discussions between the assembled parties.

The captain in command of the Bomb Disposal Unit stressed that under no circumstances could the escape and evasion exercise continue with an unexploded bomb in the middle of it. Some wit said it would add an air of reality to the exercise, especially as it was a genuine enemy bomb, but after a lot of hot air, swearing, discussions about army protocol and procedures, it was decided that Claude must first show the captain the bomb. The captain would then make an assessment upon which to order any further action.

So we all trooped into the plantation of young conifers, plodding along an identifiable but little-used footpath for about four hundred yards until Claude halted. Alfred halted at his side and sniffed the air. Claude then pointed ahead and there, some ten yards away and very close to the edge of the footpath, was the distinct shell of a bomb. It was clearly showing where Claude had scraped away the peaty earth and seemed to be in reasonably good condition with little rust or serious deterioration.

The bomb disposal wizards crept forward to carry out their preliminary inspection. It took them but a few seconds to declare that the bomb was a relic of the Second World War; it was German, it was not particularly large or powerful, but it was alive. Closer inspection showed that the fuse was still in position and there was some slight corrosion; it could, in fact explode at any time. It wouldn't require much to set it off.

'I'm off!' said Claude.

'Me too,' I said.

And at that point Alfred wandered towards the bomb. Claude saw him and yelled, 'Alfred, you daft bat! Come here. Here, heel . . .'

But Alfred ignored his lord and master, if only for a few seconds. He instinctively approached the bomb, sniffed at it while those present held their breath, then he cocked his leg and directed a steady stream at the bomb. Thus he had marked the bomb; it was now upon Alfred's territory.

'Alfred!' There was pain and worry in Claude's voice, and Alfred then came to heel. At this stage the captain, whose name was Chambers, advised everyone to get well away from the bomb; the vehicles we had left on the track should be at a safe enough distance, he said. They were parked in a hollow, the edge of which provided a barrier between them and the bomb. He reckoned that if the bomb did explode it could kill at three hundred yards, with flying rocks and debris being a danger over a far greater distance, even up to five or six hundred yards, although that danger would be lessened by the density of the growing conifers.

The trees near the bomb would be destroyed, but those at a distance would act as a barrier to the effect of the blast, as would mounds of earth which were dotted around the forest. Many trees could withstand such a blast, depending upon their distance from the point of the explosion. He said he felt confident that the bomb would not explode unless it received a severe knock or direct hit; he also said he felt sure he could defuse it and make it safe without an explosion. Nevertheless, the problem of the concealed soldiers remained. If the bomb did explode, any soldiers hidden within a hundred yards of it could be killed. And they would resist any moves to tempt them out of hiding simply because they thought that such pleas were trickery.

'Can you really find them, Claude?' I asked him.

'Aye,' he said. 'Me and Alfred can. We can find 'em using our sixth sense. I was a wartime scout, me, tracking through the jungles of Burma and moving like a wraith . . . But I can't track with a bomb waiting to go off!'

'It won't go off unless it's knocked or damaged,' said Captain Chambers. 'I can assure you of that. It will be perfectly safe unless it receives a severe knock. I'll stand near the bomb while you do a recce within four hundred yards. Any soldier you find will be considered taken by the enemy – but as I said earlier, you must be accompanied by an enemy soldier suitably marked.'

And so Claude found himself exercising his considerable tracking skills in the wood, aided by the sensitive nostrils of Alfred his lurcher and accompanied by an 'enemy' soldier.

Together they found five soldiers hiding within range of the bomb and these were 'captured' by the enemy; Alfred angered one of them by peeing upon his helmet as he lay prone. It seemed Alfred liked marking things in his own specialized manner. Then a loud-hailer message was broadcast to those who were not caught, warning them of an unexploded bomb. The location was given. Captain Chambers moved in quickly, saying it would take at least an hour to complete his work, and so the testing time began. We all worried that the soldiers who had not been found might begin to move around, but that was a risk which had to be taken. But Chambers did a good job. By one o'clock, he had defused the bomb, saying it had been in remarkably good condition and that the fuse had been somewhat complicated. It could have exploded but it was now safe. The exercise could continue.

The SAS major was not very pleased that his men had been found by a poacher and his dog; the enemy major said that if a local man and his dog could find the concealed soldiers, then so could his experts, while Captain Chambers thanked Claude for his assistance. He showed his appreciation to Alfred too, by giving him a bar of chocolate; Alfred showed his appreciation by raising his leg against the wheel of his vehicle.

And so our drama was over. Claude was silent on the way back to Aidensfield, clearly thinking over what might have happened. I told him how pleased I was that he had volunteered his services in that way – he could have saved a life.

'There's only one thing bothering me,' he said at length. 'Me being an old soldier, like.'

'What's that, Claude?' I asked.

'I was working for the enemy wasn't I? Helping them to find our men. Me, a good, loyal member of His late Majesty's forces.'

'But you helped to defuse a real enemy bomb,' I reminded him.

'Aye, so I did. Me and Alfred. Alfred doesn't remember the war, Mr Rhea, he wasn't even born then.'

'He'd have made a good spy,' I said. 'The Allies could have dropped him in France. I wonder if he likes parachutes?'

8 Ladies of the Village

When he has ladies to please, every feature works!
Jane Austen (1775–1817)

Police officers and authors have one thing in common – they enjoy observing people.

For the police officer on foot patrol, the practice of watching people going about their daily routine can be both productive and fascinating. The productive side comes from knowing what is happening on one's patch and many a crime has been solved through the observational skills of a uniformed constable. Knowing who the person was and why he or she was at that place at that time has always been a good aid to the detection of crime.

The fascination comes from studying, in very real terms, the behaviour of human beings. One peculiarity is that one sees the same people in the same place each day; they are buying the same items from the same grocer's, they are seen sitting on the same park bench to rest their feet or catching the same bus back home after standing at the same bus stop facing the same way while carrying the same shopping bag.

We are all creatures of habit and we do not realize that others are keenly aware of those habits; it is only when we cease to follow our daily pattern that others miss us.

Many old folk have been saved from death because neighbours and friends have noted that these vulnerable members of society have not undertaken their daily rituals. If old Mr Brown isn't buying his bread at the usual time, his absence is noted and becomes a cause for alarm; if Mrs Green doesn't come into the post office at 10.15 a.m. on Thursday like she always does, we worry about her; if Mr Grey is walking along the street without the overcoat he wears every day of the year, then we know he's having problems and we do something about it.

One skill which develops from years of observing others is that it is sometimes possible to foretell a person's next move. Many is the time I have been standing on a street corner, knowing that a motorist is going to turn left or right in spite of that driver never having signalled his or her intention. There is some indefinable indication in the way the car and its driver behave that provides a clue to the immediate future.

Likewise, one instinctively knows that the lady walking in front of you will suddenly stop, turn around and hurry back to the shop she has just left; one knows that a child on the pavement will suddenly dart across the road or that the old lady with the puzzled frown on her face and clutching a pile of cheap novels will ask for directions to the nearest library. Groups of little old ladies always manage to get lost in shopping precincts and bus stations, old men catch the wrong trains and young mums often manage to lose infants in crowded places. Tourists always ask for directions to the car parks, the toilets and the nearest café, while Americans ask the way to Buckingham Palace, Scotland or Herriot country.

One interesting pastime when observing the public is to try to work out a person's occupation from their appearance; this is particularly fascinating if travelling by InterCity train, when one may spend up to two hours sitting opposite another traveller. Business men with notions of their own importance in the world are readily identifiable by their smart suits, black briefcases and statutory portable telephones, even if they are merely going to a seminar about brass screws or a new range of scented air-fresheners. Others are not so easy to identify.

Teachers are fairly easy to pick out, as are off-duty police officers, nurses or fire officers. Salesmen and saleswomen often look harassed but especially so if the train is even two minutes late; they usually have piles of forms which need to be filled in at every minute of the day. Holidaymakers tend to be excited and noisy, people going for interviews or exams are nervous and read their notes over and over again, pensioners read the *Sun* because they can't afford anything else, shoppers repeatedly make new lists of their requirements and students spend their time walking the corridors drinking from cans of lager or coke they've brought on board. Male students will walk time and time again past a group of pretty female students, hoping to make some favourable impression. European nationals seem to think that every seat is booked automatically upon purchase of one's ticket and Scotsmen speak in long sentences of incomprehensible dialect which is delivered with the speed of a machine gun. Long train journeys are a rich source of material for authors.

Shoes are often a give-away to a person's status in the world, highly polished ones indicating someone in a position of importance, casual ones revealing someone who pays more attention to comfort than appearance and those with thick soles indicating a person with a complex about their lack of height. I think the modern term for short people is 'vertically challenged' – I'm not sure what the term is for people who dream up such political daftness.

Authors tend to observe others in a continual search for characters suitable for inclusion in their novels. There are times when a person's appearance can be deceptive – it is easy for a writer to look at a smart person and then to describe the style of clothing. It takes a vastly different technique to understand the character who is wearing those clothes – to create a totally fictitious character so that the person appears to be real, with feelings and ambitions, is never easy. In fact, it is extremely difficult.

Many authors tend to base their creations on people they know well or whom they meet during their travels. Quite often, for example, a very smart and confident appearance will conceal a confidence trickster; an old person in cheap, ragged clothing might be a titled and wealthy individual; the fun-loving, chip-eating buffoon you meet on holiday might well be a highly successful company director back home while the man with dark glasses and a pipe might be a detective watching us all.

It was this habit of observing others that drew my attention to the curious world of Miss Mabel Hibbard, sometimes known to the children of Aidensfield as Old Mother Hubbard. She was a rather squat and heavily built lady with iron-grey hair done in a bun and she always wore a heavy royal blue overcoat; she topped it with a curious old-fashioned hat. Her bun protruded from the back of her hat rather like a rabbit's tail.

She always carried a round shopping basket with nothing inside. Her shoes were flat and well-worn, while her stockings were of old-fashioned lisle and full of wrinkles. She walked with a slight limp in her left leg; her gait was rather like that of a rolling sailor. Even so she would walk very rapidly, almost trotting along when she was out and about in Aidensfield. It did not take long for me to realize that she was a regular sight in the village and was one of the local 'characters'.

Miss Hibbard lived in a large detached house overlooking the green; it was a splendid, if neglected, dwelling built in local moorland stone with a blue slate roof. It was constantly in need of a coat of paint and the garden was overgrown but I was to learn that the interior was full of antique furniture and a wonderful collection of rare Staffordshire pottery. In spite of her run-down appearance, Miss Hibbard was known to have a substantial private income and she could be very generous.

Although she rarely spent much money on herself, she did, from time to time, reveal flashes of true benevolence by donating cash to the church, to any village charity and to the Missions to Seamen or the Royal National Lifeboat Institution.

She was a very familiar figure in the village, pottering around the shops, going along to the church, visiting friends, helping at functions in the village hall or simply enjoying the fresh moorland air on long and lonely walks. But as she pottered about her business in Aidensfield, she began to intrigue me. I was first drawn to observing her after seeing her waiting for Arnold Merryweather's bus.

At ten o'clock one morning I was standing near the telephone kiosk, from where I could see the bus stop. Mabel Hibbard was standing there, empty basket in hand, as she waited for Arnold's service bus which would take her to Ashfordly. It was Friday: market day in Ashfordly.

There was no one else at the bus stop; other people would be going to town later or perhaps using their own cars. And so Mabel waited alone. As she waited, her eyes caught something in the window of the village shop. She pottered across a few yards of green to examine it. But as she started that manoeuvre, Arnold's bus appeared at the far end of Aidensfield, rising up the hill and heading for the bus stop. I felt sure Mabel would have seen or heard the oncoming bus, but she hadn't. I was too far away to shout at her, although I did try.

The bus rumbled past without halting and quickly disappeared around the corner as it made for Ashfordly. Mabel then returned to the bus stop, never realizing she'd missed it.

I decided to help. I drove to the bus stop in the police minivan and said, 'Hop in, Mabel, we can catch the bus.'

'Pardon?' she cupped an ear with her free hand.

'Bus!' I shouted. 'We can catch it.'

'No, it's not come yet,' she said. 'I'm waiting for it.'

'You've missed it,' I shouted again. 'When you were looking in the shop window; it came past and didn't stop. It's gone round the corner.'

'I never saw any bus,' she looked puzzled.

I realized for the first time that she was as deaf as a proverbial post and went closer, shouting that if we hurried we could catch Arnold's bus before it left the outskirts of Aidensfield.

It took some time for her to get the gist of my shouting and arm-waving and I know she was worried about getting into my police minivan, but I did catch the bus for her. With a cheery wave she boarded the rickety old vehicle and I saw the gigantic conductress, Hannah, come and take her fare.

From that time onwards, whenever I saw Mabel out and about in Aidensfield, I realized that she always missed seeing those things she wanted to see. She was always looking the wrong way at precisely the wrong moment.

One example occurred at the annual church fête. It was known that one of her nephews was a squadron leader in the RAF; he was a flying instructor at RAF Leeming and, as a special favour for the village, Mabel had been approached by the chairman of the organizing committee to ask her nephew if he could arrange a fly-past of jet aircraft while the fête was being held. Mabel had written to her nephew, Squadron Leader Hibbard, but he had stressed that it was impossible to make an official fly-past of jets for something as minor as Aidensfield church fête. He did say however, that, weather permitting, he would be in the air that day with five of his pupils in jet trainers, and he would arrange for them to fly over the village at 3 p.m. His own aircraft would make it six, and they would fly in formation, doing three runs over the village. It was all very unofficial, but the committee was delighted. They announced the flypast at 3 p.m. on all their publicity material and invited Mabel to be their guest of honour.

For the fly-past she would be seated on a platform with the vicar, the chairman, the doctor and other dignitaries. On the morning of the fête, Squadron Leader Hibbard telephoned his aunt to say that the weather was ideal for flying and that he would take to the air as planned, except that another commitment had arisen which meant that only one pass across Aidensfield was possible, not three as originally suggested. It meant that Aidensfield would still have its very own unofficial fly-past, however. There was great excitement about this event and it certainly attracted the crowds to the fête.

At a few minutes to three, therefore, a loudhailer announcement reminded the gathering of the impending arrival of six jet aircraft. Everyone assembled to wait. And then, in the distance across the moor, they could hear the distinctive sound of jet engines; Squadron Leader Hibbard had been true to his word and I saw the tiny outline of six distant aircraft as they flew ever so slowly towards the village.

It was at that precise moment, that Mabel decided to look in her handbag for a toffee. As she bent down to open her bag and rummage inside, I wanted to shout at her and tell her to look skywards but I was too far away and the crowd was shouting with happiness as they sighted the planes. Everyone else was looking at the sky; no one was bothering to observe Mabel except me. I was switching my gaze between Mabel and the oncoming aircraft.

It was almost as if I knew what was going to happen. Soon everyone was cheering as the six planes, in arrowhead pattern, swept across the moors. Mabel was oblivious to all this. Head down, she was rummaging in her bag while everyone else was gazing skywards – I continued to alternately look at her and at the planes, willing her to forget whatever she was seeking, but no one else was paying her the slightest attention. All eyes were on the heavens.

And then, with a roaring and whistling sound, the six shining aircraft, flying as slowly and as low as permissible, came directly over the church fête. They waggled their wings and flew on. Within seconds, they were disappearing over the horizon to the cheers of the crowd. I looked at Mabel.

Only then, as the jets whistled out of sight, did she find her toffee; she sat erect with a smile on her face, popped the sweet into her mouth and settled down to wait for her nephew. By then, of course, he was heading for the North Sea, never to return that day. She had neither seen nor heard the fly-past.

Everyone was so sorry that Mabel had missed the moment, but as I talked to people afterwards, I heard lots more similar tales about her. I was to learn, for example, that years earlier she had been invited to a friend's house to watch the Coronation on television, then a real national treat. Mabel was an ardent royalist and loved anything connected with the Royal Family. But seconds before the Archbishop of Canterbury had placed the crown on Her Majesty's head, Mabel had left the room to go to the toilet. When she'd returned, the supreme moment was over – and in those days there were no such things as video recorders to tape highlights from television.

Then, when she had watched a replay years later, she missed the crowning again because she dropped her spectacles on the floor at that precise moment and spent some minutes trying to find them. So far as anyone knew, Mabel had never actually seen Her Majesty being crowned – she had always been looking the other way whenever the ceremony had been repeated on television.

Some friends had tried to rectify those omissions when a local lass, Katherine Worsley of Hovingham, married the Duke of Kent to become Her Royal Highness the Duchess of Kent. The date was 8 June 1961 and the entire population of the villages on the edge of the moors had become extremely excited. Her Majesty was a guest at the wedding and she would be driving through the countryside following the ceremony.

Locations and timings of Her Majesty's journey from Hovingham were publicized, so the people of Aidensfield felt they should take Mabel to a suitable position so that she would see the Queen. Having never seen a royal person in the flesh, Mabel had said she would cherish that moment for the rest of her life. To see the Queen in the flesh was like meeting God!

A small group of her friends had taken her to a knoll just outside Hovingham which was a superb vantage point. From there one could look along the road towards Hovingham and so gain a superb aspect of the royal cars as they sped towards us. Although this was before I became the village constable at Aidensfield, I was there too, on duty, because this was a busy road and there was a set of crossroads at which I had to halt all oncoming traffic to allow the royal procession to speed past. We knew the car would be travelling at a very fast speed for security reasons and we would be warned, by police radio, when the royal motorcade left Hovingham Hall.

At that time, of course, I did not know Mabel, although in fact she would have been waiting within a few yards of my traffic duty position. And then we got word – the royal party was leaving; Her Majesty was to travel from Hovingham Hall to Malton to catch the royal train back to York and thence to London. That was my signal to halt all traffic at the crossroads. I shouted to the crowd that Her Majesty was en route, and would arrive in about five minutes. Everyone grew excited as I stood on the crossroads, ensuring an open run for the royal motorcade.

It was when I became village constable at Aidensfield that I heard about Mabel's mishap during her vigil. She had been among a crowd of friends and seconds before the royal cars appeared in the distance, Mabel decided she would have an orange.

She had brought some sandwiches, a flask of tea and an orange to eat during the long wait. And, oblivious to the cheers around her, she had ducked down to the grassy knoll upon which she stood and had begun to ferret in her basket for an orange. Then, having found one among the other picnic paraphernalia, she had sought a knife with which to cut the skin so she could peel it. And as she had squatted on her haunches among the crowds, hunting for the knife, the Queen's motorcade had flashed past at seventy miles an hour. As Mabel had straightened up, orange in hand, the last police car of the royal motorcade was heading out of sight. Mabel had missed the Queen.

I did learn that there was a saying in the village that Miss Mabel had missed again; she missed seeing the presentation of the World Cup to Bobby Moore, captain of the winning England soccer team in July 1966. She had just popped out to make herself a cup of tea; she missed the thrilling sight of Neil Armstrong stepping on to the moon in 1969, the first man to do so, because she realized she'd forgotten to switch on her oven to warm up so that she could cook herself a casserole.

Mabel's great love, however, was the church. A committed Anglican, she thought God was an Englishman and believed that the British Royal Family was somehow descended from Him. Thus, for her, the Church of England with the British Sovereign as its Supreme Governor was something founded and approved of by God himself.

But being deaf she missed most of the points raised by the Reverend Roger Clifton in his sermons. She also missed advance information about church events such as parochial parish council meetings, weddings, baptisms, confirmations and funerals. None the less, she was a regular attender, relying on the church notice board for times of special services, additional functions and visits by the bishop.

It would take a long time to catalogue all the important events that Mabel had managed to miss; she managed to miss most of the local sights and occasions, and also contrived to miss those of national interest which appeared on television. And then one July, she died. She passed away very quickly due to heart failure and so the time came for her own funeral.

The vicar of Aidensfield, the Reverend Roger Clifton, was on holiday and his place had been taken for three weeks by the Reverent Austin Threadgill who hailed from Scotland. Six feet six inches tall, with a shock of black hair, he lived in the vicarage for those three weeks, and it was soon known that his strong point was his stentorian voice.

It was thunderous. Rumour was that he had been a sergeant-major in the war, but I have never heard such a powerful voice. It was deafening, even from a distance, and in the confines of the church it echoed about the building, reverberating from the walls and waking up the bats which slept in the belfry.

When the Reverent Threadgill opened up on Sunday mornings, his sermon could be heard by anyone walking past the church; I passed on one occasion when he was lecturing about sin, and his voice sounded like a clarion call to arms. His enunciation was clear though, and no one could avoid his message, nor could anyone go to sleep during his thunderclap sermons.

And, of course, Mabel had missed him. By dying when she did she had missed the only vicar whose voice she would have heard, but at least she had the honour of having this clamorous voice to conduct her funeral. The reverend's powerful and sonorous tones filled the church and brought tears to those who listened (probably because he was hurting their ear-drums), but Mabel did receive a loud and very fitting send-off.

Even at the graveside the roar of his words drowned the sound of passing traffic and we all felt that Mabel, wherever she was, would have heard him. Some said he had been sent by God especially to provide Mabel with a perfect end to her time on earth.

Later, though, a new bus stop was built in Aidensfield. It was right outside Mabel's old house. I wondered whether, if she had been alive, she would have missed the buses which came to that stop. Somehow, I think she would. I could envisage her standing there, waiting for Arnold's bus to appear and then, seconds before it arrived, hurrying back into the house for her purse.

Miss Mabel had gone through life missing things; sometimes I wondered if that was why she had never married. Maybe she had missed every opportunity to fall in love, but actually, after she died, she was missed by everyone in Aidensfield.

Another busy lady, who never missed anything, was Mrs Fiona Tucker-Smith. Her husband worked away from home during the week, doing something mysterious but very financially rewarding in the City of London. He commuted to London from York station on Sunday nights and returned to Aidensfield on Friday evenings. While he earned his weekly crust in pin-stripe trousers and bowler hat he left Fiona to occupy herself during the week and so she did.

Her only source of interest outside her home was the church. She was a very tall and slim lady in her late forties who dressed in expensive but old-fashioned clothes, always of a dark colour but always immaculately kept. Her hair was pulled tightly back and she wore it in two ringlets curled around her ears where they looked like a cross between sea shells, curled-up fossil snakes and ear-muffs. Pale faced and devoid of make-up, she seldom smiled and tackled every aspect of life with the utmost severity and efficiency. A capable organizer, she did take part in many village events, particularly those which had a strong link with the Anglican parish church.

She spent her time raising funds for the parish, helping with the Remembrance Day distribution of red poppies, running raffles, coffee mornings, wine and cheese tastings and a host of other fairly upper-class functions, all of which were linked in some way with Aidensfield's Anglican parish church. She ignored the Catholic church in the village, even though some of the 'best' people in the village followed the ancient faith of this land, and she would not be caught dead in a bingo session, whist drive or beetle drive. Another character trait was that she tended to socialize only with people superior to herself. There were many such people in the district, some titled and others of aristocratic bearing, but she seemed able to distinguish between those whose money was 'new' and those whose ancestry could be traced in blue blood.

She ignored those with 'new' money, preferring to cultivate the local blue-bloods, even if they were impoverished. She was one of the villagers with whom I had a lot of official contact.

This was because she was either chairman or secretary of all the parish church organizations (and in those days, chairmen were chairmen irrespective of sex, and they were not described as pieces of furniture, i.e. chairs). Fiona was chairman of the Parochial Church Council, chairman of the Church Fund-Raising Committee, secretary of the parish council, secretary of the Mothers' Union, secretary and president of the Women's Institute, organizer of the rota for church flower ladies, organizer of the rota for church cleaners, selector of hymns for Sunday services, compiler and typist for the parish magazine, organizer of sidesmen's duties, collector of Sunday collections and distributor of hymn books. She would also look after any official guests to the church, such as the bishop or visiting clergy, organizing coffee, lunch or tea for them.

She had not actually reached the stage of taking a service, administering communion or preaching the sermon, but she did tend the altar linen, polish the candlesticks and select the readings, both on Sundays and during the week.

The Reverend Roger Clifton seemed content to allow her this freedom. A charming bachelor, he was very busy because he ministered at several smaller neighbouring parishes and was a member of an ecumenical committee at York. He did once indicate to me, off the record, that he allowed Fiona to undertake all these duties because she did fulfil some of the roles traditionally undertaken by the wife of a clergyman, but in addition he did feel sorry for her; her husband was away such a lot and she needed something to occupy her. For Fiona, the church in all its aspects provided some kind of fulfilment; she was in fact, a stand-in for the vicar's wife. And there is no doubt she did a very good job.

The snag was that none of the other willing and able ladies got a look in. Fiona kept them all at bay by ruling the committees and other organizations with remarkable efficiency, always being in charge and giving them menial tasks. They wanted to feel useful, but in fact, they felt used. Throughout her work she used her considerable committee skills to keep the lesser ladies at a respectful and harmless distance. Fiona did everything; she even monitored the vicar's diary to ensure that he shared himself equally between his parishes, his duties for the York diocese and her village organizations.

But all good things come to an end and in this instance it happened with the transfer of Roger Clifton to an important post at York Minster. Clearly, his part-time church work in York had impressed those in authority. God, and the diocesan authorities, had more work for him and it seemed he was destined for a fine clerical career. The village was happy for him because he was such a charming and capable man, with a genuine love of his faith and respect for his congregation. Although the people of Aidensfield were sad to lose Roger, they were pleased for him. He had been a good, caring man of the church. Accompanying the news of his departure was a notice that his replacement would be a vicar from the Lake District with the unlikely name of the Reverend Christian Lord.

At this news the ladies of the parish scented dramatic changes because the Reverend Lord was married. Fiona might find herself thrust into a less prominent position, they hoped, and this might enable some of them to take more responsibility. They waited with considerable pleasure for the arrival of the new incumbent.

I was aware of all these manoeuvrings, simply because I

spent a lot of time in Aidensfield and, like the rest of the village, I wondered what was to befall Fiona. In due course, the Reverend and Mrs Christian Lord moved into the vicarage and, after allowing them a few days to settle in, I went to introduce myself as the village constable. Mrs Lord, a quietly spoken lady, was smothered in white emulsion and carrying a paint brush when she answered my knock. Though a headscarf protected some of her hair, I could see the rest was streaked with the emulsion. She looked very down-to-earth and practical and I found myself liking her.

'Sorry for the mess,' she beamed. 'But I thought I'd brighten up this spot. I've got more on me than the walls! It's had a bachelor vicar living here, you can always tell. No flowers in the place, no bright colours, sombre wallpapers. I'm going to make the vicarage a bright and breezy place!'

That was good news and after I'd briefly introduced myself, she ushered me into the book-lined study where her husband was working on some papers. He stood up and shook my hand. I was quite surprised to see that he was a very small man, scarcely more than five feet two inches tall. He had a round, happy face and very thin fair hair on his head. He wore half-rimmed spectacles and peered over these as he greeted me.

'So God's law and man's law meet,' he laughed. 'You might be the inspiration for my first sermon, I need to make an impact. Sin and law-breaking . . . now there's an idea.'

'Is it a sin to break the law?' I asked him. 'It is a sin to commit murder or theft, but is it a sin to ride a bike without lights or drink after time in the pub?'

'I might just take up those points,' he smiled. 'But let's get the important things settled first – has Ruth said anything about coffee?'

'Ruth will break off her decorating and organize coffee for the constable and the vicar!' sang a voice from outside the door.

'I don't know what I'd do without my wife,' he said with an infectious chuckle. 'How some vicars cope without wives I'll never know! I could never have been a Catholic priest, I just don't know who would have tidied my study and made my coffee.'

And so I introduced myself, making it known that I was a Catholic and therefore not one of his flock. We had a long, fun-laden talk about the village, its people, its environs, its problems and those in need. He listened intently, asking me lots of direct questions, and I came to the rapid conclusion that he would be an asset to Aidensfield. As I was about to take my leave, however, he indicated that I should stay a moment longer. 'I have one curious favour to ask,' he said.

'Fire away,' I invited.

'Have you come across a lady called Fiona Tucker-Smith?' he asked.

My response must have told him everything he wanted to know because when I answered in a somewhat guarded way that I did know her, he said, 'I get the impression that she runs things around here? The church, I mean.'

'She is either secretary or chairman of every organization linked to your church,' I said.

'She's already trying to organize me,' he smiled. 'She's told me I'm to attend a wine and cheese party next Wednesday, that I must not fail to have one service a month for the Mothers' Union, that she will see to the prayer books, bell-ringing, flowers and church cleaners and that she will take care of my appointments diary.'

I decided I would explain to him the villagers' view of Fiona and so I did, saying that there were lots of other very capable and willing ladies who would love to become involved in village events. But Fiona had cornered the market.

'Thank you, Mr Rhea.'

'Nick,' I said. 'Everyone calls me Nick.'

'Nick, nick!' he chortled. 'I'll bet everybody says that?'

'I'm used to it,' I said.

'And me! Fancy my parents christening me Christian with a surname like Lord, and fancy me becoming a vicar! Sometimes when I'm leading prayers, I sound as if I'm calling my own name . . . Is there any word from the Lord . . . Lord be with you . . . For thou Lord, art good and ready to forgive . . . I could go on for ever! Anyway, back to Mrs Fiona What's-her-name.'

'She does mean well,' I said in her favour.

'I'm sure she does. But thank you for telling me about her. Ruth will take care of her, and she will do it in a most kind and gentle way. Ruth will see that the other ladies get their share of responsibility and take their part in helping Aidensfield church and its congregation.'

As I left, I had no idea how Mrs Lord would achieve the impossible, but within a month things began to happen. I was due to speak to the Mothers' Union about my work and on the morning of the event, I received a call from Fiona.

'Mr Rhea,' she said in her firm voice. 'When I booked you for this talk, I said I would be chairman for the evening and that I would introduce you to our members. Well, I have been asked to join a committee at Ashfordly, Lord Ashfordly is chairman, you know, it's a committee aimed at helping young people appreciate the church. I am very honoured to be asked to serve his Lordship in this way, but it means I cannot chair your meeting. Both meetings are on the same night. Mrs Burley, the auctioneer's wife, is vice-chairman, and she will act for me at the Mothers' Union. I thought you ought to know.'

I thanked her for keeping me informed but, so far as I knew, this was the first time that Fiona had not fulfilled one of her many functions. When I arrived at the meeting, I found Mrs Burley firmly in the chair, with the vicar's wife at her side. After my talk, we had coffee and I managed to catch Ruth Lord for a few moments' talk. After the preliminaries, I found myself alone with her and made the comment, 'Fiona Tucker-Smith is attending another meeting?'

She smiled sweetly. 'I felt that a woman of her skills and determination had so much to offer and when I heard of a vacancy on Lord Ashfordly's committee, I felt it was perfect for her. And, Nick,' she smiled. 'I do know that the Archbishop is seeking someone to represent the diocese on the Church of England Children's Society, a most worthy charity. I have nominated Fiona for that too; they meet once a month in York. I did tell her that several past members of that committee have featured in the Queen's Birthday Honours lists . . . I believe Fiona is very keen to become involved.'

'It would mean her giving up some of her local work?'

'It would indeed,' smiled Ruth Lord. 'And I'm sure we can find lots of capable replacements. I have a feeling we might need quite a lot.'

I smiled at her. She was a very pleasant lady and she was removing Fiona in a most graceful manner, and at the same time not dominating the organizations herself. This was the art of delegation; I felt that the Reverend and Mrs Lord would do the Lord's work at Aidensfield in a very acceptable way.

9 Faith, Hope and Charity

Man is by his constitution a religious animal.
Edmund Burke (1729–1797)

There is little doubt that the arrival of the Reverend Christian Lord and his admirable wife did result in an upsurge of interest in church matters at Aidensfield. The new vicar could preach an interesting and thought-provoking sermon, he had a sense of humour, he loved meeting the public and his wife soon began to take an active, but not domineering, part in the varied events of the village. Within a very short time the congregation at the Anglican parish church began to increase while the entire village welcomed the Reverend Lord and Mrs Lord to our peaceful rural community.

That is not to say that the previous vicar, Roger Clifton had been ineffective – he hadn't. Roger had been a very capable, kind and successful vicar and he had served Aidensfield as well as anyone could. He was right for that time. If anything, though, he lacked charisma; steady and reliable, he maintained a close and devoted following, but did not attract any new members of the faithful. His congregations were very static, comprising the same few each Sunday.

But in life, change is inevitable and the acceptance of change is important. The 1960s were times of great change, both in attitudes and in organizations in this country and overseas. The police service was changing and so was the church – and all change should be welcomed if it is harnessed for the good of the community. With Roger Clifton's departure, therefore, the Anglican parish was bound to experience changes and so it did.

The Catholic community of Aidensfield, of which I was part, also welcomed the new vicar; although the true spirit of ecumenism had not yet filtered to Aidensfield, it is fair to say that the Catholics and the Anglicans of Aidensfield and district did exist in mutual friendship even if they could not understand, or did not wish to understand, one another's long-held and cherished beliefs.

The older and more entrenched Anglicans continued to refer to the Catholics as Romans. They seemed to think we were foreigners or had some unwholesome allegiance to a foreign power. It seemed beyond their reasoning to credit Christ with having established a universal church which was not centred upon the United Kingdom – I'm sure some of them thought that Bethlehem and Jerusalem should really have been part of the British Empire. Those older Protestants never called us Catholics; they believed *they* belonged to the one, true Catholic church even though the law of England said the head of their church must be a Protestant.

The law also said that the head of the Church of England could never marry a Catholic. What the Protestants failed to realize was that the term 'Roman' Catholic did not come into use until the end of the sixteenth century – and then only in Britain. It is by no means a universal term. It seems to have been coined in England, a typically English means of implying there was something not quite English about the older, world-wide Catholic faith.

I was quite astonished to find that a lot of Anglicans had, and still have, no idea of the history of their own church, not knowing the drama and cruelty of the Reformation, not realizing that their church was not formed until the sixteenth century. There had been a church in England from the time of St Augustine's arrival in Canterbury in AD 596 – and he was a Catholic, having been sent by Pope Gregory I to convert the English. He was the first Archbishop of Canterbury, almost a thousand years before the Church of England was formed, the faith he brought came from God and from Rome. It was not the Church of England nor was it the Protestant faith. Augustine brought the church to England, he helped to establish the church *in* England, not the Church of England.

That church, with its new and protestant faith, was not established until 1559 – and it was then imposed on this country by the law of the land.

Thus the Church of England is less than 450 years old with no apostolic origins, it is state-controlled and paradoxically claims to be both Catholic and Protestant. It was members of that ancient Catholic church who built all those fine abbeys and churches which Henry VIII later crushed as he was trying to eradicate all evidence of the former church from this land.

Many of the faithful Anglicans of Aidensfield could not understand the ancient impact of English law upon their church – statutes such as the Acts of Supremacy and of Treason, laws by which Catholics who refused to accept the English sovereign as Supreme Head of the church were found guilty of treason and executed. The King, Henry VIII, declared himself head of the new Church of England; it was treason to deny him that office, and treason carried the death penalty. From the time of Henry VIII, therefore, the English sovereign would be head of the church, not the Pope, and as a consequence it was in January 1547 that King Edward VI became Supreme Head of the Church of England. He was nine years old at the time. Later Elizabeth I became the first female head of a church that is still fretting about the appointment of women priests.

In the centuries which followed, the law of England governed the new church in such a way that church and state became almost inextricably entwined. Even today, the Anglican church is governed by Parliament, which comprises people of many faiths or none at all. It seem strange that the British Parliament, through its laws, has any say in the running of God's church. To those outside the Church of England it seems an odd way to govern a church.

The Catholics, on the other hand, viewed the Anglicans with some suspicion, blaming them for the destruction of all their medieval monasteries and abbeys, for seizing all their finest churches, for taking over their lands and executing their leaders. But it wasn't the Anglican church leaders who did these things; it was the state, although by then church and state were as one.

With the loss of their lands and church buildings, denied the right to practise their faith from the time of the Reformation, the Catholics went into hiding for more than a couple of centuries. In spite of the risks to their lives, many men did become priests, returning in secret to spread the gospel. So the old Catholic religion survived, often in secret and often at risk of a cruel death to those who practised it. In spite of their treatment,

Catholics remained true to their country and to their church, but could not accept that the British sovereign was head of their religion. They did accept him as head of their country, but not of their church.

With the passage of some 270 years, Catholics eventually regained some of their old lost rights through the Catholic Emancipation Act of 1829. This restored the rights of Catholics to sit in Parliament, to inherit land, to join HM Forces, to act as judges and to enjoy a university education. Those and more rights had been denied them since the Reformation, but even now no Catholic can become Prime Minister nor can the British sovereign be a Catholic. If a member of the Royal Family marries a Catholic, then he or she forfeits all rights to the succession. I don't think the same stricture applies if the sovereign marries a member of any other faith or even an atheist. So, even in the 1990s, there are still restrictions upon Catholics in Britain; religious bias still exists in our fine country. But even if the constitution of Britain continues to be discriminatory in matters of religion, most of the people either do not care or prefer to ignore those old divisions.

For some of the people of Aidensfield, though, those old divisions did cause hurt and anger, and from time to time ancient prejudices did surface. In spite of an outward attitude of tolerance between the faiths, there were still undercurrents which had roots in the badly-named 'Reformation' which had occurred more than 430 years earlier.

On one occasion, there was a fight outside a dance hall and I found myself having to sort out something which had all the appearances of an unprovoked attack upon a young man.

The assailant was a powerful farmer called Jack MacKay

and he had a pretty daughter of seventeen. She was called Rebecca and she had attended a dance in Elsinby village hall. Jack had driven her to the hall at eight o'clock and had said he would return at 11.45 p.m. to collect her. I was on duty outside the hall, as was my normal practice on dance nights, when I heard a commotion. It was just after 11.45 p.m. and the dancers were leaving, many of them in pairs. Some had been established as couples long before the dance started but other pairings had been formed only that evening. New romances were blossoming, I felt; this was not surprising, of course, because village dances were one of the places where the young people of Aidensfield and district met and fell in love.

My attention was drawn to the fracas by a lot of shouting and cursing; it was in the car park beside the hall and as I turned to investigate the disturbance, somebody shouted, 'Mr Rhea, there's a fight near the gate!'

I ran across the car park in the darkness to find two men scuffling and shouting; the younger one clearly on the defensive and his older, larger assailant was shouting abuse before a curious gathering of friends who tried to separate them. I waded in, shouting 'Police', and managed to seize the collar of one assailant. I hauled him backwards, the tightness of his collar restricting his breathing and so forcing him to break his hold on the other.

I found I'd got in my grip a man in his early forties, not a youth in his teens as I might have expected. I recognized him as Jack MacKay, a farmer from Elsinby. The other fighter was much younger, probably in his late teens or early twenties. He was Gerry O'Connell, the son of an electricity board worker from Aidensfield.

'Now just calm down, the pair of you,' I shouted.

'He just came for me,' the younger man was straightening his clothes and tidying his hair. 'I never said a word . . . the man's crazy . . . he just lashed out!'

And it was only then that I saw Rebecca in the background, biting her lip as she suddenly found herself a reluctant focus of attention in this strange affair.

'What's all this about, Jack?' I asked the older man.

'I'm having no Papist courting my lass,' he said in a strong Scots accent. 'I want no Romish offspring near me, no Papist trash in my family . . .'

'I'm a Papist,' I said quietly. 'But I'm sure that young man isn't trash. Catholic, yes, trash no.'

'He called me that,' said the youngster, licking his lips where Jack's first blow had landed. 'I don't know what's got to him.'

Jack belonged to a fiery Scots religion, one of the so-called Wee Frees, and I'd long known of his religious intolerance. He was a very charming man otherwise, a good farmer and a successful businessman, but his deep religious bias could surface at the most awkward moments. And when he'd seen his daughter kissing a Catholic 'good-night' outside the dance hall, he'd been unable to restrain himself. 'Love thy neighbour as thyself' was not a commandment which was accepted by members of his church; they hated Catholics and made no secret of it, in spite of calling themselves Christians.

'Jack, calm down or you'll be arrested,' I bellowed at him to rouse him from his fanatical stupor.

My voice so very close to his ear seemed to do the trick and he suddenly relaxed, as if all his anger had evaporated.

'Sorry, Nick,' quite suddenly he was as calm and rational as ever. 'Sorry, I didn't mean to do that . . . it's just that . . .'

'Jack, you've got to learn to control this dislike of Catholics. I'm a Catholic but I don't go around clouting members of the Scottish Free Churches . . . and I don't go around arresting them without good cause.'

'He was kissing my daughter.'

'Is that a crime? Would Christ have reacted like you did? For most of the time, you live a good Christian life, Jack, I know that – no alcohol, prayers on Sundays, no swearing . . . yet you blow up like this!'

'It's those Papists . . .'

'Look, I suggest you shake hands with young Gerry and then we can forget this. I'm sure he wouldn't want me to prosecute you for assaulting him, the press would have a field day with this story, you know – religious strife in Elsinby!'

'I can never shake hands with a Papist,' he said.

'If I was St Peter, would you shake hands with me?'

'Aye, of course, Peter was a good man.'

'He was the first Pope,' I said. 'That's not religious dogma, it's part of world history. And he was appointed to the job by Christ himself, even your Bible will tell you that! Thou art Peter and upon this rock I will build my church . . . you've heard the words, surely?'

'You're playing with words, Mr Rhea.'

'And you're playing with fire, Jack. Hell fire, I shouldn't be surprised.'

At this point, Rebecca came forward and took her father's arm. 'Come along, dad, take me home.'

He looked at Rebecca, then at me, then at the crowd which

had gathered and nodded, 'Aye, right,' was all he said. He did not apologize for his actions and I decided to let him go rather than inflame the situation any further. There was absolutely no point in arresting him or bringing about a prosecution – it would serve no useful purpose at all. As I made my decision, he turned his back on Gerry O'Connell and walked away without a word. Rebecca trotted after him.

'You'll not press charges, Mr Rhea?' said Gerry as he came over to me, still nursing his jaw with his hand.

'No,' I said. 'But next time you fancy the daughter of one of the Wee Frees of Scotland, make sure her dad's not around to see you in action!'

'I've been seeing her a while,' said the lad. 'She never said anything about her dad being likely to blow up like that.'

'She knows you're a Catholic?' I asked.

'Yes, we often have talks about religion, she's very interested in my church, she says her mum wanted to leave Scotland to get away from the influence of the Wee Frees, to gain a wider perspective, she said. But her dad won't give up.'

'Give him time,' I said. 'If he was brought up in that mould, he'll never shake off the shackles. It's up to you to show the Jack MacKays of this world that Catholics haven't got forked tails, that the Pope isn't an Antichrist, and that we are all human beings with a love of God.'

'It's not easy, coping with a man like that,' he said. 'I'll be scared even to let him see me with Rebecca, he might turn violent again.'

'Just don't give him chance, and don't react the same way as him,' I advised. 'Keep calm – in fact, you made a very good start tonight. You could have flattened him, I'd guess.'

'If you hadn't turned up, I reckon I could have floored him,' grinned Gerry. 'I was my school boxing champion, I can use my fists.'

And so the drama was over. Gerry walked home without his girlfriend, while Rebecca drove her father back to his farm. Later, I saw Gerry and Rebecca going for walks together on the moors or visiting Strensford or the coastal villages, but whenever I met them I never referred to that incident.

Several years later, Rebecca did marry Gerry; they married in Elsinby Catholic church before a happy gathering of friends and family. The only man missing was Jack MacKay. He died three weeks before the wedding; some said his death was an act of God. I wondered if it was from a broken heart.

I think a lot of people are interested in religion, probably out of curiosity; many who never go near a church or attend a service frequently express their views on religion in a manner which shows they often think about it. I knew a man who claimed to be an atheist; he had no belief whatsoever in God or divinity, and yet he peppered his conversation with phrases like, 'God willing', 'God only knows' and 'God help me'.

Another such character was Geoffrey Ditchburn, A retired chemical worker. He found religion something of a puzzle and often tried to rationalize his thoughts in conversations with those who attended church.

He'd worked all his life in the chemical industry on Teesside, being an expert on man-made fibres, and he retired to a life of rural bliss in Aidensfield. During my patrols I would often see him out for a brisk walk with his two labradors, Bill and Ben. Geoffrey, a rounded, cheerful-looking man with a bald head and tiny ears, walked swiftly with the aid of a walking stick. He spent hours roaming the moors and woods looking for unusual insects. Whenever he saw me, however, he would stop for a chat and he did have a tremendously wide knowledge of politics and world affairs; he also had a wonderful sense of humour. It was due to the arrival of the Reverend Lord that, one day when he met me on the village green, his topic of conversation was the church. After the usual pleasantries, he asked if I had met the new vicar.

'Yes,' I said. 'Several times,' and I followed by expressing a favourable opinion of Christian Lord.

'I never go to church,' he said solemnly. 'I can say my prayers whenever and wherever I want; I don't need pews and walls and incense and colourful robes to help me meet God.'

'You believe in God?' I asked.

'Yes, although not necessarily in the form of a bad-tempered old man sitting on a throne and delegating responsibility to St Peter. We all know St Peter finished up as nothing more than a heavenly bouncer, deciding who comes into heaven and who doesn't. What a job – it must be worse than being a bouncer at a night-club, having to make all those decisions. And he won't get paid either. Imagine being faced with villains – Hitler or Stalin or Henry VIII – would you have let any of that lot into heaven? Remember, once they're in, you can't turf them out again; it's worse than a night-club, at least at a night-club you can get rid of unwanted guests. And suppose Peter refused to let somebody in, and God said he was wrong? I mean, Peter might not have admitted Martin Luther but God might have thought he was a decent chap. There again, Peter might have admitted William and Conqueror but God might not have wanted him even though he was a Catholic who built lots of churches and abbeys; God might have been frightened he would try to take over the entire kingdom of heaven and besides, not everybody likes Norman architecture. Then there was Hannibal and all his elephants to look after; do you reckon St Peter wanted him in heaven with all those elephants? I mean, you can't just assume that whatever Peter wanted God would agree to, and nobody wants their boss altering their decisions . . .'

'I'd never looked at it like that,' I had to admit. 'Do you always see religion like this?'

'I think I see it logically,' he smiled. 'I often believe there were politicians in the universe long before God created the world.'

'How on earth do you come to that conclusion?' I asked.

'Well, the Old Testament says God created the world out of chaos, and politicians always cause chaos!' he grinned.

I chuckled at this view, but he went on, 'So what about Noah's Ark?'

'What about it?' I responded.

'Well, with all those animals on board in such a small place, and on wooden boards. If animals pee or crap on wood, it raises one hell of a stink. So what about that stink? You can't wash it away, it lingers for months with just one dropping, so can you imagine what it would be like after months of droppings from every one of those animals and birds! God, the thought is appalling! There were no air fresheners in those days, you know, and posies of violets wouldn't be much of a help. You imagine having all those wild creatures on board, all needing to be fed and watered and mucked out. Who did all that? I can't believe that yarn about Noah and the Ark, nobody could tolerate that stink all that time! There's no wonder the bloody dove left, is there?'

I had to chuckle at the picture his words produced in my mind, then he went on.

'I often think of the church as a football team,' he said. 'Every church I mean, not just the Catholics or the Protestants or Aidensfield church.'

'A football team?' I was puzzled.

'Yes. Think of a football as containing all the sins of the world. Now God doesn't want it in heaven, does he? He doesn't want all those sins being kicked about in heaven, so the goal is heaven.'

'And the devil's the striker?'

'Yes, the devil is the other side – he's trying to get sin into heaven. God wants to stop him.'

'So you see God as the goalkeeper?' I asked.

'Got it in one!' he beamed. 'God is there trying to keep sin out of heaven, but it's a tough job, so he needs help. That's who the other team members are. The Pope is the centre forward and the others in the front line are the outside left and outside right, and inside left and inside right, depending on the opinions of the cardinals. Left wingers and right wingers.'

'So the half backs?' I asked. 'Centre half?'

'The Orthodox churches,' he said. 'Greek Orthodox, Eastern Orthodox and Russian Orthodox. Centre half, left half and right half.'

'And the backs? Left and right full backs?'

'Church of England on the right, other Protestants on the left. They're there in case all else fails. And when they're in play, they all kick the ball to one another; all the churches are trying to pass the blame for sin to one another, aren't they? If sin gets past any of them, then it's up to God to become the goalie and stop it from reaching heaven.'

'But in a real football match a lot of goals are scored,' I put to him.

'And I reckon the devil gets a lot of sinful folks into heaven,' he grinned. 'Including a lot of churchmen and women.'

'So where does the ref come into your scheme of things?' I asked.

'St Peter,' he said. 'He's the ref and the apostles are linesmen, all working to reach decisions about what's fair and what isn't, what's sinful and what isn't. I mean, a lot of fouls are committed in the name of religion.'

'And some goals are not counted due to the off-side rule,' I added.

'Some things which are not sins now might have been sins in the past, like sex before marriage,' he said.

'I suppose, in your scheme of things, countries who fight battles in the name of religion also commit fouls?' I said.

'Got it,' he grinned. 'So you see, Nick, I can't really take religion seriously. Every time I hear a priest or vicar preaching I think he's a commentator at a football match. I finish up wondering which side will win.'

'I wonder if God does the football pools?' I asked him.

'The thing that worries me,' he grinned, 'are the spectators. I often wonder which team they want to win!'

One of the innovations from the new vicar was the venue of the harvest festival.

He decided to hold it in the pub instead of the parish church, one reason being that all members of the community, irrespective of their religious persuasion, could attend.

He had a word with the Catholic priest, Father Adrian, who felt it was a superb idea, although the Methodist minister, Pastor Smith, felt that the alcohol being served might detract from the solemnity of the occasion. Anything more than a glass of dry sherry was, in the view of some of his parishioners, rather sinful, even if the fruit of the vine did feature strongly in many church services. In spite of his reservations, however, he did agree to participate after Father Adrian reminded him that Christ was born in an inn and that he later produced some very good wine for the wedding at Cana, his very first miracle. Clearly, added the Reverend Lord, Jesus was not against a moderate tipple.

The inn's harvest festival was probably the first truly ecumenical service in the district. It raised one question though – if this was to be a joint service, should the Catholics and Methodists go ahead with their own normal services, or should this be the *Aidensfield* harvest festival rather than the Anglican parish harvest festival? Decisions would have to be made, in parochial church council of course.

Meanwhile George Ward, the landlord, was delighted and readily gave his consent. He even said he would not charge a fee for the use of his premises. A large attendance was expected, so the service would have to be held in the bar because there was no other suitable room at the inn. The only consideration that George requested was that the regulars were not barred from their own pews in the bar.

Christian Lord said, 'That's the whole idea, George. We want everybody there, pub faithful and church regulars. This will be one way of getting people to a church service who would never normally venture through my doors.'

'Like Claude Jeremiah Greengrass?' smiled George.

'And others, like you,' beamed the genial vicar. 'Now, as you know, the congregation always bring samples of their produce for display in church during the harvest festival – vegetables, fruit, cereals, potatoes and so forth, and when the festival is over, we donate those offerings to charity.'

'Yes, a very nice idea,' George agreed.

'Well, in my view,' said the vicar, 'few charities need fruit and vegetables these days. They're more in need of funds. They need money for furniture, premises, equipment, maintenance and so forth, so on this occasion, I propose holding an auction of the produce after the service. In your pub, I might add. I believe we shall raise a lot of money which we can donate to a worthwhile charity or charities.'

'It sounds a great idea,' enthused George. And so the vicar's plans were put into action. In due course he selected his date, in October, and the announcement was made. Notices were printed and distributed around the village and they asked for the faithful to bring their fruit and vegetables to decorate the pub instead of the church. In the meantime, the Catholics and the Methodists decided not to hold their own harvest festivals this year. Instead, they would all join the village harvest festival in the pub. There were some objections, as all the clergymen had expected, but it was hoped that the objectors would reconsider their decisions for next year.

The produce flooded in. George was overwhelmed with cabbages, carrots and broccoli, corn dollies, jars of strawberry jam and scrubbed potatoes of massive dimensions. In the week before the festival the pub's appearance changed to resemble that of a fruit and vegetable stall. There were apples on his optics, rhubarb behind the till and celery in the lager glasses. Mushrooms filled ashtrays, plums adorned the domino boards and sprigs of mint decorated the dart board.

Ladies of all religious persuasions came to arrange the produce in the most tasteful manner and, it is rumoured, even Miss Wisdom, the chapel caretaker, sampled one of George's free sherries. Preparation for the festival was a jolly occasion in itself, and then the great night arrived.

The first noticeable fact was that the wives of the pub regulars turned up; the effect of this was to double immediately the number of early customers in the bar. Some of their older children came too because their mums and dads felt that, if mum was going to the pub, then so could Johnny and Jenny. Thus the evening was already guaranteed to be a success. George was beginning to think it was his lucky night and that his foresight in appointing two extra bar staff for the night had been wise.

Claude Jeremiah Greengrass turned up too, with Alfred on a lead and with an offering of parsnips tied to his collar. Then the church congregations began to arrive, accompanied by relations and friends. The pub-shy Methodists crept into this sinful place with eyes wide as they sought signs of the devil; the Anglicans came with slightly more bravado, while for most of the Catholics the pub was a regular haunt. Many of them came here on Sunday mornings straight after Mass. But on this night, the choirs came too and to avoid arguments as to who should play the pub piano during the service (Anglican, Methodist or Catholic?), George said he would do so.

I was there, in uniform, to keep order should this crowd

become over-enthusiastic for the fruit of the vine or the ears of the barley field, but there was no trouble. It was a most friendly and good-humoured occasion. The joint service, with the lovely, practised voices of the Methodists leading the singing, was a joy; everyone joined in. Even Alfred raised his voice to the heavens when the singers reached the higher notes, his lone wolf-like howling adding a touch of melancholy to 'We plough the fields and scatter', and also in 'Come to God's own temple, come; Raise the song of harvest-home!' Alfred's greatest moment, however, was in his accompaniment to 'All things bright and beautiful, all creatures great and small'.

When the singing was over and sore throats had been eased with several drops of George's finest ale, tomato juice, vodka, soft drinks, whisky with green ginger or other throat-relieving potions, it was time for the auction. The auctioneer was Rudolph Burley, whose fine bass voice could be heard over any other human din. After suggesting that the congregation gather in to their bosoms yet another drink or two to keep them going 'Ere winter storms begin', he began his auction of the vegetable produce. The resultant income would be equally divided between the three denominations represented here, and they could then allocate the monies to the charities of their choice.

With apples being knocked down for ten times their normal price, farmers buying back their own potatoes and beetroot, and jars of jam raising the cost of a meal of caviare, it was a very successful occasion. Well over £175 was raised, a large sum in those days, and everyone felt it was a success. Even Pastor Smith, with two malt whiskies, a pint of best bitter and a brandy beneath his belt, was beginning to appreciate the merits of singing hymns in a pub. Claude's parsnips raised three shillings and some of my raspberries fetched half a crown.

The evening concluded with a famous harvest hymn but I'm sure that I heard George mispronounce one word. The harvest hymn 'To thee, O Lord, our hearts we raise' contains the line 'The hills with joy are ringing'. As the massed choirs of Aidensfield raised the pub roof with their voices in a grand finale, and as Alfred's dulcet tones drowned the accompanying piano music, I was sure I heard George's fine voice singing, 'The tills with joy are ringing.'

10 All Change

Fear of change perplexes monarchs.
John Milton (1608–1674)

If the fear of change perplexed monarchs, then it most certainly perplexed police officers, especially those serving in the 1960s. In the years immediately following the turmoil of the Second World War, police forces had settled into a cosy routine laced with mutual respect between themselves and the public. They were quite content to potter along in their comfortable, old-fashioned way. Police officers had no false notions of their place in society – they sought not wealth but a means of providing an efficient if sometimes out-moded service to those by whom they were paid.

Modern contraptions like personal radio sets had not yet reached the rural beats – there is a tale of one sergeant being issued with twenty brand new radio sets for his officers whereupon he promptly locked them in a cupboard, saying to his men, 'These things are too expensive and too good for you to use.' Bicycles were quite suitable for patrol work, feet were even better, and if a constable wished to go somewhere at high speed he would commandeer a passing car or jump on to a bus.

Ordinary constables were not expected to use cars and most certainly they were not expected to own a motor car.

In that leisurely era, crime fighting and crime prevention was done at a rather gentle pace. It is not surprising that there was some resistance to constables driving cars while on duty – hitherto, the method of patrolling a town beat had been restricted to a pair of whopping size elevens, although rural constables did have motor cycles and eventually minivans. But their town colleagues had to plod around the streets without a thought of the current concern about Incident Response Times, while motor vehicles were used almost exclusively by exalted ranks like sergeants, inspectors and superintendents. In the minds of those in authority over constables, there was something almost obscene in a constable actually being allowed to drive a police car, unless he was a member of the élite Road Traffic Division. Certainly ownership of a motor car by a constable was treated with some suspicion – questions were asked, such as where did he get the money to run a car? How can a constable afford such a luxury? And most certainly, police houses were never equipped with garages for one's private car.

As the 1960s progressed, however, police constables could afford to buy motor cars, and this coincided with rumours of massive changes within the police service. Sergeant Blaketon had already had a whiff of change, but that whiff was soon to turn into a gale of impressive power. The oncoming changes were not contained in the proverbial breath of fresh air – they were to be borne upon typhoon-style gusts.

For example, new ranks were being created – there was to be a new rank of chief inspector (between inspector and superintendent) and another new rank of chief superintendent which would be higher than a superintendent. In addition, a rank of deputy chief constable would be created and this would be higher than the existing assistant chief constable. With the arrival of a deputy chief constable, there would be two assistant chief constables who would function at a lower level, one being responsible for the administration of the force and the other supervising operational matters. To cater for this influx of senior officers police divisions were to be enlarged to accommodate the new chiefs and to give them something useful to do, and so the new top brass would be able to spend more days driving around in expensive cars with a sense of importance. In the terminology of the force at that time, the changes meant there were going to be far more chiefs than Indians.

With these rumoured (and eventually imposed) developments, rural beats were to be enlarged with inevitable changes to the boundaries of sections and sub-divisions. There would be fewer sections, sub-divisions and divisions, but the new ones would be far larger than the old. It was probably the advent of motorized constables that was the basis for these changes.

There was no doubt that these developments, when they arrived, would affect rural beats like Aidensfield. The village constable (me, in other words) would, if the rumours were correct, be expected to operate in areas previously covered by neighbouring constables. Rural constables might even be drafted into the local towns to perform duties – not a very nice prospect. That notion was even worse for sergeants like poor old Blaketon – if he was ordered to patrol the streets of a town he would be subservient to the local hierarchy, not king of his own midden as he was at Ashfordly. There is little wonder that these moves were resisted, if only for personal reasons. It could be argued that they were necessary for the efficiency of the force and our service to the public but the personal trauma they created might even be counter-productive. Good man-management was not a strong feature of the service at that time – we simply obeyed orders.

If the trend towards wholescale modernization was adopted, then some rural police houses would close and be sold, their occupants being moved into town for routine patrol duties. Areas hitherto policed by, say, three or four constables could now be made the responsibility of only one. In some cases, it was rumoured, village constables would work as a team, three or four of them covering an increased area in a motor vehicle and having their day's duty divided into three eight-hour shifts. In this way the rural bobby, with his twenty-four hour responsibility for a handful of small communities, would disappear. Instead, he would work eight-hour shifts, like a town officer, but over a wider patch with more villages. His colleagues would work similar shifts, thus ensuring that all communities, however small, were served twenty-four hours a day by a motor car containing a police officer. That's how the theory was explained but the system rarely worked in practice because one constable can only be in one place at any one time. If he was dealing with a traffic accident on the outskirts of Ashfordly, he could not be expected to supervise the pub at Elsinby.

I could see that the public would begin to believe there were fewer police officers, and indeed these projected changes did mean that a rural constable's proud commitment to his very own rural beat would be reduced or even eliminated.

But perhaps the most awesome and threatening of all these rumoured changes was that police forces themselves were to be altered. During the 1960s the Boundary Commission was in the throes of examining the geography of the British counties, county boroughs and cities with a view to reshaping them. It was said that city police forces like York, Leeds and Hull would vanish upon being absorbed by their neighbouring counties. The counties themselves would change too, with the famous Yorkshire Ridings being abolished in favour of new counties with names like North Yorkshire, West Yorkshire, South Yorkshire, Humberside and Cleveland.

The East Riding of Yorkshire would vanish without trace, becoming the northern part of Humberside. Rumours of this kind of 'progress' produced horror stories among police officers who realized that if new counties were created with their new county councils and new police authorities, then new police forces would also be formed. There would be new procedures, new bosses, new demands and lots of new problems.

During my time at Aidenfield, however, all these changes were little more than rumours but some rumours have a habit of becoming fact. It is fair to say that many of us did worry about our jobs because the amalgamation of police forces would inevitably mean that some top jobs would be lost. And if the top jobs were lost, then the chances of promotion were reduced. For example, if three police forces were merged to become only one, then at least two chief constables would lose their posts. The same would apply to the lower ranks but none of us felt this would affect mere constables. Any police force could function without superintendents but none could function without the humble constables on the beat.

But if the authorized establishment of a new police force was, say, 1,500 constables and the amalgamated constituent forces between them had 1,700 constables, then two hundred constables would have to disappear. Admittedly, this would be done by natural wastage such as retirements or resignations, so there would be no redundancies or sackings.

None the less, I do know that the constant rumours about such far-reaching changes did create a cloud of worry among a lot of officers, old and young, in high ranks and low ranks, in town and country. Another of the horrors awaiting officers in ancient cities was that they would have to patrol rural areas and deal with ghastly things like swine fever, sheep pox, epizootic lymphangitis, glanders or farcy. These were all diseases of animals, something of a problem for a city-bred officer who couldn't distinguish a pheasant from a ferret or a Friesian. And to patrol a lonely moorland road at night, without the benefit of street lighting and with an owl hooting in the distance, was something not relished by townie constables.

While long-serving officers like Sergeant Blaketon were fretting about their careers due to these threatened changes, young whizz-kids like Inspector Pollock were not. The highly educated, police college trained Pollocks of the police service saw themselves as the new wave of senior officers; they regarded themselves as the chosen few, men charged with the duty of modernizing a stagnating service and bringing to it all the techniques and skills of those trained in skilled man-management and organizational efficiency. Pollock saw himself as a future chief constable in a most modern and efficient police force; in fact, he saw himself as something of a saviour to the public he had sworn to serve.

I felt he would never achieve very senior rank because he was something of a twit; one of his failings was that he could never remember the names of his subordinates. This became apparent to me when, for some reason, he began to call me PC MacTavish.

This was something of a departure from the normal. Many senior officers referred to constables by their surnames – I was just Rhea. The force was full of Smiths, Jones, Browns and Greens in addition to some more colourful names like Fox, Hare and Fowler, Martin, Swift and Swallow to name but a few. But, as constables, they were known by their surnames to all ranks higher than their own. Sergeants and above called constables by their surnames. Sergeants were addressed as sergeant by all ranks, while inspectors and all higher ranks were called sir by their subordinates.

In some smaller forces, however, particularly in cities and boroughs, the constables were known by the numbers they wore upon their uniforms. Thus PC 6 Brown would be known simply as 'Six'. One would therefore receive messages like 'What duty is Six working this weekend?' or 'Has Six been seen since 9 a.m.?' This was even carried into off-duty periods so that news came along that Six was getting married, or his wife had had a child or that Six was sick with influenza. I've attended many social functions where officers called each other by their official numbers; quite literally, therefore, some officers were mere numbers in their force. Some police officers went through their entire service not knowing the real identity of Six or Ten or Ninety-Nine. In similar vein, one of the best known fictional police constables just after the Second World War was widely known to the public as simply PC 49.

Some recruiting officers had great fun allocating numbers to police officers – we had a PC Walls who was given the number 4, one called Fawcett who was given 444, another called Goode

who was given number 2, one called Green who was given
number 10 and one called Steeples who was given the number
200.

Thus we had Four Walls; Four, Four, Four Fawcett; Two
Goode, Ten Green (who was nicknamed Ten Green Bottles)
and Two Hundred Steeples as members of our constabulary. I
was the very ordinary PC 575 Rhea. Later, when the police
forces did amalgamate, one unfortunate officer was given the
number 999 – his name was Ward. Thus he became known as
Emergency Ward and another, with the number 1001, became
known as the Carpet Cleaner because of a popular advert for a
fluid known as 1001. The advertisement, sung to a jingle, said
that you could clean a big, big carpet for less than half a crown.
That is 12½p in modern money.

To be called by someone else's name, however, was somewhat
unusual, even by police standards. It was especially unusual if
this was done by one's local inspector. I had met our new senior
officer, Inspector Pollock, on several occasions whilst I was at
Aidensfield and in each case he had addressed me as either Rhea
or PC Rhea.

But one Saturday evening I was patrolling Ashfordly during
a shortage of officers when Inspector Pollock arrived by car. He
climbed out, as smart as ever, and I saluted him.

'Good evening, PC MacTavish,' he said. 'All in order?'

'Yes, sir, all correct,' I informed him, wondering if I had
heard the name MacTavish or whether I had misunderstood
some other word or phrase. I did not correct his error on that first
occasion and he joined me in a short patrol around the streets
with me indicating pubs where trouble might spill on to the
Saturday night streets. He asked me several questions about the

town, its local people and problem areas, and I got the impression he was quizzing me about my knowledge of Ashfordly.

He spent about fifteen minutes with me before departing. As he was leaving I slung up a departing salute and he said, 'Carry on, PC MacTavish.'

'I'm PC Rhea, sir,' I corrected him as he was entering his car, but he didn't hear me as he drove away. I puzzled over his error but thought little more about it until I was on early morning patrol about a week later. I had to make a tour of my own beat, in my minivan, between 6 a.m. and 9 a.m., making points outside the telephone kiosks of Elsinby at 7 a.m. and Briggsby at 8 a.m. These were check points in case anyone wanted to contact; it was a daft system because I had a police radio fitted to my vehicle. Through it, I was in constant contact with my sectional, divisional and headquarters offices.

However, as I was standing outside the kiosk in Elsinby, Inspector Pollock hove to in his smart official car. He climbed out, slung up a salute and asked, 'All correct, PC MacTavish?'

'It's PC Rhea, sir,' I told him.

'Really, where?' he asked, turning around to seek PC Rhea.

'No, sir, I'm PC Rhea,' I sighed. 'I'm not PC MacTavish; you called me MacTavish!'

'Did I really? But you are MacTavish, surely?'

'No, sir, I'm PC Rhea.'

'Are you sure?'

'Very sure, sir. Rhea is my surname, I've never been called MacTavish.'

'Oh, well, sorry about that. You do look like MacTavish, though. Remarkable. A most remarkable likeness. You could be brothers, twins even. Astonishing.'

'I'm afraid I don't know a PC MacTavish, sir,' I had to admit.

'So you are Rhea! Well, well, fancy me not recognizing you. You're the Aidensfield constable, aren't you?'

'Yes, sir.'

'Then where is PC MacTavish stationed? Why did I mistake you for MacTavish? Tell me that.'

'I don't know, sir, perhaps he's new to the area.'

'Of course! That's it! A new arrival, he's been with us a couple of months, a probationer constable, straight from training school. PC Alastair MacKenzie MacTavish, a Scotsman.'

'Really, sir?'

'He's stationed at Strensford. But my goodness. Rhea does look like you, MacTavish . . .'

'Rhea, sir.'

'Who?'

'Me, sir. I'm Rhea.'

'My goodness, so you are.'

'MacTavish is the other one, sir.'

'Yes, you're right, of course. You really are both so alike, it's incredible. Now, how's things otherwise?'

'Very quiet this morning, sir, no problems.'

And so, after chatting to me for about ten minutes, off he went. I felt he'd left in a cloud of utter confusion but was sure that assertion of my identity, uncertain though it had been, would establish my name in his mind. I was wrong. Whenever he met me in Aidensfield village, or at my police house, he called me PC Rhea, but whenever I encountered him away from Aidensfield, he always called me PC MacTavish.

As this absurdity continued, I decided to find out a little more of PC Alastair MacKenzie MacTavish of Strensford Police. From friends stationed there, I discovered he was a new recruit with a strong Scots accent, but that he was indeed about my height and had my colouring. Furthermore, one of my friends did say he had a partial resemblance to me and, like Pollock, did state we might be taken for brothers. But the most distinctive difference was MacTavish's voice – he had a very pronounced Scots accent while I spoke with a distinct Yorkshire voice.

It was inevitable that I should meet MacTavish and our first meeting occurred when we were both selected for duty at Redcar Races. This was one of our regular and enjoyable extra duties; every one of us looked forward to duty at one or more of the local racecourses.

In the 1960s the North Riding Constabulary was responsible for policing several racecourses, including Redcar, Thornaby, Catterick, Thirsk and owing to some accident of geography, York racecourse, although not the city of York itself. Our responsibility was the Knavesmire. For race duties, we were collected at our stations by a small personnel carrier and on this occasion, as we were heading for Redcar, I settled in my seat and found myself next to a young constable with a Scots accent. The number on his epaulette was 557. I was 575.

'Are you PC MacTavish?' I asked, thinking that he did have a look of me. We could indeed have been brothers . . .

'Aye, Alastair,' and he extended his hand.

'Nick Rhea,' I said.

'Oh, you're PC Rhea!' he grinned. 'Inspector Pollock keeps calling me PC Rhea.'

'And he keeps calling me PC MacTavish,' I smiled.

We exchanged a few tales about Pollock's inability to tell us

apart and then discovered that Pollock was the duty officer at
the races. At that news, I reckoned we were in for a fun-laden
day. Both MacTavish and I were allocated duties in the car park
prior to the first race, and then, once the races started, we were
to patrol in the paddock to keep the peace, deter drunks and
watch out for pickpockets. Our briefings were given by a local
sergeant who had no difficulty with our identities and we
proceeded to our places of duty.

MacTavish, being new to the chore of racecourse car parking,
was positioned on the entrance to our car park, which offered
the simplest of our duties. Inside there were me and several
other officers; we operated at the end of each row of cars, filling
in the gaps by a well-tested system of hand-signals. We had to
guide the cars in at a rapid rate and park them in herring-bone
fashion to facilitate a smooth and swift exit once racing was
over. MacTavish's job was simply to keep traffic moving
towards us and to help in preventing queues of cars forming in
the town on the approaches to the racecourse. But, as the
sergeant told us, 'Change places from time to time, Rhea and
MacTavish; Rhea, you give young MacTavish an opportunity
to do the herring-bone parking . . . help him, though, we don't
want a cock-up.'

As MacTavish was waving his cars towards me, Inspector
Pollock passed by the youngster and I heard him ask, 'Everything
in order, Rhea?'

'MacTavish, sir. I'm MacTavish. Rhea is over there, parking
the cars in rows.'

'Oh, yes, of course. Well, carry on, things are going smoothly.'

Pollock then came to me and beamed. 'You're Rhea, aren't
you? MacTavish is on the entrance?'

'Yes, sir,' I smiled. 'You've got it right this time!'

'Yes, I can tell you apart now. Well, no problems? The drivers are behaving? Obeying your signals?'

'Yes, sir, they're very experienced at this anyway, well, most of them, that is. The newcomers can cause hold-ups, but nothing serious. We're coping very well.'

Half an hour later, MacTavish and I were told to change our places. I was on the entrance now, waving in the never-ending stream of cars, and MacTavish was having his first real attempt at herring-bone parking. He was coping quite well when Inspector Pollock arrived at my point.

'Well done, MacTavish, you've learned this very well.'

'Rhea, sir. I'm PC Rhea. MacTavish is over there, parking them in rows.'

He looked into the ranks of cars and shook his head. 'But I thought Rhea was there . . .'

'No, I'm here, sir, we've changed places. Sergeant's orders.'

'I ought to memorize your number, MacTavish . . .'

'Rhea, sir.'

'So you are 575, Rhea.'

'Yes, sir, and MacTavish is 557.'

'That's not going to help, is it?' he grumbled, shaking his head. 'Well, I'd better go and see how MacTavish is getting along.'

By the time he returned for his third visit, we had swopped places again, and the confusion continued; it was even worse when we left the car parking to assume our duties in the paddock because in there we were free to roam anywhere and were not restricted to fixed points. But as the afternoon wore on, Inspector Pollock, being an officer of superior intellect, found a compromise. He ceased to address us by name. He merely addressed us as 'Constable'.

And he did this thereafter. Thus I had lost my identity and the next time he saw me at Ashfordly, he asked, 'All correct, Constable?'

'Yes, sir, all's quiet.'

'That was a very good report you submitted about the careless driving incident,' he said. 'Seeing it was the first traffic accident you've had to deal with, you did a very good job. A very well-presented file.'

'That wasn't me, sir,' I smiled. 'That would be PC 557 MacTavish.'

'Aren't you MacTavish?'

'No, sir, I'm Rhea.'

Sadly, about a year later, PC MacTavish was asked to resign from the force because, under the terms of his probationary period, it was felt he would never make an efficient constable. I have often wondered if I had done something wrong or sloppily which might have been entered in his personal record by error and which might have soured his chances of being accepted as a constable in our force. But I never knew the reason for his early departure. Then, about two years later, a Scotsman stopped me in Strensford to ask directions to the harbourside.

'You're Jock MacTavish's lad, aren't you?' he suddenly asked as he looked into my face.

'No,' I said. 'My name is Rhea.'

'Are ye sure?' he grinned. 'You're not pulling my leg?'

'No,' I spoke in a strong Yorkshire accent. 'I'm the one with the Yorkshire accent.'

And he went away, shaking his head. 'I think you're kidding me, Alastair,' he said. 'Your dad said I'd find you here, at Strensford . . .'

And to this day, I have no idea what became of Alastair MacKenzie MacTavish; if his father did not know where he was, then clearly there was a mystery about that ex-constable.

And, on reflection, I don't know the identity of the Scotsman who thought I was Alastair MacKenzie MacTavish, but for a long time after the departure of MacTavish, Inspector Pollock continued to call me 'Constable'.

Another occasion when Inspector Pollock became confused occurred when the Strensford Police football team won the Chief Constable's Cup and decided to hold their celebration party at the Aidensfield Arms. It was a Friday night and the team had booked a supper at the pub; George had applied for an extension of hours and promised to make a superb ham buffet, Arnold Merryweather's bus had been booked to convey the team to and from Strensford. The party promised to be a happy occasion.

Although the party was for team members and their spouses, the captain, Bob Oliver, did invite me to pop in. He also extended his invitation to the officers of Ashfordly Section. When the day of the party arrived I was dismayed to find that I was on duty, and so were Alf Ventress and Phil Bellamy, both of whom were keen football fans. But the fact that Phil was on duty that night was not necessarily a drawback – he said he might just pop in and so I said likewise. It would be churlish to avoid the party, we felt.

On that Friday night the heavens opened and the rain poured

down. In my little van with its radio crackling in the comfort of the cab, I found nothing to do. I chugged around the moors and dales but found nothing to occupy me; everyone was sheltering from the storm but I had to patrol until midnight. I found myself getting utterly bored – and then I remembered the party at the inn. I had an invitation, but I was on duty – I decided I would pop in, as invited, but would not, of course, drink alcohol. I might be tempted to a soft drink or two, and some sandwiches. I convinced myself that I was not doing wrong because pub visits were part of my duty.

And so, at about 10.30, I parked my minivan at the rear of the pub under a carport and entered. Inside, the place was heaving with large off-duty policemen with their wives or girlfriends, and the regulars were there too. Among the packed crowd, I spotted the familiar shape of Claude Jeremiah Greengrass; his dog, Alfred, was dozing before the fire. And then I saw two police uniforms. At first, I thought the team was organizing some kind of joke, but I quickly realized that the uniformed men were Phil Bellamy and Alf Ventress. As I pushed through the crowd towards them, somebody thrust a pint of beer into my hand and disappeared before I could refuse it. Clutching the pint high above my head to avoid spillage, I managed to reach Alf and Phil.

'What are you two doing here? I thought you were on duty!'

'We are, we've sneaked over here for some supper,' grinned Bellamy.

Alf added, 'There's nobody about, the town's dead and we've got to close the police station for several hours a day now, part of the new plans, so me and Phil thought we'd drive out to this party. We were invited . . .'

'What about Blaketon? Won't he wonder where you are?'

'He's on his long weekend off, he's gone away to the Lake District.'

'So who's in charge?'

'That dopey new inspector,' grinned Alf. 'Pollock. And he won't even know where to find the pub, let alone find us. Relax, Nick, we've left the car outside the back window with the radio on full volume; look, the window's open at the bottom, we'll hear our call sign if we're wanted for anything urgent.'

I could see the rear bar window was open a few inches, but the rain was not entering. And I could see the bodywork of their official car just outside. It meant that two official police vehicles were parked at the rear of the pub. There is a saying within police circles that a good policeman never gets wet, so we were helping to perpetuate that myth. We all knew, however, that if we got caught, we should be in serious trouble for being absent from our beats. That did not necessarily apply to me, of course, because I *was* on my beat and I could claim that I was performing a routine pub visit. Normally pub visits lasted two or three minutes, but this one would last all night!

The snag with radios in official vehicles was that every thirty minutes, at quarter to and quarter past the hour, we received a request from Control to state our current location. This meant that either Alf or Phil had to rush out of the pub every thirty minutes to respond to 'locations', as we termed the call. And in response to each call he gave a vague response such as 'Patrolling Ashfordly area' or 'Patrolling the A169 heading south' or 'Thackerston Moor, intend Elsinby and Crampton' or 'Rannockdale towards Whemmelby'. And so, in the minds of Control, the Ashfordly car appeared to be busily patrolling the

district in pouring rain when in fact it was parked behind
George's busy inn at Aidensfield. I could quite easily respond to
each call by saying 'Patrolling Aidensfield and district.'

So, on that awful night, our cars remained at the inn while we
talked football, had our suppers and socialized with the victorious
Strensford team. The extension of hours had been granted until
midnight and by half-past eleven the entire football team was
well fed and watered. I must admit I had sipped from the pint
which had been earlier thrust into my hands, but had restricted
myself to that one alcoholic drink, although I did have a
whopping big supper, several soft drinks and copious cups of
coffee. Alf had sipped one pint of beer too and had then turned
to orange juice, but Bellamy, not driving, had weakened – he
had dealt with several pints and enough food to satiate a family
of five.

And then I heard the distinctive sound of the Ashfordly car's
official radio. It was Ventress's call sign, but it was not
'locations' – it was a duty call!

'Alf, Phil,' I said, 'you're wanted. Division's calling you
up!'

Alf rushed out to the rear of the premises to respond. The rain
was cascading from the skies in a ferocious downpour and in the
few seconds that it took to reach the car door he got drenched.
He came back and said, 'That was Inspector Pollock, he asked
for my location.'

'What did you say?' asked Phil, now very nervous.

'Well, he said he'd been checking our locations all night,
driving to the places I'd mentioned hoping to rendezvous
with us, and had missed us every time.'

'Oh God,' groaned Bellamy.

Ventress continued, 'He wants to know where the hell we've been! He wants an explanation – he said we could not have driven from Thackerston to Whemmelby without meeting him and if we'd been in Elsinby, he would have seen us . . .'

'Where is he now?' I asked.

'Aidensfield,' and the expression on Alf's face told us that his ruse had been rumbled. 'He's parked right outside the front door of this pub!'

It meant the three of us were trapped inside. Our police vehicles were at the back and there was no way out other than by the main entrance. We knew that Pollock would wait outside the pub. He was not as daft as we'd thought. We were in trouble.

'I'll check,' I said.

I rushed up to the first landing of George's staircase and peered through the window that overlooked the street; sure enough, Pollock's car was parked right opposite, its lights shining in the pouring rain. I could see him in the driver's seat, his white shirt collar gleaming through the damp window. We were in a dilemma now . . . we had to find a logical reason why we had been here all this time, Alf and Phil had to find a reason to explain their mysterious non-tour of the district . . . and the fact that the pub was full of off-duty policemen would make any excuse sound very feeble. But, as the Bible says, 'In the multitude of counsellors, there is safety.'

And there were lots of counsellors in the premises. I returned to the bar to impart my bad news to Alf and Phil, whereupon George approached me.

'Trouble, Nick?'

I explained our dilemma, urging George to be sure to close

the premises on time, having regard to his extension of hours, of course, because Pollock was lingering outside. George said, 'This lot are leaving early, some have got to be on duty at 1 a.m., they were given three hours off for this. They'll be on their way before we have to shut.'

'That's not my real concern, George,' I said, 'We need a good reason for being here now, Alf, Phil and me.'

'Well, it's a foul night, Nick; nobody with any sense would be out in this weather, you'd never turn a dog out on a night like this!'

'That's it!' I had the answer. 'Dogs! We've been doing a humanitarian act, we've been out looking for Claude Jeremiah's dog. Claude told us the dog had got lost and he was worried, so we've been looking for it. How's that for a story? Claude will co-operate, surely?'

'It might cost you a few free pints for him, but you're not wet!' said George. 'Your uniforms are all dry!'

'Then we must go outside and stand in the downpour until we look wet . . .' I said.

'And Alfred's as dry as a bone, Nick, he's been lying near that fire all night, he's as clean as a whistle . . .'

'Then we'll have to wet him, we could bath him!' I said.

'Bath him? You're not using the hotel bathroom to bath that flea-ridden mongrel!' snapped George.

'You've an outbuilding and a bucket?' I asked.

'There's an old tin bath hanging inside that bottle shed round the back,' said George. 'You can use that if you want . . .'

And so the urgent plot was hatched. In the few minutes that remained, and as the football team began to sing their final song, I asked Claude Jeremiah if we could borrow Alfred.

'Borrow my Alfred?' he frowned. 'He's very particular who he mixes with, is my Alfred.'

'He's been happy enough to eat all those bits of ham the policemen have given him,' I said. 'He likes these coppers, Claude. Besides, we could come to some arrangement about free drinks in here, for you, I mean.'

'Aye, well, if it's business you're talking . . .'

And so, for the price of three free pints of beer every night for a week, Claude agreed to lend us Alfred and to say he had reported to us that Alfred had been lost in the storm. Silently, Alf Ventress, Phil Bellamy and I crept out of the rear door with Alfred on a lead, leaving the footballers to sing as loudly as possible so that Inspector Pollock would hear their dulcet tones. Outside, we allowed the rain to drench our uniforms and, from an outside tap, we filled an old bucket with water and threw it over the startled Alfred. We stood him in the old tin bath and swished gallons over the miserable dog until he looked as if he truly had been lost on the moors.

The poor dog was baffled by this treatment and did not like it one bit; he whined and struggled, he thrashed about which made us even wetter and shook himself so that each one of us was very wet very soon.

Eventually satisfied with his bedraggled appearance, we replaced the bath and bucket, climbed over the fence behind the pub into a ploughed field, got our boots, uniforms and the dog well and truly filthy with mud, and then trudged down a narrow path back into the village. I knew we could appear some distance from the pub's entrance.

The three of us, drenched and dirty, with Alfred resisting at the end of the lead, trudged through the street until we arrived at the pub door. There we could see the lights of Pollock's car, so we made towards them.

'Good evening, sir,' said Ventress, hauling Alfred to his side as he approached the car.

Pollock wound down the window and peered at the three of us. We must have been a sorry sight.

'What on earth's going on, Ventress? I've been touring the moors and dales looking for you, and for you, Rhea, and not a sign, not a sound . . . not one of you answered my radio calls . . . I came to the locations . . .'

'We've been looking for this dog, sir, he's a valuable animal. He escaped from his owner and so, as a humanitarian act, we decided to look for him. Sorry we missed you, that would be when we got off the beaten track, into side roads, up farm lanes, along bridleways, looking for Alfred . . . anyway, sir, we've found him.'

'It doesn't look like a very valuable animal to me,' said Pollock. 'In fact, it looks like a downright mongrel . . . where's it from?'

'Aidensfield, sir,' I said. 'His owner is in the pub, we're just returning the dog to him.'

At that moment, the front door of the pub burst open and the Strensford Police football team poured forth.

Singing some bawdy song, they traipsed out of the pub and headed for their bus in the car park. Pollock watched them with a frown on his face.

'Isn't that Sergeant Jowett?' asked Pollock.

'Is it, sir?' said Alf Ventress. 'Your eyesight's better than mine . . .'

'And PC Bateman . . . and Campbell . . . and Wood . . .'

'Oh, they'll have been celebrating their win, sir, the Chief Constable's Cup,' I said 'It had slipped my mind because of this dog . . . the pub was granted an extension of hours, sir, for the party. You'll remember – the licence was approved by Ashfordly magistrates a month ago.'

'Yes, of course. I do remember. You know, it would have been nice to have joined them,' smiled Pollock. 'Especially on a night like this.'

'Yes, sir, but one's constabulary duty must be done,' said Alf with water dripping from the peak of his cap. And at that moment the door of the pub opened to reveal Claude Jeremiah Greengrass who stood in the light cast from within.

Playing his part like a hero, Claude shouted, 'Alfred, you old bugger, are you out there?'

Alfred whined and leapt towards his master; his sudden move meant that the wet lead slipped from Ventress's hands. The happy dog galloped across to Claude and leapt up to greet him. Alfred made a huge fuss and wagged his tail as Claude hugged him.

'A most touching scene,' smiled Inspector Pollock. 'Is that the owner?'

'Yes, sir,' I said.

'It's five minutes to midnight,' smiled Pollock, glancing at his watch. 'Five minutes to go before closing time, so I think that man ought to buy us all a drink, to thank you gentlemen for making such an effort to trace his dog.'

'A great idea!' beamed Ventress.

'I say, you,' said Pollock leaping from his car. 'You with the dog!'

Claude halted as the inspector galloped across the road.

'Me?' asked Claude, in amazement at the sight. 'What have I done now?'

'These men, officers of mine, I might add, have worked jolly hard tonight to find your dog, I believe.'

'Aye, they have. And I'm very grateful . . .' Claude played his part very well. 'It's not often I'm grateful to the police but, well, on a night like this . . .'

'There's just time for you to buy them all a drink, I can authorize them to take a drink on duty, being their senior officer, and there are just a few minutes left before the inn must close . . . so might I suggest you buy us all a drink, to celebrate the recovery of your dog? And there are more of my men on the car park, just about to leave . . . I might even persuade them to stay a few minutes more, just to celebrate the return of this dog . . .'

'Me? Buy a load of coppers a drink?' blustered Claude. 'It's them that ought to be buying me a drink or two . . .'

'Consider it an investment, Claude,' I said softly.

'Aye, well, if you put it like that. I'm just pleased I've got Alfred back safe and sound!' He meant every word of that final remark and so he trudged back into the pub with Alfred on his lead. Pollock brought in the bus-load of officers and we all had a drink, paid for by Claude Jeremiah Greengrass. George was astounded, I was worried but Alfred was happy. He shook himself all over Claude and then went to lie by the fire once more.

'Alfred, an odd name for a dog,' said Pollock.

'He's named after me,' said Alf Ventress. 'I rescued him as a puppy, somebody threw him in the river and I found him. I gave him to Mr Greengrass, who named the dog after me. So you see, sir, there was a sentimental reason for our work tonight.'

In the touching moments that followed, Claude leaned over to Ventress and said, 'You don't half talk a load of old mush! That dog was never named after a copper . . .'

'It is now,' smiled Alf.

And so the police officers of Ashfordly, Strensford and district settled down to await the impending changes. Most worried of all was poor Sergeant Blaketon. He could see himself plodding the beat in Strensford as a shift sergeant rather than being in charge of his own section. This worry was compounded when a sergeant and a constable from the Research and Development department at force headquarters suddenly arrived at Ashfordly police station.

'We've come to measure your office, Oscar,' announced Sergeant Higgins.

'Measure it? What on earth for?' bellowed Blaketon.

'We can't say, it's confidential,' said Higgins. 'It's all to do with changes to the force structure, new divisions being created, sections disappearing, that sort of thing.'

And for the next half-hour, Sergeant Higgins and PC Dawson measured Sergeant Blaketon's office and the enquiry office with a long tape-measure. Dawson wrote down the details in a shorthand notebook as the two men discussed matters like offices for secretaries, toilets for women and parking places for senior officers' cars.

Poor Sergeant Blaketon just sat with a defeated look on his face. He knew that Headquarters theorists worked in strange ways but he did now think that Ashfordly police station was earmarked for some future role of great importance. He also got the impression that his humble office was being earmarked for someone of high rank. It would be three weeks after that visit, when I took my van into Headquarters garage for its regular service, that I saw PC Alan Dawson.

'I was on your patch the other week, Nick,' he said. 'With Dan Higgins. We played a joke on Oscar Blaketon.'

'A joke?' I asked. 'What kind of joke?'

'Well, years ago, Blaketon dropped Higgins into the mire, something pretty minor, it was. Blaketon should have delivered a message from Higgins to the superintendent, but he forgot. It was petty stuff, but as a result, Higgins got a bollocking from the superintendent.'

'So what was the joke?' I pressed.

'We were on our way to Scarborough police station,' smiled Alan Dawson. 'We just dropped into Ashfordly police station and measured it. Measuring someone's office always gets the incumbent worried – we told him it was confidential, something to do with impending changes in the Force structure. He'll worry about that for months now.'

'The Serious Rumour Squad in action?' I smiled.

'Some rumours have a habit of becoming fact,' he said, leaving me to ponder *that* statement. So was something important really going to happen at Ashfordly and Aidensfield? Or was it just a rumour? I could only wait and see.

HEARTBEAT

CONSTABLE ACROSS THE MOORS
AND OTHER TALES OF A YORKSHIRE VILLAGE BOBBY

NOW AN ITV SERIES

Nicholas Rhea

Of the millions who have enjoyed ITV's popular series HEARTBEAT, none will forget characters such as Claude Jeremiah Greengrass, Sergeant Blaketon and PC 'Vesuvius' Ventress. And they will be familiar with the village of Aidensfield, at the heart of Constable Nick Rowan's North Yorkshire beat. Set in 1960s Aidensfield, this omnibus collection of stories, which together with Nicholas Rhea's other tales of a village policeman originally inspired the HEARTBEAT TV series, tells of all these characters and many more: of Claude Jeremiah's dog Alfred and his unfortunate incident with the budgerigar, of young PC Nick's first merry New Year's Eve in Aidensfield, and of the funeral of the ancient tramp, Irresponsible John. Humorous, touching and imbued with a deep affection for the Yorkshire countryside and its people, this heartwarming collection is a treat no HEARTBEAT fan will want to miss.

'Witty, warm-hearted and full of lovable rogues'
Northern Echo

Heartbeat is a Yorkshire Television series derived from the Constable Books by Nicholas Rhea

FICTION / TV TIE-IN 0 7472 4125 2

HEARTBEAT

CONSTABLE AMONG THE HEATHER
AND OTHER TALES OF A YORKSHIRE VILLAGE BOBBY

NOW AN ITV SERIES

Nicholas Rhea

In the quiet North Yorkshire village of Aidensfield
a policeman's lot is often a very happy one. So
found PC Nicholas Rhea whose colourful and
warm-hearted stories of his countryside beat in the
1960s are the inspiration behind ITV's enormously
popular drama HEARTBEAT, starring Nick Berry.
From skulduggery at the Aidensfield village whist
drive to Sergeant Blaketon's trials with a stranded
Humber Snipe, from Gold Top Gareth, the
kleptomaniac milkman, to Roy the devoted
sheepdog who stays with his master to the very end,
even in a hospital ward, PC Nick Rhea paints a
delightful, poignant and amusing picture of a police
constable's life in some of England's most beautiful
countryside thirty years ago.

'As with the Herriot series, the best humour comes
from the author's close understanding and
affectionate portrayals of the character of Yorkshire
country folk' *Northern Echo*

Heartbeat is a Yorkshire Television series derived
from the Constable Books by Nicholas Rhea

FICTION / TV TIE-IN 0 7472 4012 4

A selection of bestsellers from Headline

OXFORD EXIT	Veronica Stallwood	£4.99	☐
BOOTLEGGER'S DAUGHTER	Margaret Maron	£4.99	☐
DEATH AT THE TABLE	Janet Laurence	£4.99	☐
KINDRED GAMES	Janet Dawson	£4.99	☐
MURDER OF A DEAD MAN	Katherine John	£4.99	☐
A SUPERIOR DEATH	Nevada Barr	£4.99	☐
A TAPESTRY OF MURDERS	P C Doherty	£4.99	☐
BRAVO FOR THE BRIDE	Elizabeth Eyre	£4.99	☐
NO FIXED ABODE	Frances Ferguson	£4.99	☐
MURDER IN THE SMOKEHOUSE	Amy Myers	£4.99	☐
THE HOLY INNOCENTS	Kate Sedley	£4.99	☐
GOODBYE, NANNY GRAY	Staynes & Storey	£4.99	☐
SINS OF THE WOLF	Anne Perry	£5.99	☐
WRITTEN IN BLOOD	Caroline Graham	£5.99	☐

All Headline books are available at your local bookshop or newsagent, or can be ordered direct from the publisher. Just tick the titles you want and fill in the form below. Prices and availability subject to change without notice.

Headline Book Publishing, Cash Sales Department, Bookpoint, 39 Milton Park, Abingdon, OXON, OX14 4TD, UK. If you have a credit card you may order by telephone – 01235 400400.

Please enclose a cheque or postal order made payable to Bookpoint Ltd to the value of the cover price and allow the following for postage and packing:

UK & BFPO: £1.00 for the first book, 50p for the second book and 30p for each additional book ordered up to a maximum charge of £3.00.

OVERSEAS & EIRE: £2.00 for the first book, £1.00 for the second book and 50p for each additional book.

Name ....

Address ....

....

....

If you would prefer to pay by credit card, please complete:
Please debit my Visa/Access/Diner's Card/American Express (delete as applicable) card no:

Signature .... Expiry Date ....